STUDY GUIDE FOR

ENGINEERING ECONOMIC ANALYSIS

ELEVENTH EDITION

Donald G. Newnan
Ted G. Eschenbach
Jerome P. Lavelle

Prepared by
Ed Wheeler

D1456690

New York   Oxford
OXFORD UNIVERSITY PRESS

Oxford University Press, Inc., publishes works that further Oxford University's objective of excellence in research, scholarship, and education.

Oxford New York
Auckland Cape Town Dar es Salaam Hong Kong Karachi
Kaula Lampur Madrid Melbourne Mexico City Nairobi
New Delhi Shanghai Taipei Toronto

With offices in
Argentina Austria Brazil Chile Czech Republic France Greece Guatemala Hungary
Italy Japan Poland Portugal Singapore South Korea Switzerland Thailand Turkey
Ukraine Vietnam

Published by Oxford University Press, Inc.
198 Madison Avenue, New York, NY 10016
http://www.oup.com

Oxford is a registered trademark of Oxford University Press

ISBN: 978-0-19-977819-5

Printing number: 9 8 7 6 5 4 3 2 1

Printed in the United States of America
on acid-free paper

Contents

Foreword

Over the years I have determined that students often do not have study materials that are truly useful to them. They usually have the course textbook and the lecture notes that they have managed to take or someone has taken for them. Often these lecture notes leave much to be desired in terms of clear, organized, useful information. Occasionally a student will have copies of old exams given by his or her professor. These exams can be treasure troves of information for the student. For the past several years I have made my old quizzes and exams available to my students and have been told that they are the most useful of all the resources available for studying for an exam.

This study guide is the product of the revision of the guide that accompanied the tenth edition of *Engineering Economic Analysis*. Chapters have been reorganized and new problems added. The great majority of problems in this study guide are actual exam problems used in an introductory course in engineering economy. In general, the exam problems are just as they appeared on the actual course examination. Every chapter in *EEA* has a companion chapter in this study guide

This study guide begins with a summary of basic engineering economy principles. The main section of the book consists of almost 400 problems with solutions. The problems offer a wide range of complexity and different solution formats. The last section contains a set of compound interest tables typically used in the solution of engineering economy problems.

I would like to thank Dr. Ted Eschenbach for initially recommending me to the publisher of this guide. And I would like to thank Rachael Zimmermann for asking me to participate once more in this revision. Special thanks go to my engineering economy students who have allowed me to use the rough manuscript in class in order to debug it. And the biggest thanks of all go to my wife, Ellen, and daughter, Abby, for their patience and understanding while I worked on this project.

If you find any errors in the problems or solutions, please inform the editor in care of the Department of Engineering at the University of Tennessee at Martin or by e-mail at ewheeler@utm.edu. If you would like to submit a problem or problems for a future edition, please use the same addresses. I hope you find that this material facilitates a better understanding of engineering economy and that it helps you to succeed in your course!

Ed Wheeler
Editor

Formulas

Compound Amount: To find F, given P

$(F/P, i, n)$ $\qquad F = P(1+i)^n$

Present Worth: To find P, given F

$(P/F, i, n)$ $\qquad P = F(1+i)^{-n}$

Series Compound Amount: To find F, given A

$(F/A, i, n)$ $\qquad F = A\left[\dfrac{(1+i)^n - 1}{i}\right]$

Sinking Fund: To find A, given F

$(A/F, i, n)$ $\qquad A = F\left[\dfrac{i}{(1+i)^n - 1}\right]$

Capital Recovery: To find A, given P

$(A/P, i, n)$ $\qquad A = P\left[\dfrac{i(1+i)^n}{(1+i)^n - 1}\right]$

Series Present Worth: To find P, given A

$(P/A, i, n)$ $\qquad P = A\left[\dfrac{(1+i)^n - 1}{i(1+i)^n}\right]$

Arithmetic Gradient Uniform Series: To find A, given G

$(A/G, i, n)$ $\qquad A = G\left[\dfrac{(1+i)^n - in - 1}{i(1+i)^n - i}\right]$ or $A = G\left[\dfrac{1}{i} - \dfrac{n}{(1+i)^n - 1}\right]$

Arithmetic Gradient Present Worth: To find P, given G

$(P/G, i, n)$ $\qquad P = G\left[\dfrac{(1+i)^n - in - 1}{i^2(1+i)^n}\right]$

Geometric Gradient: To find P, given A_1, g

$(P/G, g, i, n)$ $\qquad P = A_1\left[n(1+i)^{-1}\right]$ $\qquad P = A_1\left[\dfrac{1 - (1+g)^n(1+i)^{-n}}{i - g}\right]$

$\qquad\qquad\qquad\qquad$ when $i = g$ $\qquad\qquad\qquad\qquad$ when $i \neq g$

Continuous Compounding at Nominal Rate r

Single Payment: $\qquad F = P\left[e^{rn}\right]$ $\qquad\qquad P = F\left[e^{-rn}\right]$

Uniform Series: $\qquad A = F\left[\dfrac{e^r - 1}{e^{rn} - 1}\right]$ $\qquad A = P\left[\dfrac{e^{rn}(e^r - 1)}{e^{rn} - 1}\right]$

$$F = A\left[\frac{e^{rn} - 1}{e^r - 1}\right] \qquad P = A\left[\frac{e^{rn} - 1}{e^{rn}(e^r - 1)}\right]$$

Compound Interest

i = Interest rate per interest period

n = Number of interest periods

P = A present sum of money

F = A future sum of money

A = An end-of-period cash receipt or disbursement in a uniform series continuing for n periods

G = Uniform period-by-period increase or decrease in cash receipts or disbursements

g = Uniform rate of cash flow increase or decrease from period to period; the geometric gradient

r = Nominal interest rate per interest period

m = Number of compounding subperiods per period

Effective Interest Rates

For noncontinuous compounding: i_{eff} or $i_a = \left(1 + \dfrac{r}{m}\right)^m - 1$

where r = nominal interest rate per year
m = number of compounding periods in a year

OR

i_{eff} or $i_a = (1 + i)^m - 1$

where i = effective interest rate per period
m = number of compounding periods in a year

For continuous compounding: i_{eff} or $i_a = (e^r) - 1$

where r = nominal interest rate per year

Values of Interest Factors When n Equals Infinity

Single Payment: **Uniform Payment Series:**

$(F/P, i, \infty) = \infty$ $(A/F, i, \infty) = 0$ $(F/A, i, \infty) = \infty$

$(P/F, i, \infty) = 0$ $(A/P, i, \infty) = i$ $(P/A, i, \infty) = 1$

Arithmetic Gradient Series:

$(A/G, i, \infty) = 1/i$

$(P/G, i, \infty) = 1/i^2$

COURSE SUMMARY

This chapter is a brief review of engineering economic analysis/engineering economy. The goal is to give you a better grasp of the major topics in a typical first course. Hopefully, this overview will help you put the course lectures and your reading of the textbook in better perspective. There are 28 example problems scattered throughout the engineering economics review. These examples are an integral part of the review and should be worked to completion as you come to them.

CASH FLOW

The field of engineering economics uses mathematical and economic techniques to systematically analyze situations that pose alternative courses of action.

The initial step in engineering economics problems is to resolve a situation, or each alternative course in a given situation, into its favorable and unfavorable consequences or factors. These are then measured in some common unit—usually money. Those factors that cannot readily be reduced to money are called intangible, or irreducible, factors. Intangible or irreducible factors are not included in any monetary analysis but are considered in conjunction with such an analysis when one is making the final decision on proposed courses of action.

A cash flow table shows the "money consequences" of a situation and its timing. For example, a simple problem might be to list the year-by-year consequences of purchasing and owning a used car:

Year	Cash Flow	
Beginning of first year, or Year 0	−4500	Car purchased "now" for $4500 cash. The minus sign indicates a disbursement.
End of Year 1	−350	
End of Year 2	−350	Maintenance costs are $350 per year
End of Year 3	−350	
	−350	
End of Year 4	+2000	The car is sold at the end of the 4th year for $2000. The plus sign represents receipt of money.

This same cash flow may be represented graphically:

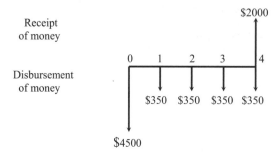

The upward arrow represents a receipt of money, and the downward arrows represent disbursements.

The x axis represents the passage of time.

EXAMPLE 1
In January 2000, a firm purchased a used plotter for $500. Repairs cost nothing in 2001 or 2002. Repairs were $85 in 2003, $130 in 2004, and $140 in 2005. The machine was sold in 2005 for $300. Compute the cash flow table.

Solution

Unless otherwise stated in problems, the customary assumption is a beginning-of-year purchase, followed by end-of-year receipts or disbursements, and an end-of-year resale or salvage value. Thus the plotter repairs and the plotter sale are assumed to occur at the end of the year. Letting a minus sign represent a disbursement of money, and a plus sign a receipt of money, we are able to set up this cash flow table:

Year	Cash Flow
Beginning of 2000	−$500
End of 2001	0
End of 2002	0
End of 2003	−85
End of 2004	−130
End of 2005	+160

Notice that at the end of 2005, the cash flow table shows +160. This is the net of −140 and +300.

If we define Year 0 as the beginning of 2000, the cash flow table becomes:

Year	Cash Flow
0	−$500
1	0
2	0
3	−85
4	−130
5	+160

From this cash flow table, the definitions of Year 0 and Year 1 become clear. Year 0 is defined as the *beginning* of Year 1. Year 1 is the *end* of Year 1. Year 2 is the *end* of Year 2, and so forth.

TIME VALUE OF MONEY

When the money consequences of an alternative occur in a short period of time—say, less than one year—we might simply add up the various sums of money and obtain the net result. But we cannot treat money this same way over longer periods of time. This is because money today does not have the same value as money at some future time.

Consider this question: Which would you prefer, $100 today or the guarantee of receiving $100 a year from now? Clearly, you would prefer the $100 today. If you had the money today, rather than a year from now, you could use it for the year. And if you had no use for it, you could lend it to someone who would pay interest for the privilege of using your money for the year.

EQUIVALENCE

In the preceding section we saw that sums of money at different points in time (for example, $100 today or $100 one year from today) may be equal in the sense that they both are $100, but $100 a year from today is not an acceptable substitute for $100 today. When we have acceptable substitutes, we say they are *equivalent* to each other. Thus at 8% interest, $108 a year from today is equivalent to $100 today.

EXAMPLE 2
At a 10% per year interest rate, $500 today is *equivalent* to how much three years from today?

Solution

The $500 now will increase by 10% in each of the 3 years.

Now	=		$500.00
End of 1st year	= 500 + 10%(500)	=	550.00
End of 2nd year	= 550 + 10%(550)	=	605.00
End of 3rd year	= 605 + 10%(605)	=	665.50

Thus $500 now is *equivalent* to $665.50 at the end of 3 years.

Equivalence is an essential factor in engineering economic analysis. Suppose we wish to select the better of two alternatives. First, we must compute their cash flows. An example would be:

	Alternative	
Year	*A*	*B*
0	−$2000	−$2800
1	+800	+1100
2	+800	+1100
3	+800	+1100

The larger investment in Alternative *B* results in larger subsequent benefits, but we have no direct way of knowing if Alternative *B* is better than Alternative *A*. Therefore we do not know which alternative should be selected. To make a decision, we must resolve the alternatives into *equivalent* sums so they may be compared accurately, which will allow a decision to be made.

COMPOUND INTEREST FACTORS

To facilitate equivalence computations, a series of compound interest factors will be derived and their use illustrated.

Symbols

i = Interest rate per interest period. In equations, the interest rate is stated as a decimal (that is, 8% interest is 0.08).

n = Number of interest periods.

P = A present sum of money.

F = A future sum of money. The future sum F is an amount, n interest periods from the present, that is equivalent to P with interest rate i.

A = An end-of-period cash receipt or disbursement in a uniform series continuing for n periods, the entire series equivalent to P or F at interest rate i.

G = Uniform period-by-period increase in cash flows; the arithmetic gradient.

g = Uniform *rate* of period-by-period increase in cash flows; the geometric gradient.

Functional Notation

	To Find	*Given*	*Functional Notation*
Single Payment			
Compound Amount Factor	*F*	*P*	(*F/P, i, n*)
Present Worth Factor	*P*	*F*	(*P/F, i, n*)
Uniform Payment Series			
Sinking Fund Factor	*A*	*F*	(*A/F, i, n*)
Capital Recovery Factor	*A*	*P*	(*A/P, i, n*)
Compound Amount Factor	*F*	*A*	(*F/A ,i ,n*)
Present Worth Factor	*P*	*A*	(*P/A , i, n*)
Arithmetic Gradient			
Gradient Uniform Series	*A*	*G*	(*A/G, i, n*)
Gradient Present Worth	*P*	*G*	(*P/G, i, n*)

From the foregoing table, we can see that the functional notation scheme is based on writing (To Find / Given, *i, n*). Thus, if we wished to find the future sum *F,* given a uniform series of receipts *A,* the proper compound interest factor to use would be (*F/A, i, n*).

Single Payment Formulas

Suppose a present sum of money P is invested for one year at interest rate i. At the end of the year, we receive back our initial investment P together with interest equal to Pi or a total amount $P + Pi$. Factoring P, the sum at the end of one year is $P(1 + i)$. If we agree to let our investment remain for subsequent years, the progression is as follows:

	Amount at Beginning of Period	+	Interest for the Period	=	Amount at End of the Period
1st year	P	+	Pi	=	$P(1 + i)$
2nd year	$P(1 + i)$	+	$Pi\,P(1 + i)$	=	$P(1 + i)^2$
3rd year	$P(1 + i)^2$	+	$Pi\,P(1 + i)^2$	=	$P(1 + i)^3$
n^{th} year	$P(1 + i)^{n-1}$	+	$Pi\,P(1 + i)^{n-1}$	=	$P(1 + i)^n$

The present sum P increases in n periods to $P(1 + i)^n$. This gives us a relationship between a present sum P and its equivalent future sum F:

Future Sum = (Present Sum)$(1 + i)^n$

$$F = P(1 + i)^n$$

This is the Single Payment Compound Amount formula. In functional notation it is written

$$F = P(F/P, i, n)$$

The relationship may be rewritten as

Present Sum = (Future Sum)$(1 + i)^{-n}$

$$P = F(1 + i)^{-n}$$

This is the Single Payment Present Worth formula. It is written

$$P = F(P/F, i, n)$$

EXAMPLE 3

At a 10% per year interest rate, $500 today is equivalent to how much 3 years from today?

Solution

This problem was solved in Example 2. Now it can be solved using a single payment formula.

$P = \$500$ $F =$ unknown
$n = 3$ years $i = 10\%$

$$F = P(1 + i)^n = 500(1 + 0.10)^3 = \$665.50$$

This problem may also be solved using the Compound Interest Tables.

$$F = P(F/P, i, n) = 500(F/P, 10\%, 3)$$

From the 10% Compound Interest Table, read $(F/P, 10\%, 3) = 1.331$.

$$F = 500(F/P, 10\%, 3) = 500(1.331) = \$665.50$$

EXAMPLE 4

To raise money for a new business, a friend asks you to loan her some money. She offers to pay you $3000 at the end of 4 years. How much should you give her now if you want to earn 12% interest per year on your money?

Solution

$F = \$3000$ $P =$ unknown
$n = 4$ years $i = 12\%$

$$P = F(1 + i)^{-n} = 3000(1 + 0.12)^{-4} = \$1906.55$$

Alternate computation obtained by using the Compound Interest Table:

$$\begin{aligned} P = F(P/F, i, n) &= 3000(P/F, 12\%, 4) \\ &= 3000(0.6355) \\ &= \$1906.50 \end{aligned}$$

Note that the solution based on the Compound Interest Table is slightly different from the exact solution obtained by using a hand calculator. In economic analysis, the Compound Interest Tables are always considered to be sufficiently accurate.

Uniform Payment Series Formulas

A uniform series is identical to n single payments, where each single payment is the same and there is one payment at the end of each period. Thus, the present worth of a uniform series is derived algebraically by summing n single-payments. The derivation of the equation for the present worth of a uniform series is shown below.

$$P = A\,[\qquad\qquad 1/(1 + i)^1 + 1/(1 + i)^2 + \cdots + 1/(1 + i)^{n-1} + 1/(1 + i)^n]$$
$$(1 + i)\,P = A\,[1/(1 + i)^0 + 1/(1 + i)^1 + 1/(1 + i)^2 + \cdots + 1/(1 + i)^{n-1}]$$
$$(1 + i)P - P = A\,[1/(1 + i)^0 \qquad\qquad\qquad\qquad\qquad\quad - 1/(1 + i)^n]$$
$$iP = A\,[1 - 1/(1 + i)^n]$$
$$= A\,[(1 + i)^n - 1]/(1 + i)^n]$$
$$P = A\,[(1 + i)^n - 1]\,/\,[i(1 + i)^n] \quad \text{Uniform Series Present Worth formula}$$

Solving this equation for A:

$$A = P\,[i(1 + i)^n]\,/\,[(1 + i)^n - 1] \quad \text{Uniform Series Capital Recovery formula}$$

Since $F = P(1 + i)^n$, we can multiply both sides of the P/A equation by $(1 + i)^n$ to obtain

$$(1 + i)^n P = A\,[(1 + i)^n - 1]\,/i \quad \text{which yields}$$
$$F = A\,[(1 + i)^n - 1]\,/i \quad \text{Uniform Series Compound Amount formula}$$

Solving this equation for A, we obtain

$$A = F\,[i\,/(1 + i)^n - 1] \quad \text{Uniform Series Sinking Fund formula}$$

In functional notation, the uniform series factors are

Compound Amount(F/A, i, n)

Sinking Fund(A/F, i, n)

Capital Recovery(A/P, i, n)

Present Worth(P/A, i, n)

EXAMPLE 5

If $100 is deposited at the end of each year in a savings account that pays 6% interest per year, how much will be in the account at the end of 5 years?

Solution

$A = \$100$ $F = $ unknown

$n = 5$ years $i = 6\%$

$F = A(F/A, i, n) = 100(F/A, 6\%, 5) = 100(5.637) = \$563.70$

EXAMPLE 6

A woman wishes to make a quarterly deposit into her savings account so that at the end of 10 years the account balance will be $10,000. If the account earns 6% annual interest, compounded quarterly, how much should she deposit each quarter?

Solution

$F = \$10,000$ $A = $ unknown
$n = 40$ quarterly deposits $i = 1\frac{1}{2}\%$ per quarter year

$A = F(A/F, i, n) = 10,000(A/F, 1\frac{1}{2}\%, 40) = 10,000(0.0184) = \$184$

EXAMPLE 7

An individual is considering the purchase of a used automobile. The total price is $6200 with $1240 as a down payment and the balance to be paid in 48 equal monthly payments with interest of 12% compounded monthly. The payments are due at the end of each month. Compute the monthly payment.

Solution

The amount to be repaid by the 48 monthly payments is the cost of the automobile *minus* the $1240 down payment.

$P = \$4960$ $A = $ unknown
$n = 48$ monthly payments $i = 1\%$ per month

$A = P(A/P, i, n) = 4960(A/P, 1\%, 48) = 4960(0.0263) = \$130.45$

EXAMPLE 8

A couple sold their home. In addition to a cash down payment, they financed the remaining balance for the buyer. The loan will be paid off by monthly payments of $232.50 for 10 years. The couple decides to sell the loan to a local bank. The bank will buy the loan, based on 1% per month interest. How much will the bank pay the couple for the loan?

Solution

$A = \$232.50$ $P = $ unknown
$n = 120$ months $i = 1\%$ per month

$P = A(P/A, i, n) = 232.50(P/A, 1\%, 120) = 232.50(69.701) = \$16,205.48$

Arithmetic Gradient

At times one will encounter a situation in which the cash flow series is not a constant amount A. Instead, it is an increasing series like:

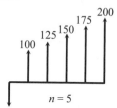

$$n = 5$$

This cash flow may be resolved into two components:

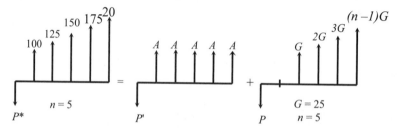

We can compute the value of P^* as equal to P' plus P. We already have an equation for $P' =$

$$P' = A(P/A, i, n)$$

The value for P in the right-hand diagram is

$$P = G\left(\frac{(1+i)^n - in - 1}{i^2(1+i)^n}\right)$$

This is the Arithmetic Gradient Present Worth formula. In functional notation, the relationship is

$$P = G(P/G, i, n)$$

EXAMPLE 9

The maintenance on a machine is expected to be \$155 at the end of the first year, then increasing by \$35 each year for the next 7 years. What sum of money would need to be set aside now to pay the maintenance for the 8-year period? Assume 6% interest.

Solution

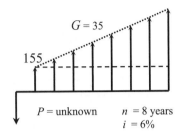

$$P = 155(P/A, 6\%, 8) + 35(P/G, 6\%, 8) = 155(6.210) + 35(19.841) = \$1656.99$$

In the gradient series, if instead of the present sum P, an equivalent uniform series A is desired, the problem becomes

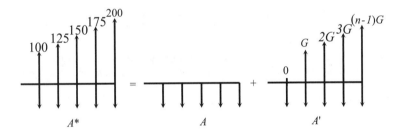

The relationship between A' and G in the right-hand diagram is

$$A' = G\left(\frac{(1+i)^n - in - 1}{i(1+i)^n - 1}\right)$$

In functional notation, the Arithmetic Gradient (to) Uniform Series factor is

$$A = G(A/G, i, n)$$

It is important to note carefully the diagrams for the two arithmetic gradient series factors. In both cases the first term in the arithmetic gradient series is zero and the last term is $(n-1)G$. But we use n in the equations and functional notation. The formula derivations were done on this basis, and the arithmetic gradient series Compound Interest Tables are computed this way.

EXAMPLE 10
Consider again the situation in Example 9. We wish now to know the uniform annual equivalent maintenance cost. Compute an equivalent A for the maintenance costs.

Solution

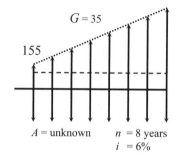

A = unknown n = 8 years
                   i = 6%

Equivalent uniform annual maintenance cost:

$$A = 155 + 35(A/G, 6\%, 8) = 155 + 35(3.195) = \$266.83$$

Geometric Gradient

The arithmetic gradient is applicable when the period-by-period change in the cash flow is a uniform amount. In other cases, the period-by-period change is a *uniform rate, g*. A diagram of this situation is

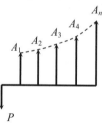

where $A_n = A_1(1 + g)^{n-1}$
   g = Uniform rate of period-by-period change; the geometric gradient stated as a
       decimal (8% = 0.08)
   A_1 = Value of A at Year 1
   A_n = Value of A at any Year n

Geometric Series Present Worth formulas:

When $i = g$, $P = A_1[n(1 + i)^{-1}]$

When $i \neq g$, $P = A_1\left(\dfrac{1 - (1 + g)^n (1 + i)^{-n}}{i - g}\right)$

EXAMPLE 11

It is likely that airplane tickets will increase 8% in each of the next 4 years. The cost of a plane ticket at the end of the first year will be $180. How much money would need to be placed in a savings account now to have money to pay a student's travel home at the end of each year for the next 4 years? Assume that the savings account pays 5% annual interest.

Solution

The problem describes a geometric gradient where $g = 8\%$ and $i = 5\%$.

$$P = A_1 \left(\frac{1 - (1+g)^n (1+i)^{-n}}{i - g} \right)$$

$$P = 180.00 \left(\frac{1 - (1.08)^4 (1.05)^{-4}}{0.05 - 0.08} \right) \quad = \quad 180.00 \left(\frac{-0.119278}{-0.03} \right) \quad = \quad \$715.67$$

Thus, $715.67 would need to be deposited now.

As a check, the problem can be solved without using the geometric gradient:

Year		Ticket
1	$A_1 =$	$180.00
2	$A_2 = 180.00 + 8\%(180.00) =$	194.40
3	$A_3 = 194.40 + 8\%(194.40) =$	209.95
4	$A_4 = 209.95 + 8\%(209.95) =$	226.75

$P = 180.00(P/F, 5\%, 1) + 194.40(P/F, 5\%, 2) + 209.95(P/F, 5\%, 3) + 226.75(P/F, 5\%, 4)$
$= 180.00(0.9524) + 194.40(0.9070) + 209.95(0.8638) + 226.75(0.8227)$
$= \$715.66$

NOMINAL AND EFFECTIVE INTEREST

Nominal interest is the annual interest rate without considering the effect of any compounding.

Effective interest is the annual interest rate taking into account the effect of any compounding during the year.

Frequently an interest rate is described as an annual rate, even though the interest period may be something other than one year. A bank may pay $1\frac{1}{2}\%$ interest on the amount in a savings account every 3 months. The *nominal* interest rate in this situation is 6%($4 \times 1\frac{1}{2}\% = 6\%$). But if you deposited $1000 in such an account, would you have 106%(1000) = $1060 in the account at the end of one year? The answer is no, you would have more. The amount in the account would increase as follows:

			Amount in Account
	At beginning of year	=	$1000.00
End of 3 months:	1000.00 + 1½%(1000.00)	=	1015.00
End of 6 months:	1015.00 + 1½%(1015.00)	=	1030.23
End of 9 months:	1030.23 + 1½%(1030.23)	=	1045.68
End of one year:	1045.68 + 1½%(1045.68)	=	1061.37

The actual interest rate on the $1000 would be the interest, $61.37, divided by the original $1000, or 6.137%. We call this the *effective* interest rate. The formula for calculating the effective rate is

$$\text{Effective interest rate} = (1 + i)^m - 1 \text{ , where}$$

$i =$ Interest rate per interest period
$m =$ Number of compoundings per year

EXAMPLE 12

A bank charges 1½% per month on the unpaid balance for purchases made on its credit card. What nominal interest rate is it charging? What is the effective interest rate?

Solution

The nominal interest rate is simply the annual interest ignoring compounding, or 12(1½%) = 18%. Effective interest rate = $(1 + 0.015)^{12} - 1 = 0.1956 = 19.56\%$.

SOLVING ECONOMIC ANALYSIS PROBLEMS

The techniques presented so far illustrate how to convert single amounts of money, and uniform or gradient series of money, into some equivalent sum at another point in time. These compound interest computations are an essential part of economic analysis problems.

Typically, we have a number of alternatives, and the question is, Which alternative should be selected? The customary method of solution is to resolve each of the alternatives into some common form and then choose the best alternative (taking both the monetary and intangible factors into account).

Criteria

Economic analysis problems inevitably fall into one of these categories:

1. Fixed Input   The amount of money or other input resources is fixed.

   Example: A project engineer has a budget of $450,000 to overhaul a plant.

2. Fixed Output   There is a fixed task, or other output to be accomplished.

   Example: A consulting engineer must purchase a new computer.

3. Neither Input nor Output Fixed   This is the general situation: neither the amount of money or other inputs is fixed, nor is the amount of benefits or other outputs fixed.

Example: A mechanical engineering firm has more work available than it can handle. It is considering paying the staff for working evenings to increase the amount of design work it can perform.

There are five major methods of comparing alternatives: present worth; annual worth; future worth; rate of return; and benefit/cost ratio. These are presented in the following sections.

PRESENT WORTH

In present worth analysis, the approach is to resolve all the money consequences of an alternative into an equivalent present sum. For the three categories given above, the criteria are:

Category	*Present Worth Criterion*
Fixed Input	Maximize the Present Worth of benefits or other outputs.
Fixed Output	Minimize the Present Worth of costs or other inputs.
Neither Input nor Output Fixed	Maximize [Present Worth of benefits *minus* Present Worth of costs] or, stated another way: Maximize Net Present Worth.

Application of Present Worth

Present worth analysis is most frequently used to determine the present value of future money receipts and disbursements. We might want to know, for example, the present worth of an income-producing property, like an oil well. This should provide an estimate of the price at which the property could be bought or sold.

An important restriction in the use of present worth calculations is that there must be a common analysis period when alternatives are being compared. It would be incorrect, for example, to compare the present worth (PW) of cost of Pump *A*, expected to last 6 years, with the PW of cost of Pump *B*, expected to last 12 years.

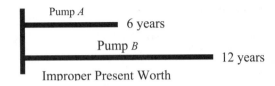

Pump *A*   6 years

Pump *B*   12 years

Improper Present Worth

In situations like this, the solution is either to use some other analysis technique (generally the annual worth method) or to restructure the problem so there is a common analysis period. In the foregoing example, it would be customary to assume that a pump is needed for 12 years and that Pump *A* will be replaced by an identical unit (Pump *A*) at the end of 6 years. This gives a 12-year common analysis period.

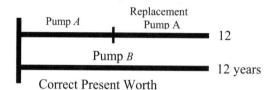

This approach is easy to use when the different lives of the alternatives have a practical least common multiple life. When this is not true (for example, life of *J* equals 7 years and the life of *K* equals 11 years), either some assumptions must be made to select a suitable common analysis period, or the present worth method should not be used.

EXAMPLE 13

Machine *X* has an initial cost of $10,000, annual maintenance of $500 per year, and no salvage value at the end of its 4-year useful life. Machine *Y* costs $20,000. The last year there is no maintenance cost. The second year, maintenance is $100, and it increases $100 per year in subsequent years. The machine has an anticipated $5000 salvage value at the end of its 12-year useful life. If interest is 8%, which machine should be selected?

Solution

The analysis period is not stated in the, problem. Therefore we select the least common multiple of the lives, or 12 years, as the analysis period.

Present Worth of Costs, Machine *X*

$$= 10,000 + 10,000(P/F, 8\%, 4) + 10,000(P/F, 8\%, 8) + 500(P/A, 8\%, 12)$$
$$= 10,000 + 10,000(0.7350) + 10,000(0.5403) + 500(7.536)$$
$$= \$26,521$$

Present Worth of Costs, Machine *Y*

$$= 20,000 + 100(P/G, 8\%, 12) - 5000(P/F, 8\%, 12)$$
$$= 20,000 + 100(34.634) - 5000(0.3971)$$
$$= \$21,478$$

Choose Machine *Y*, with its smaller Present Worth of Costs.

EXAMPLE 14

Two alternatives have the following cash flows:

| | Alternative | |
Year	A	B
0	−$2000	−$2800
1	+800	+1100
2	+800	+1100
3	+800	+1100

At a 5% interest rate, which alternative should be selected?

Solution

Solving by Present Worth analysis:

$$\text{Net Present Worth (NPW)} = \text{PW of benefits} - \text{PW of costs}$$

$$\begin{aligned} \text{NPW}_A &= 800(P/A, 5\%, 3) - 2000 \\ &= 800(2.723) - 2000 \\ &= \$178.40 \end{aligned}$$

$$\begin{aligned} \text{NPW}_B &= 1100(P/A, 5\%, 3) - 2800 \\ &= 1100(2.723) - 2800 \\ &= \$195.30 \end{aligned}$$

To maximize NPW, choose Alternative *B*.

Capitalized Cost

In the special situation where the analysis period is infinite ($n = \infty$), an analysis of the present worth of cost is called *capitalized cost*. There are a few public projects for which the analysis period is infinity. Other examples would be permanent endowments and cemetery perpetual care.

When *n* equals infinity, a present sum *P* will accrue interest of *Pi* for every future interest period. For the principal sum *P* to continue undiminished (an essential requirement for *n* equal to infinity), the end-of-period sum *A* that can be disbursed is *Pi*.

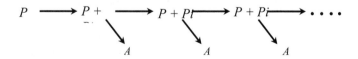

When $n = \infty$, the fundamental relationship between *P*, *A*, and *i* is

$$A = Pi$$

Some form of this equation is used whenever there is a problem with an infinite analysis period.

EXAMPLE 15

In his will, a man wishes to establish a perpetual trust to provide for the maintenance of a small local park. If the annual maintenance is $7500 per year and the trust account can earn 5% interest, how much money must be set aside in the trust?

Solution

When $n = \infty$, $A = Pi$ or $P = A/i$

Capitalized cost $P = A/i = \$7500/0.05 = \$150,000$

ANNUAL WORTH

The annual worth method is more accurately described as the method of Equivalent Uniform Annual Cost (EUAC) or, where the computation is of benefits, the method of Equivalent Uniform Annual Benefits (EUAB).

For each of the three possible categories of problems, there is an annual worth criterion for economic efficiency.

Category	*Annual Worth Criterion*
Fixed Input	Maximize the Equivalent Uniform Annual Benefits; that is, maximize EUAB.
Fixed Output	Minimize the Equivalent Uniform Annual Cost; that is, minimize EUAC.
Neither Input nor Output Fixed	Maximize EUAB – EUAC; or, stated another way, maximize Annual Worth.

Application of Annual Worth Analysis

In the section on present worth, we pointed out that the present worth method requires that there be a common analysis period for all alternatives. This same restriction does not apply in all annual cost calculations, but it is important to understand the circumstances that justify comparing alternatives with different service lives.

Frequently the goal of an analysis is to provide for a more or less continuing requirement. One might need to pump water from a well, for example, as a continuing requirement. Regardless of whether the pump has a useful service life of 6 years or 12 years, we would select the one whose annual cost is a minimum. And this would still be the case if the pump useful lives were the more troublesome 7 and 11 years, respectively. Thus, if we can assume a continuing need for an item, an annual cost comparison among alternatives of differing service lives is valid.

The underlying assumption made in these situations is that when the shorter-lived alternative has reached the end of its useful life, it can be replaced with an identical item with identical costs, and so forth. This means the annual worth of the initial alternative is equal to the annual worth for the continuing series of replacements. The underlying "continuing requirement" assumption is often present, so the annual worth comparison of unequal-lived alternatives is an appropriate method of analysis.

If, on the other hand, there is a specific requirement in some situation to pump water for 10 years, then each pump must be evaluated to see what costs will be incurred during the analysis period and what salvage value, if any, may be recovered at the end of the analysis period. The annual worth comparison needs to consider the actual circumstances of the situation.

EXAMPLE 16

Consider the following alternatives:

	A	B
First cost	$5000	$10,000
Annual maintenance	500	200
End-of-useful-life salvage value	600	1000
Useful life	5 years	15 years

Based on an 8% interest rate, which alternative should be selected?

Solution

Assuming that both alternatives perform the same task and that there is a continuing requirement, the goal is to minimize EUAC.

Alternative A:
$$EUAC = 5000(A/P, 8\%, 5) + 500 - 600(A/F, 8\%, 5)$$
$$= 5000(0.2505) + 500 - 600(0.1705) = \$1650$$

Alternative B:
$$EUAC = 10,000(A/P, 8\%, 15) + 200 - 1000(A/F, 8\%, 15)$$
$$= 10,000(0.1168) + 200 - 1000(0.0368) = \$1331$$

To minimize EUAC, select Alternative *B*.

FUTURE WORTH

In present worth analysis, the comparison is made in terms of the equivalent present costs and benefits. But the analysis need not be made at the present time. It could be made at any point in time: past, present, or future. Although the numerical calculations may look different, the decision is unaffected by the point in time selected. Of course, in certain cases we do want to know what the future situation will be if we take some particular course of action now. An analysis that is made based on some future point in time is called a future worth analysis.

Category	Future Worth Criterion
Fixed Input	Maximize the Future Worth of benefits or other outputs.
Fixed Output	Minimize the Future Worth of costs or other inputs.
Neither Input nor Output Fixed	Maximize [Future Worth of benefits *minus* Future Worth of costs]; or, stated another way: Maximize Net Future Worth.

EXAMPLE 17

Two alternatives have the following cash flows:

		Alternative	
Year	A		B
0	−$2000		−$2800
1	+800		+1100
2	+800		+1100
3	+800		+1100

At a 5% interest rate, which alternative should be selected?

Solution

In Example 14, this problem was solved by Present Worth analysis at Year 0. Here it will be solved by Future Worth analysis at the end of Year 3.

$$\text{Net Future Worth (NFW)} = \text{FW of benefits} - \text{FW of cost}$$

$$\begin{aligned}
NFW_A &= 800(F/A, 5\%, 3) - 2000(F/P, 5\%, 3) \\
&= 800(3.152) - 2000(1.158) \\
&= \$205.60
\end{aligned}$$

$$\begin{aligned}
NFW_B &= 1100(F/A, 5\%, 3) - 2800(F/P, 5\%, 3) \\
&= 1100(3.152) - 2800(1.158) \\
&= \$224.80
\end{aligned}$$

To maximize NFW, choose Alternative B.

RATE OF RETURN

A typical situation is a cash flow representing the costs and benefits. The rate of return may be defined as the interest rate, where

   PW of benefits = PW of costs   or   PW of benefits − PW of costs = 0

   or

   EUAB = EUAC   or   EUAB − EUAC = 0

EXAMPLE 18

Compute the rate of return for the investment represented by the following cash flow:

Year	Cash Flow
0	−$595
1	+250
2	+200
3	+150
4	+100
5	+ 50

Solution

This declining arithmetic gradient series may be separated into two cash flows for which compound interest factors are available:

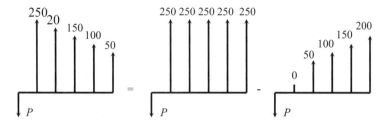

Note that the gradient series factors are based on an *increasing* gradient. Here, subtracting an increasing arithmetic gradient, as indicated by the diagram, solves the declining cash flow.

PW of benefits – PW of costs = 0
$$[250(P/A, i, 5) - 50(P/G, i, 5)] - 595 = 0$$

Try $i = 10\%$:
$$[250(3.791) - 50(6.862)] - 595 = -9.65$$

Try $i = 12\%$:
$$[250(3.605) - 50(6.397)] - 595 = +13.60$$

The rate of return is between 10% and 12%. It may be computed more accurately by linear interpolation:

$$\text{Rate of return} = 10\% + 2\%\left(\frac{9.65 - 0}{13.60 - (-9.65)}\right) = 10.83\%$$

Application of Rate of Return with Two Alternatives

To properly compare two alternatives by using rate of return, compute the incremental rate of return on the cash flow representing the difference between the two alternatives. Since we want to look at increments of *investment,* the cash flow for the difference between the alternatives is computed by taking the higher-initial-cost alternative *minus* the lower-initial-cost alternative. If the incremental rate of return is greater than or equal to the predetermined minimum attractive rate of return (MARR), choose the higher-cost alternative; otherwise, choose the lower-cost alternative.

EXAMPLE 19

Two alternatives have the following cash flows:

Year	Alternative A	B
0	-$2000	-$2800
1	+800	+1100
2	+800	+1100
3	+800	+1100

If 5% is considered to be the minimum attractive rate of return (MARR), which alternative should be selected?

Solution

These two alternatives were examined earlier (Examples 14 and 17) by present worth and future worth analysis. This time, the alternatives will be resolved by using rate of return analysis.

Note that the problem statement specifies a 5% minimum attractive rate of return (MARR), while Examples 14 and 17 referred to a 5% interest rate. These are really two different ways of saying the same thing: the minimum acceptable time value of money is 5%.

First, tabulate the cash flow that represents the increment of investment between the alternatives. Taking the higher-initial-cost alternative minus the lower-initial-cost alternative does this:

Year	Alternative A	B	Difference between Alternatives B − A
0	-$2000	-$2800	-$800
1	+800	+1100	+300
2	+800	+1100	+300
3	+800	+1100	+300

Then compute the rate of return on the increment of investment represented by the difference between the alternatives:

PW of benefits = PW of costs

$300(P/A, i, 3) = 800$

$(P/A, i, 3) = 800/300$

$= 2.67$

$i \approx 6.1\%$

Since the incremental rate of return exceeds the 5% MARR, the increment of investment is desirable. Choose the higher-cost alternative, Alternative B.

Before leaving this example problem, one should note something that relates to the rates of return on Alternative A and on Alternative B. These rates of return, if computed, are:

	Rate of Return
Alternative A	9.7%
Alternative B	8.7%

The correct answer to this problem has been shown to be Alternative *B*, and this is true even though Alternative *A* has a higher rate of return. The higher-cost alternative may be thought of as the lower-cost alternative plus the increment of investment between them. Looked at this way, the higher-cost Alternative *B* is equal to the desirable lower-cost Alternative *A* plus the desirable differences between the alternatives.

The important conclusion is that computing the rate of return for each alternative does not provide the basis for choosing between alternatives. Instead, incremental analysis is required.

EXAMPLE 20

Consider the following:

Year	Alternative A	Alternative B
0	−$200.0	−$131.0
1	+77.6	+48.1
2	+77.6	+48.1
3	+77.6	+48.1

If the minimum attractive rate of return (MARR) is 10%, which alternative should be selected?

Solution

To examine the increment of investment between the alternatives, we will examine the higher-initial-cost alternative minus the lower-initial-cost alternative, or *A* − *B*.

Year	Alternative A	Alternative B	Increment A − B
0	−$200.0	−$131.0	−$69.0
1	+77.6	+48.1	+29.5
2	+77.6	+48.1	+29.5
3	+77.6	+48.1	+29.5

Solve for the incremental rate of return:

PW of benefits = PW of costs
$$29.5(P/A, i, 3) = 69.0$$
$$(P/A, i, 3) = 69.0/29.5$$
$$= 2.339$$

From the Compound Interest Tables, 12% < ROR_{A-B} < 15%, Therefore we select the higher-initial-cost alternative, Alternative *A*.

Application of Rate of Return with Three or More Alternatives

When there are three or more mutually exclusive alternatives, one must proceed following the same general logic presented for two alternatives. The components of incremental analysis are:

1. Compute the rate of return for each alternative. Reject any alternative for which the rate of return is less than the given MARR.

2. Rank the remaining alternatives in order of their increasing initial cost.

3. Examine the increment of investment between the two lowest-cost alternatives as described for the two-alternative problem. Select the better of the two alternatives and reject the other one.

4. Take the preferred alternative from Step 3. Consider the next higher-initial-cost alternative and proceed with another two-alternative comparison. (An alternative is to use the two highest-cost alternatives first.)

5. Continue until all alternatives have been examined and the best of the multiple alternatives has been identified.

EXAMPLE 21

Consider the following:

Year	Alternative A	Alternative B
0	−$200.0	−$131.0
1	+77.6	+48.1
2	+77.6	+48.1
3	+77.6	+48.1

If the minimum attractive rate of return (MARR) is 10%, which alternative, if any, should be selected?

Solution

One should carefully note that this is a three-alternative problem; the alternatives are *A, B,* and "*Do Nothing.*" (Neither *A* nor *B* must be chosen.)

In this solution we will skip Step 1 because we have previously solved for the ROR_A and ROR_B. Reorganize the problem by placing the alternatives in order of increasing initial cost:

Year	Alternative Do Nothing	B	A
0	0	-$131.0	-$200.0

Examine the "*B – Do Nothing*" increment of investment:

Year	B	−	Do Nothing		
0	−$131.0	−	0 =	−$131.0
1	+48.1	−	0 =	+48.1
2	+48.1	−	0 =	+48.1
3	+48.1	−	0 =	+48.1

Solve for the incremental rate of return:

PW of benefits = PW of costs
$$131.0 = 48.1(P/A, i, 3)$$
$$(P/A, i, 3) = 131.0/48.1$$
$$= 2.723$$

From Compound Interest Tables, the incremental rate of return is 5%. Since the incremental rate of return is less than 10%, the $B - Do\ Nothing$ increment is not desirable. Reject Alternative B.

Next, consider the increment of investment between the two remaining alternatives:

Year	A	$-$	Do Nothing	
0	$-\$200.0$	$-$	$0 =$	$-\$200.0$
1	$+77.6$	$-$	$0 =$	$+77.6$
2	$+77.6$	$-$	$0 =$	$+77.6$
3	$+77.6$	$-$	$0 =$	$+77.6$

Solve for the incremental rate of return:

PW of benefits = PW of costs
$$200.0 = 77.6(P/A, i, 3)$$
$$(P/A, i, 3) = 200/77.6$$
$$= 2.577$$

From Compound Interest Tables, the incremental rate of return is 8%. Since the rate of return on the $A - Do\ Nothing$ increment of investment is less than the desired 10%, reject the increment by rejecting Alternative A. We select the remaining alternative: Do nothing!

If you have not already done so, you should go back to Example 20 and see how the slightly changed wording of the problem radically altered it. Example 20 required the choice between two undesirable alternatives. Example 21 adds the do-nothing alternative, which is superior to A or B.

EXAMPLE 22

Consider four mutually exclusive alternatives:

		Alternative		
	A	B	C	D
Initial Cost	$\$400.0$	$\$100.0$	$\$200.0$	$\$500.0$
Uniform Annual Benefit	100.9	27.7	46.2	125.2

Each alternative has a 5-year useful life and no salvage value. If the minimum attractive rate of return (MARR) is 6%, which alternative should be selected?

Solution

Mutually exclusive means that selecting one alternative precludes selecting any of the other alternatives. This is the typical "textbook" situation. The solution will follow the several steps in incremental analysis.

1. The rate of return is computed for the four alternatives.

Alternative	A	B	C	D
Computed rate of return	8.3%	11.9%	5%	8%

Since $ROR_C < MARR$, it may be eliminated from further consideration.

2. Rank the remaining alternatives in order of increasing initial cost and examine the increment between the two lowest-cost alternatives.

	Alternative		
	B	A	D
Initial Cost	$100.0	$400.0	$500.0
Uniform Annual Benefit	27.7	100.9	125.2

	A – B
ΔInitial Cost	$300.0
ΔUniform Annual Benefit	73.2
ΔROR_{A-B}	7%

Since the incremental ROR exceeds the 6% MARR, Alternative *A* is the better alternative.

3. Take the preferred alternative from Step 2 and consider the next-higher-cost alternative. Do another two-alternative comparison.

	D - A
ΔInitial Cost	$100.0
ΔUniform Annual Benefit	24.3
ΔROR_{D-A}	6.9%

The incremental ROR exceeds the 6% MARR, Alternative *D* is preferred over Alternative *A*.

Conclusion: Select Alternative *D*. Note that once again the alternative with the highest rate of return (Alt. *B*) is not the proper choice.

BENEFIT/COST RATIO

Generally in public works and governmental economic analyses, the dominant analytical tool is the benefit/cost ratio. It is simply the ratio of benefits divided by costs, taking into account the time value of money.

$$B/C = \frac{\text{PW of benefits}}{\text{PW of costs}} = \frac{\text{Equivalent Uniform Annual Benefits}}{\text{Equivalent Uniform Annual Costs}}$$

For a given interest rate, a B/C ratio ≥ 1 reflects an acceptable project. The method of analysis using B/C ratio is parallel to that of rate of return analysis. The same kind of incremental analysis is required.

Application of B/C Ratio for Two Alternatives

Compute the incremental B/C ratio for the cash flow representing the increment of investment between the higher-initial-cost alternative and the lower-initial-cost alternative. If this incremental B/C ratio is ≥ 1, choose the higher-cost alternative; otherwise, choose the lower-cost alternative.

Application of B/C Ratio for Three or More Alternatives

Follow the procedure used for rate of return, except that the test is whether or not the incremental B/C ratio is ≥ 1.

EXAMPLE 23
Use benefit/cost analysis to solve Example 22. Consider four mutually exclusive alternatives:

	Alternative			
	A	*B*	*C*	*D*
Initial Cost	$400.0	$100.0	$200.0	$500.0
Uniform Annual Benefit	100.9	27.7	46.2	125.2

Each alternative has a 5-year useful life and no salvage value. Based on a 6% interest rate, which alternative should be selected?

Solution
1.   B/C ratio computed for the alternatives:

Alt. A $B/C = \dfrac{\text{PW of benefits}}{\text{PW of cost}} = \dfrac{100.9(P/A,\ 6\%,\ 5)}{400} = 1.06$

Alt. B $B/C = \dfrac{\text{PW of benefits}}{\text{PW of cost}} = \dfrac{27.7(P/A,\ 6\%,\ 5)}{100} = 1.17$

Alt. C $B/C = \dfrac{\text{PW of benefits}}{\text{PW of cost}} = \dfrac{46.2(P/A,\ 6\%,\ 5)}{200} = 0.97$

Alt. D $B/C = \dfrac{\text{PW of benefits}}{\text{PW of cost}} = \dfrac{125.2(P/A,\ 6\%,\ 5)}{500} = 1.05$

Alternative C with a B/C ratio less than 1 is eliminated.

2. Rank the remaining alternatives in order of increasing initial cost and examine the increment of investment between the two lowest-cost alternatives.

	Alternative		
	B	*A*	*D*
Initial Cost	$100.0	$400.0	$500.0
Uniform Annual Benefit	27.7	100.9	125.2

	A – B
ΔInitial Cost	$300.0
ΔUniform Annual Benefit	73.2

$$\text{Incremental B/C ratio} = \frac{73.2(P/A, 6\%, 5)}{300} = 1.03$$

The incremental B/C ratio exceeds 1.0 therefore Alternative *A* is preferred over *B*.

3. Take the preferred alternative from Step 2 and consider the next-higher-cost alternative. Do another two-alternative comparison.

	D – A
Δ Initial Cost	$100.0
Δ Uniform Annual Benefit	24.3

$$\text{Incremental B/C ratio} = \frac{24.3(P/A, 6\%, 5)}{100} = 1.02$$

The incremental B/C ratio exceeds 1.0; therefore Alternative *D* is preferred over *A*.

Conclusion: Select Alternative *D*.

BREAKEVEN ANALYSIS

In business, "breakeven" is defined as the point at which income just covers the associated costs. In engineering economics, the breakeven point is more precisely defined as the point at which two alternatives are equivalent.

EXAMPLE 24
A city is considering a new $50,000 snowplow. The new machine will operate at a savings of $600 per day, compared with the equipment presently being used. Assume that the minimum attractive rate of return is 12% and the machine's life is 10 years with zero resale value at that time. How many days per year must new snowplow be used to justify its purchase?

Solution

This breakeven problem may be readily solved by annual cost computations. We will set the equivalent uniform annual cost of the snowplow equal to its equivalent uniform annual benefit, and solve for the required annual utilization.

Let X = breakeven point = days of operation per year.

$$\text{EUAC} = \text{EUAB}$$
$$50{,}000(A/P, 12\%, 10) = 600\,X$$
$$X = \frac{50{,}000(0.1770)}{600}$$
$$= 14.7 \text{ days/year}$$

DEPRECIATION

Depreciation of capital equipment is an important component of after-tax economic analysis. For this reason, one must understand the fundamentals of depreciation accounting.

Depreciation is defined in its accounting sense as the systematic allocation of the cost of a capital asset over its useful life. *Book value* is defined as the original cost of an asset, minus the accumulated depreciation of the asset.

In computing a schedule of depreciation charges, three items are considered:

1. Cost of the property, P
2. Depreciable life in years, n
3. Salvage value of the property at the end of its depreciable life, S

Straight-Line Depreciation

$$\text{Depreciation charge in any year} = \frac{P - S}{n}$$

Sum-of-Years'-Digits Depreciation

$$\text{Depreciation charge in any year} = \frac{\text{Remaining Depreciable Life at Beginning of Year}}{\text{Sum of Years Digits' for Total Useful Life}}(P - S)$$

$$\text{where Sum of Years' Digits} = 1 + 2 + 3 + \cdots + n = \frac{n}{2}(n + 1)$$

Double Declining Balance Depreciation

$$\text{Depreciation charge in any year} = \frac{2}{n}(P - \text{Depreciation charges to date})$$

Modified Accelerated Cost Recovery System Depreciation

Modified accelerated cost recovery system (MACRS) depreciation is based on a property class life that is typically less than the actual useful life of the property and on zero salvage value. The varying depreciation percentage to use must be read from a table (based on declining balance with conversion to straight line). To calculate the depreciation charge in any given year, the proper MACRS property class must first be determined. The following tables are used with MACRS depreciation. Table 1 categorizes assets by recovery period. Table 2 provides the percentage depreciation allowed each year.

Depreciation charge in any year $n = P$(percentage depreciation allowance)

Table 1 Recovery Periods for MACRS

Property Class	Personal Property (all except real estate)
3-Year	Special handling devices for food and beverage manufacture
	Special tools for the manufacture of finished plastic products, fabricated metal products, and motor vehicles
	Property with ADR $\leq$ 4 years
5-Year	Automobiles, buses, trucks, noncommercial aircraft
	Computers
	Construction equipment, petroleum drilling equipment and R&D equipment
	Property with 4 years $<$ ADR $<$ 10 years
7-Year	And items not assigned to another class
	Office furniture, fixture, and equipment
	Most manufacturing equipment and mining equipment
	Property with 10 years $\leq$ ADR $<$ 16 years
10-Year	Marine vessels and water transportation equipment
	Petroleum refining equipment
	Single-purpose agricultural structures, trees and vines that bear nuts or fruits
	Property with 16 years $\leq$ ADR $<$ 20 years
15-Year	Steam and electric generation and distribution systems
	Telephone distribution facilities
	Municipal wastewater (sewage) treatment facilities
	Property with 20 years $\leq$ ADR $<$ 25 years
20-Year	Municipal sewers
	Property with ADR $\geq$ 25 years
Property Class	**Real Property (real estate)**
27.5-Year	Residential rental property (does not include hotels and motels)
39-Year	Nonresidential real property

Table 2 MACRS Percentages

Applicable Percentages for Property Class

Year	3-year	5-year	7-year	10-year	15-year	20-year
1	33.33	20.00	14.29	10.00	5.00	3.750
2	44.45	32.00	24.49	18.00	9.50	7.219
3	14.81	19.20	17.49	14.40	8.55	6.677
4	7.41	11.52	12.49	11.52	7.70	6.177
5		11.52	8.93	9.22	6.93	5.713
6		5.76	8.92	7.37	6.23	5.285
7			8.93	6.55	5.90	4.888
8			4.46	6.55	5.90	4.522
9				6.56	5.91	4.462
10				6.55	5.90	4.461
11				3.28	5.91	4.462
12					5.90	4.461
13					5.91	4.462
14					5.90	4.461
15					5.91	4.462
16					2.95	4.461
17						4.462
18						4.461
19						4.462
20						4.461
21						2.231

EXAMPLE 25

A piece of construction machinery costs $5000 and has an anticipated $1000 salvage value at the end of its 5-year depreciable life. Compute the depreciation schedule for the machinery by:

a. Straight-line depreciation
b. Sum-of-years'-digits depreciation
c. Double declining balance depreciation
d. MACRS

Solution

$$\text{Straight-line depreciation} = \frac{P - S}{n} = \frac{5000 - 1000}{5} = \$800$$

Sum-of-years'-digits depreciation:

$$\text{Sum-of-years'-digits} = \frac{n}{2}(n+1) = \frac{5}{2}(6) = 15$$

1st-year depreciation $= \dfrac{5}{15}(5000 - 1000) = \$1333$

2nd-year depreciation $= \dfrac{4}{15}(5000 - 1000) = 1067$

3rd-year depreciation $= \dfrac{3}{15}(5000 - 1000) = 800$

4th-year depreciation $= \dfrac{2}{15}(5000 - 1000) = 533$

5th-year depreciation $= \dfrac{1}{15}(5000 - 1000) = \underline{\ \ 267}$

$\$4000$

Double declining balance depreciation:

1st-year depreciation $= \dfrac{2}{5}(5000 - 0) = \$2000$

2nd-year depreciation $= \dfrac{2}{5}(5000 - 2000) = 1200$

3rd-year depreciation $= \dfrac{2}{5}(5000 - 3200) = 720$

4th-year depreciation $= \dfrac{2}{5}(5000 - 3920) = \cancel{432}\quad 80$

5th-year depreciation $= \dfrac{2}{5}(5000 - 4352) = \underline{\cancel{259}}\quad \underline{\ \ 0}$

$\$4611\quad \$4000$

Since the problem specifies a $1000 salvage value, the total depreciation cannot $4000. The double declining balance depreciation must be stopped in the 4th year, when it totals $4000.

MACRS

Since the asset is specified as construction equipment, the 5-year recovery period is determined. Note that the depreciation will be over a 6-year period. This is because only ½-year depreciation is allowed in the first year. The remaining ½-year is recovered in the last year. If an asset is disposed of midlife, then only ½ of the disposal year's depreciation is taken. Also note that the salvage value is not used in the depreciation calculations.

1st-year depreciation $= 0.2000(5000) = \$1000$
2nd-year depreciation $= 0.3200(5000) = 1600$
3rd-year depreciation $= 0.1920(5000) = 960$
4th-year depreciation $= 0.1152(5000) = 576$
5th-year depreciation $= 0.1152(5000) = 576$
6th-year depreciation $= 0.0576(5000) = \underline{\ \ 288}$
$\$5000$

The depreciation schedules computed by the four methods are as follows:

Year	SL	SOYD	DDB	MACRS
1	$800	$1333	$2000	$1000
2	800	1067	1200	1600
3	800	800	720	960
4	800	533	80	576
5	800	267	0	576
6				288

INCOME TAXES

Income taxes represent another of the various kinds of disbursements encountered in an economic analysis. The starting point in an after-tax computation is the before-tax cash flow. Generally, the before-tax cash flow contains entries of three types:

1. Disbursements of money to purchase capital assets: these expenditures create no direct tax consequence for they are the exchange of one asset (cash) for another (capital equipment).

2. Periodic receipts and/or disbursements representing operating income and/or expenses: these increase or decrease the year-by-year tax liability of the firm.

3. Receipts of money from the sale of capital assets, usually in the form of a salvage value when the equipment is removed from service: the tax consequence depends on the relationship between the residual value of the asset and its book value (cost − depreciation taken).

Residual Value	Tax Consequence
Is less than current book value	Loss on sale
Equals current book value	No loss & no recapture
Exceeds current book value	Recaptured depreciation
Exceeds initial book value	Recaptured depreciation & capital gain

The step that follows after the before-tax cash flow is to compute the depreciation schedule for any capital assets. Then, taxable income is the taxable component of the before-tax cash flow minus the depreciation. The income tax is then the taxable income times the appropriate tax rate. Finally, the after-tax cash flow is the before-tax cash flow adjusted for income taxes.

To organize these data, it is customary to arrange them in the form of a cash flow table, as follows:

Year	Before-tax Cash Flow	Depreciation	Taxable Income	Income Taxes	After-tax Cash Flow
0	—	—	—	—	—
1	—	—	—	—	—

EXAMPLE 26

A corporation expects to receive $32,000 each year for 15 years from the sale of a product. There will be an initial investment of $150,000. Manufacturing and sales expenses will be $8067 per year. Assume straight-line depreciation, a 15-year useful life, and no salvage value. Use a 46% income tax rate. Determine the projected after-tax rate of return.

Solution

$$\text{Straight-line depreciation} = \frac{P-S}{n} = \frac{150,000-0}{15} = \$10,000 \text{ per year}$$

Year	Before-tax Cash Flow	Depreciation	Taxable Income	Income Taxes	After-tax Cash Flow
0	−150,000				−150,000
1	+23,933	10,000	13,933	−6409	+17,524
2	+23,933	10,000	13,933	−6409	+17,524
.	.	.	.	.	.
.	.	.	.	.	.
.	.	.	.	.	.
15	+23,933	10,000	13,933	-6409	+17,524

Take the after-tax cash flow and compute the rate of return at which the PW of benefits equals the PW of costs.

$$17,524(P/A, i, 15) = 150,000$$
$$(P/A, i, 15) = 150,000/17,524$$
$$= 8.559$$

From Compound Interest Tables, $i = 8\%$.

INFLATION

Inflation is a decrease in the buying power of the dollar (peso, yen, or other currency). More generally, it is thought of as the increase in the level of prices. Inflation rates are usually estimated as having a constant rate of change. This type of cash flow is a geometric gradient.

Future cash flows are generally estimated in constant-value terms. The assumption is made that the inflation rates for various cash flows will match the economy's inflation rate. This allows for the use of a real interest rate.

Another approach uses the market interest rate. The market rate includes both the time value of money and an estimate of current and predicted inflation.

For exact calculation of real and market interest rates the following formula is used.

$$(1 + \text{Market rate}) = (1 + i)(1 + f)$$
where i = the real interest rate
f = the inflation rate

EXAMPLE 27

Determine the market interest rate if the inflation rate is estimated to be 2.5% and the time value of money (the real interest rate) is 6%.

Solution

(1 + Market rate) = (1 + 0.06)(1 + 0.025)
(1 + Market rate) = 1.0865
  Market rate = 0.0865 = 8.65%

Uncertainty and Probability

It is unrealistic to consider future cash flows to be known exactly. Cash flows, useful life, salvage value, and so on can all be expressed by using probability distributions. Then measures of expected or average return and of risk can be used in the decision-making process.

   Probabilities can be derived from the following:

1. Historical trends or data
2. Mathematical models (probability distributions)
3. Subjective estimates

   Probabilities must satisfy the following:

1. $0 \le P \le 1$.
2. The sum of all probabilities must = 1.

   Expected values for cash flows, useful life, salvage value, and so on can be found by using a weighted average calculation.

EXAMPLE 28

The following table summarizes estimated annual benefits, annual costs, and end-of-life value for an asset under consideration. Determine the expected value for each of the three. If the asset has a first cost of $25,950 and an anticipated life of 8 years, determine the rate of return for the asset.

	State and Associated Probability			
	$p = .20$	$p = .40$	$p = .25$	$p = .15$
Annual benefits	3000	6500	8000	11,500
Annual costs	1500	2800	5000	5,750
End-of-life value	5000	7500	9000	10,000

Solution

E(Annual Benefits)	= .20(3000) + .40(6500) + .25(8000) + .15(11,500)
	= $6,925.00

E(Annual Costs)	= .20(1500) + .40(2800) + .25(5000) + .15(5750)
	= $3,532.50

E(End-of-Life Value)	= .20(5000) + .40(7500) + .25(9000) + .15(10,000)
	= $7750.00

To determine ROR:

PW of benefits – PW of costs = 0

$[6925(P/A, i\%, 8) + 7750(P/F, i\%, 8)] – [25,950 + 3532.5(P/A, i\%, 8)] = 0$

Try 6%:

$[6925(6.210) + 7750(.6274)] - [25,950 + 3532.5(6.210)] = –\$20.22$

Try 5%:

$[6925(6.463) + 7750(.6768)] – [25,950 + 3532.5(6.463)] = \$1220.93$

By interpolation, the ROR = 5.98%.

Chapter 1

Making Economic Decisions

1-1

Many engineers earn high salaries for creating profits for their employers and then, at retirement time, find themselves insufficiently prepared financially. This may be because in college courses there is little or no discussion on using engineering economics for the direct personal benefit of the engineer. Among the goals of every engineer should be assuring that adequate funds will be available for anticipated personal needs at retirement.

A realistic goal of retiring at age 65 with a personal net worth in excess of $2 million can be accomplished by several methods. An independent study ranked the probability of success of the following methods of personal wealth accumulation. Discuss and decide the ranking order of the following five methods.

a. Purchase as many lottery tickets as possible with money saved from salary.
b. Place money saved from salary in a bank savings account.
c. Place all money saved from a salary in a money market account.
d. Invest saved money into rental properties and spend evenings, weekends, and vacations repairing and managing.
e. Invest all money saved into stock market securities, and study investments 10 to 15 hours per week.

Solution

Independent studies can be misleading. If a recent winner of a $2million lottery drawing were asked to rank wealth accumulation methods, item a would head his or her list. A workaholic with handyman talent might put item d as his Number 1 choice. Similarly, many people have become millionaires by investing in real estate and in other ways not listed here. The important thing is to learn about the many investment vehicles available and then choose the one or the several most suitable for you.

1-2

A food processor is considering the development of a new product. Depending on the quality of raw material, he can expect different yields process-wise, and the quality of the final products will also vary considerably. The product development department has identified three alternatives, which it has produced on a pilot scale. The marketing department has used those samples for surveys to estimate potential sales and pricing strategies. The three alternatives, which would use existing equipment, but different process conditions and specifications, are summarized as follows. Indicate which alternative seems to be the best according to the estimated data, if the objective is to maximize total profit per year.

	Alternative		
	1	2	3
Pounds of raw material A per unit of product	0.05	0.07	0.075
Pounds of raw material B per unit of product	0.19	0.18	0.26
Pounds of raw material C per unit of product	0.14	0.12	0.17
Other processing costs ($/unit product)	$0.16	$0.24	$0.23
Expected wholesale price ($/unit product)	0.95	1.05	1.25
Projected volume of sales (units of product)	1,000,000	1,250,000	800,000
Cost of raw material A $3.45/lb			
Cost of raw material B $1.07/lb			
Cost of raw material C $1.88/lb			

Solution

		Alternative		
		1	2	3
Cost of raw raterial A ($/unit product)	0.05×3.45 =	0.1725	0.2415	0.2587
Cost of raw raterial B ($/unit product)	0.19×1.07 =	0.2033	0.1926	0.2782
Cost of raw material C ($/unit product)	0.14×1.88 =	0.2632	0.2256	0.3196
Other processing costs ($/unit product)		$0.16	$0.24	$0.23
Total cost ($/unit product)		0.799	0.8997	1.0865
Wholesale price ($/unit product)		0.95	1.05	1.25
Profit/unit		0.151	0.1503	0.1635
Projected sales (units of product)		1,000,000	1,250,000	800,000
Projected profits		151,000	187,875	130,800

Therefore, choose Alternative 2.

1-3

Car *A* initially costs $500 more than Car *B*, but it consumes 0.04 gallon/mile versus 0.05 gallon/mile for *B*. Both vehicles last 8 years, and *B*'s salvage value is $100 smaller than *A*'s. Fuel costs $1.70 per gallon. Other things being equal, beyond how many miles of use per year (*X*) does *A* become preferable to *B*?

Solution

$$-500 + 100 + (0.05 - 0.04)\,(1.70)\,(8)X = 0$$
$$-400 + 0.136X = 0$$
$$X = 400/0.136$$
$$= 2941 \text{ miles/year}$$

1-4

Sam decides to buy a cattle ranch and leave the big-city rat race. He locates an attractive 500-acre spread in Montana for $1000 per acre that includes a house, a barn, and other improvements. Sam's studies indicate that he can run 200 cow–calf pairs and be able to market 180 500-pound calves per year. Sam, being rather thorough in his investigation, determines that he will need to purchase an additional $95,000 worth of machinery. He expects that supplemental feeds, medications, and veterinary bills will be about $50 per cow per year. Property taxes are $4000 per year, and machinery upkeep and repairs are expected to run $3000 per year.

If interest is 10% and Sam would like a net salary of $10,000 per year, how much will he have to get for each 500-pound calf?

Solution

Land cost : $500 acres × $1000/acre = $500,000
Machinery: Lump sum   =   95,000
Total fixed cost $595,000

Assume lands and machinery to have a <u>very</u> long life:
at 10% annual cost = (0.10)($595,000) = $59,500
Other annual costs:

        Feeds, medications, vet bills $50 × 200 = $10,000
        Property taxes   4,000
        Upkeep and repairs   3,000
        Salary   10,000
Total annual cost $86,500

Net sale price of each calf would have to be $86,500/180 = $480.56.

Note: If Sam were to invest his $595,000 in a suitable investment vehicle yielding 10% interest, his salary would be almost six times greater, and he could go fishing instead of punching cows.

1-5

The following letter to Joseph Priestley, the English chemist, was written by his friend Benjamin Franklin. Priestley had been invited to become the librarian for the Earl of Shelburne and had asked for Franklin's advice. What engineering economy principle does Franklin suggest Priestley use to aid in making his decision?

London, September 19, 1772
Dear Sir:

In the affair of so much importance to you wherein you ask my advice, I cannot, for want of sufficient premises, advise you what to determine, but if you please I will tell you how. When these difficult cases occur, they are difficult chiefly because while we have them under consideration, all the reasons Pro and Con are not present to the mind at the same time; but sometimes one set present themselves, and at other times another, the first being out of sight. Hence the various purposes or inclination that alternately prevail, and the uncertainty that perplexes us.

To get over this, my way is to divide a half a sheet of paper by a line into two columns; writing over the one PRO and over the other CON. Then during three or four days' consideration I put down under the different heads short hints of the different motives that at different times occur to me, for or against the measure. When I have thus got them all together in one view, I endeavour to estimate their respective weights; and where I find two (one on each side) that seem equal, I strike them both out. If I find a reason Pro equal to some two reasons Con, I strike out the three. If I judge some two reasons Con equal to three reasons Pro, I strike out the five; and thus proceeding I find at length where the balance lies; and if after a day or two of further consideration, nothing new that is of importance occurs on either side, I come to a determination accordingly. And though the weight of the reasons cannot be taken with the precision of algebraic quantities, yet when each is thus considered separately and comparatively and the whole lies before me, I think I can judge better, and am less likely to make a rash step; and in fact I have found great advantage from this kind of equation in what may be called moral or prudential algebra.

Wishing sincerely that you may determine for the best, I am ever, my dear friend, your most affectionately...

s/Ben Franklin

Solution

Decisions should be based on the differences between the alternatives. Here the alternatives are taking the job (Pro) and not taking the job (Con).

1-6

Assume that you are employed as an engineer for Wreckall Engineering, Inc., a firm specializing in the demolition of high-rise buildings. The firm has won a bid to tear down a 30-story building in a heavily developed downtown area. The crane the company owns reaches only to 29 stories. Your boss asks you to perform an economic analysis to determine the feasibility of buying a new crane to complete the job. How would you handle the analysis?

Solution

The important point of this exercise is to realize that your boss may not have recognized what the true problem is in this case. To buy a new crane is only <u>one</u> alternative, and quite likely not the best alternative. Others include:

> extension on current crane
> ramp for current crane
> renting a crane to remove the top story
> explosive demolition

If this is a fixed-output project (i.e., there is a fixed fee for demolishing building) we want to minimize costs. Weigh alternatives using economic criteria to choose the best alternative.

1-7

The total cost of a building (TC) is given by

$$TC = \left(200 + 80X + 2X^2\right)A$$

where $X =$ number of floors and $A =$ floor area (ft^2 per floor)

If the total number of square feet required is 10^6, what is the optimal (minimum cost) number of floors?

Solution

$$TC = \left(200 + 80X + 2X^2\right)\left(\frac{10^6}{X}\right)$$

$$\frac{dTC}{dx} = \left(10^6\right)\left(\frac{-200}{X^2} + 2\right) = 0$$

$$X^* = \sqrt{\frac{200}{2}} = \sqrt{100} = 10 \text{ floors}$$

1-8

By wisely saving and investing, Helen finds she has accumulated $400,000 in savings while her salaried position is providing her with $40,000 per year, including benefits, after income taxes and other deductions.

Helen's salaried position is demanding and allows her little free time, but the desire to pursue other interests has become very strong. What would be your advice to her, if you were asked?

Solution

First, Helen should decide what annual income she needs to provide herself with the things she wants. Depending on her age, she might be able to live on the interest income (maybe 10% × $400,000 = $40,000), or a combination of interest and principal. The important thing for Helen to realize is that it may be possible for her to have a more fulfilling lifestyle if she is fully aware of the time value of money. Many people keep large sums of money in bank checking accounts (drawing no interest) because they can write "free" checks.

1-9

Charles belongs to a square dance club that meets twice each month and has quarterly dues of $9 per person. The club moved its meeting place to a more expensive location. To offset the increased cost, members agreed to pay 50 cents apiece each time they attend the meeting. Later the treasurer suggests that the quarterly dues be increased to $12 per person as an alternative to the meeting charge. Discuss the consequences of the proposal. Do you think all the club members will agree to the proposal?

Solution

The members who attend regularly would pay the same amount with the new dues as with the older method: that is, $9 plus 50 cents per meeting. Many would like the added advantage of covering their quarterly expenses in one check. The members who attend infrequently would pay more under the new method and might oppose the action.

Since the people who attend infrequently are in the minority in this club, the proposal was approved when the members voted.

Chapter 2

Engineering Costs
and
Cost Estimating

2-1

A small community outside of Atlanta, Georgia, is planning to construct a new fire station. As currently planned it will have 7000 square feet under roof. The area cost factor is 86% of the 144-city average. The estimated cost per square foot for a typical 3500-ft^2 facility is $98. Based on economies of scale, a size adjustment factor of 95% can be used. Estimate the cost of the construction. Assume a cost growth factor of 1.364.

Solution

Estimated cost = 98(7000)(0.95)(0.86)(1.364)
            = $764,470

2-2

In 2009 a new 21-kW power substation was built in Gibson County, Tennessee, for $1.4 million. Weakley County, a nearby county, is planning to build a similar though smaller (18-kW) substation in 2012. The inflation rate has averaged 1.5% per year. If the power sizing exponent is .85 for this type of facility what is the estimated cost of construction of the Weakley County substation?

Solution

Cost of the 21-kW substation in 2008 dollars = $1,400,000(1.015)^3 = \$1,463,950$

$$C_x = C_k(S_x/S_k)^n$$

$$C_{21} = C_{18}(18/21)^{.85} = 1,463,950(.8772)$$
$$= \$1,284,177$$

2-3

The time required to produce the first gizmo is 1500 blips. Determine the time required to produce the 450th gizmo if the learning-curve coefficient is .85.

Solution

$$T_i = T_1 \Theta^{(\ln i/\ln 2)}$$

$$T_{450} = 1500(.85)^{(\ln 450/\ln 2)} = 358.1 \text{ blips}$$

2-4

Four operations are required to produce a certain product produced by ABC Manufacturing. Use the following information to determine the labor cost of producing the 1000th piece.

	Time Required for 1st Piece	Learning-Curve Coefficient	Labor Cost per hour
Operation 1	1 hour, 15 minutes	.90	$ 8.50
Operation 2	2 hours	.82	12.00
Operation 3	2 hours, 45 minutes	.98	7.75
Operation 4	4 hours, 10 minutes	.74	10.50

Solution

$$T_i = T_1 \Theta^{(\ln i/\ln 2)}$$

Operation 1:

$$T_{1000} = 75(.90)^{(\ln 1000/\ln 2)} = 26.25 \text{ minutes}$$
$$\text{Cost} = 26.25/60 \times 8.50 = \$3.72$$

Operation 2:

$$T_{1000} = 120(.82)^{(\ln 1000/\ln 2)} = 16.61 \text{ minutes}$$
$$\text{Cost} = 16.61/60 \times 12.00 = \$3.32$$

Operation 3:

$$T_{1000} = 165(.98)^{(\ln 1000/\ln 2)} = 134.91 \text{ minutes}$$
$$\text{Cost} = 134.91/60 \times 7.75 = \$17.43$$

Operation 4

$$T_{1000} = 250(.74)^{(\ln 1000/\ln 2)} = 12.44 \text{ minutes}$$
$$\text{Cost} = 12.44/60 \times 10.50 = \$2.18$$

Total cost = 3.72 + 3.32 + 17.43 + 2.18 = $26.65

2-5

American Petroleum (AP) recently completed construction on a large refinery in Texas. The final construction cost was $27,500,000. The refinery covers a total of 340 acres. The Expansion and Acquisition Department at AP is currently working on plans for a new refinery for the panhandle of Oklahoma. The anticipated size is approximately 260 acres. If the power-sizing exponent for this type of facility is .67, what is the estimated cost of construction?

Solution

$$C_x = C_k(S_x/S_k)^n$$

$$C_{260} = C_{340}(260/340)^{.67} = 27,500,000(.83549)$$
$$= \$22,975,975$$

2-6

A new training program at Arid Industries is intended to lower the learning-curve coefficient of a certain molding operation that currently costs $95.50/hour. The current coefficient is .87, and the program hopes to lower the coefficient by 10%. Assume that the time to mold the first product is 8 hours. If the program is successful, what cost savings will be realized when the 2000th piece is produced?

Solution

$$T_i = T_1 \Theta^{(\ln i / \ln 2)}$$

Without the training program:

$$T_{2000} = 8(.87)^{(\ln 2000/\ln 2)} = 1.74 \text{ hours}$$

With the training program:

$$T_{2000} = 8(.783)^{(\ln 2000/\ln 2)} = 0.547 \text{ hour}$$

Cost savings = $(1.74 - 0.547)(95.50) = \$113.93$

2-7

The following data concern one of the most popular products of XYZ Manufacturing. Estimate the selling price per unit.

Labor	= 12.8 hours at $18.75/hour
Factory overhead	= 92% of labor
Material costs	= $65.10
Packing cost	= 10% of materials
Sales commission	= 10% of selling price
Profit	= 22% of selling price

Solution

Labor cost	=	12.8×18.75	=	$240.00
Factory overhead	=	92% of labor	=	220.80
Material cost	=		=	65.10
Packing cost	=	10% of material costs	=	6.51
				$532.41

Let X be the selling price

$$0.10X + 0.22X + 532.41 = X$$
$$0.68X = 532.41$$
$$X = 532.41/0.68 = \$782.96$$

2-8
Draw a cash flow diagram for the following situation (EOP = end of period).

EOP	Cash Flow
0	−$1000
1	200
2	−100
3	300
4	400
5	−400
6	500

Solution

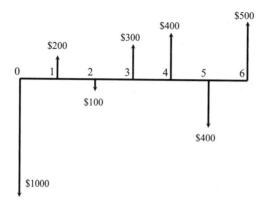

Chapter 3

Interest
and
Equivalence

3-1

Ten years ago, Jenna C. deposited $2000 into an account that paid 5% simple interest for the first 4 years and 6% compounded monthly for the remaining 6 years. The amount in the account at the end of the 10-year period is closest to

a. $3420
b. $3440
c. $3460
d. $3480

Solution

Simple interest earned at end of 4 years = $2000 \times 0.05 \times 4 = \$400$

$i = 6/12 = \frac{1}{2}\%$ $n = 12 \times 6 = 72$

$F = 2400(1.005)72 = \$3436.90$

The answer is b.

3-2

If you had $1000 now and invested it at 6%, how much would it be worth 12 years from now?

Solution

$F = 1000(F/P, 6\%, 12) = \$2012.00$

3-3

Mr. Ray deposited $200,000 in the Old and Third National Bank. If the bank pays 8% interest, how much will he have in the account at the end of 10 years?

Solution

$F = 200,000(F/P, 8\%, 10) = \$431,800$

3-4

If you can earn 6% interest on your money, how much would $1000 paid to you 12 years in the future be worth to you now?

Solution

$P = 1000(P/F, 6\%, 12) = \$497$

3-5

Downtown has been experiencing an explosive population growth of 10% per year. At the end of 2005 the population was 16,000. If the growth rate continues unabated, how many years will it take for the population to triple? Give your answer in terms of the end of the last year.

Solution

Use $i = 10\%$ to represent the growth rate.

$$48,000 = 16,000(F/P, 10\%, n)$$
$$(F/P, 10\%, n) = 48,000/16,000$$
$$= 3.000$$

From the 10% table, n is 12
Note that population would not have tripled after 11 years.

3-6

If the interest rate is 6% compounded quarterly, how long (number of quarters) will it take to earn $100 interest on an initial deposit of $300?

Solution

$$i = 6\%/4 = 1\tfrac{1}{2}\%$$

$$400 = 300(F/P, 1\tfrac{1}{2}\%, n)$$
$$(F/P, 1\tfrac{1}{2}\%, n) = 400/300$$
$$= 1.333$$

From the 1½% table, $n = 20$ quarters

3-7

A man decides to put $100 per month beginning one month from today into an account paying 12% compounded monthly. Determine how much (to the nearest penny) will be in the account immediately after the fourth deposit; use only basic concepts.

Solution

Month	Beginning Balance	Interest @ 1%	Deposit	Ending Balance	
1	$ 0.00	0.00	$100	$100.00	
2	100.00	1.00	100	201.00	
3	201.00	2.01	100	303.01	
4	303.01	3.03	100	406.04	←Answer

3-8
Determine the value of P using the appropriate factor.

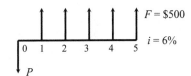

Solution

$P = F(P/F, 6\%, 5) = \$500(0.7473) = \$373.65$

3-9
One thousand dollars, deposited into an account that pays interest monthly, is allowed to remain in the account for 3 years. If the annual interest rate is 6%, the balance at the end of the 3 years is closest to

a. $1180
b. $1191
c. $1197
d. $2898

Solution

$i = 6/12 = \frac{1}{2}\%$ $n = 12 \times 3 = 36$

$F = P(1 + i)^n = 1000(1.005)^{36} = \$1196.68$

or, using interest tables,

$F = 1000(F/P, \frac{1}{2}\%, 36) = 1000(1.197) = \$1197$

The answer is c.

3-10

On July 1 and September 1, Abby placed $2000 into an account paying 3% compounded monthly. How much was in the account on October 1?

Solution

$i = 3/12 = \frac{1}{4}\%$

$F = 2000(1 + 0.0025)^3 + 2000(1 + 0.0025)^1 = \$4020.04$

or

$F = 2000(F/P, \frac{1}{4}\%, 3) + 2000(F/P, \frac{1}{4}\%, 1) = \$4022.00$

3-11

The amount of money accumulated in 5 years with an initial deposit of $10,000, if the account earned 12% compounded monthly the first 3 years and 15% compounded semiannually the last 2 years, is closest to

a. $18,580
b. $19,110
c. $19,230
d. $1,034,285

Solution

$F = [10,000(F/P, 1\%, 36)](F/P, 7.5\%, 4)$
$= 10,000(1.431)(1.075)^4$
$= \$19,110.56$

3-12

An investment of $10,000 six years ago has now grown to $20,000. The annual interest rate on this investment, assuming annual compounding, is

a. 6%
b. 8%
c. 10%
d. 12%

Solution

$F = P(1 + i)^n$
$20,000 = 10,000(1 + i)^6$
$i = 12\%$

The answer is d.

3-13

A local bank is advertising to savers a rate of 6% compounded monthly, yielding an effective annual rate of 6.168%. If $2000 is placed in savings now and no withdrawals are made, how much interest (to the penny) will be earned in one year?

Solution

Interest = Effective annual rate × Principal = $0.06168 \times 2000 = \$123.36$

Monthly compounding is irrelevant when the effective rate is known.

3-14

A small company borrowed $10,000 to expand the business. The entire principal of $10,000 will be repaid in 2 years, but quarterly interest of $330 must be paid every 3 months. What nominal annual interest rate is the company paying?

Solution

The $330 is interest for one period; therefore $i = 330/10,000 = 3.3\%$ per quarter:

$r = 3.3 \times 4 = 13.2\%$ nominal annual rate

3-15

A Cole's Home Solutions policy is to charge 1¼% interest each month on the unpaid balance. What nominal interest is Cole's charging? What is the effective interest?

Solution

(a) $r = im = 12 \times 1.25 = 15\%$

(b) $i_{eff} = (1 + i)^n - 1 = (1.0125)^{12} - 1 = 16.075\%$

3-16

E. Z. Marc received a loan of $50 from the S. H. Ark loan company; he had to repay it one month later with a single payment of $60. What was the nominal annual interest rate for this loan?

Solution

Interest = $10 for one month
$i = 10/50 = 20\%$
$r = im = 20 \times 12 = 240\%$

3-17

A college parking enforcement bureau issues parking tickets. A person receiving a ticket may pay either $5 immediately or $7 if payment is deferred one week. What nominal interest rate is implied in the arrangement?

Solution

$i = (7 - 5)/5 = 40\%$ per week

$r = im = 52 \times 40 = 2080\%$

3-18

For a nominal interest of 16%, what is effective interest if interest is

a.   compounded quarterly?
b.   compounded monthly?
c.   compounded continuously?

Solution

a. $i_{\text{eff}} = [(1 + 0.04)^4 - 1] = 16.99\%$

b. $i_{\text{eff}} = [(1 + 0.01333)^{12} - 1] = 17.22\%$

c. $i_{\text{eff}} = [e^{.16} - 1] = 17.35\%$

3-19

Which is the better investment, a fund that pays 15% compounded annually or one that pays 14% compounded continuously?

Solution

$i_{\text{eff}} = 15\%$ compounded annually $= [(1 + 0.15)^1 - 1] = 15\%$

$i_{\text{eff}} = 14\%$ compounded continuously $= [e^{0.14} - 1] = 15.03\%$

Therefore, 14% compounded continuously is slightly better.

3-20

The effective interest rate is 19.56%. If there are 12 compounding periods per year, what is the nominal interest rate?

Solution

$i_{\text{eff}} = (1 + (r/m))^m - 1 \Rightarrow r/m = (1 + i_{\text{eff}})^{1/m} - 1 = (1.1956)^{1/12} - 1 = 1.5\%$

$r = 12 \times 1.5 = 18\%$

3-21

The Block Concrete Company borrowed $20,000 at 8% interest, compounded semiannually, to be paid off in one payment at the end of 4 years. At the end of the 4 years, Block made a payment of $8000 and refinanced the remaining balance at 6% interest, compounded monthly, to be paid at the end of 2 years. The amount Block owes at the end of the 2 years is nearest to

a. $21,580
b. $21,841
c. $22,020
d. $34,184

Solution

$$i_1 = 8/2 = 4\% \qquad n_1 = (4)(2) = 8 \qquad i_2 = 6/2 = \frac{1}{2}\% \qquad n_2 = (12)(2)$$

$$F = [20,000(F/P, 4\%, 8) - 8000](F/P, \frac{1}{2}\%, 24)$$

$$= \$21,841.26$$

The answer is b.

3-22

What is the effective interest rate on a continuously compounded loan that has a nominal interest rate of 25%?

a. $e^{1.25}$
b. $e^{0.25}$
c. $e^{1.25} - 1$
d. $e^{.25} - 1$

Solution

$$i_{eff} = e^r - 1$$

$$i_{eff} = e^{0.25} - 1$$

The answer is d.

3-23

Given an annual interest rate of 5%, when continuous compounding is used rather than monthly compounding, the nominal interest rate

a. increases.
b. remains the same.
c. decreases.

Solution

The answer is b: remains the same

3-24

You borrowed $25 from a friend and after 5 months repaid $27. What nominal interest rate did you pay? What was the effective interest rate?

Solution

$$F = P(1 + i)^n$$
$$27 = 25(1 + i)^5$$
$$(27/25)^{1/5} = 1 + i$$
$$= 1.0155$$

$i = 1.55\%$ per month or 18.6% per year

$$i_{\text{eff}} = (1 + 0.0155)^{12} - 1 = 20.27\%$$

3-25

A local Qwik Kash will loan a person $2000 with a payment of $2200 due in 4 weeks. What nominal annual interest rate is the company is charging?

Solution

$i = 200/2{,}000 = 10\%$

$r = 13 \times 10\% = 130\%$

3-26

A deposit of $300 was made one year ago into an account paying monthly interest. If the account now has $320.52, what was the effective annual interest rate? Give answer to 1/100 of a percent.

Solution

$i_{\text{eff}} = 20.52/300 = 6.84\%$

3-27

How much should Abigail invest in a fund that will pay 9%, compounded continuously, if she wishes to have $60,000 in the fund at the end of 10 years?

Solution

$r = 0.09$
$n = 10$

$P = Fe^{-rn} = 60{,}000e^{-.09(10)} = \$24{,}394.18$

3-28
Given:

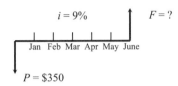

$i = 9\%$ $F = ?$

Jan Feb Mar Apr May June

$P = \$350$

Find: a. F
        b. i_{eff}

Solution

    a. $F = 350(F/P,\ 0.75\%,\ 6) = \$366.10$
    b. $i_{\text{eff}} = (1 + i)^m - 1 = (1.0075)^{12} - 1 = 9.38\%$

3-29
Five hundred dollars is deposited into an account that pays 5% interest compounded continuously. If the money remains in the account for 3 years, the account balance is nearest to

a. $525
b. $578
c. $580
d. $598

Solution

$F = e^{rn} = 500e^{.05(3)}$
        $= \$580.91$

The answer is c.

3-30
The effective interest rate on a mortgage with monthly payments is 9.38%. What is the monthly interest rate on the mortgage? What is the nominal interest rate?

Solution

$$i_{\text{eff}} = [(1 + i)^m - 1] = 9.38\%$$
$$0.0938 = [(1 + i)^{12} - 1]$$
$$1.0938 = (1 + i)^{12}$$
$$i = 0.75\% \text{ (per month)}$$

$$r = im = 0.75 \times 12 = 9\%$$

3-31

One thousand dollars, deposited into an account that pays interest monthly, is allowed to remain in the account for 3 years. The balance at the end of the 3 years is $1309.00. The nominal interest paid on this account is nearest to

a. ¾%
b. 9%
c. 9.38%
d. 10.3%

Solution

$$F = P(1 + i)^n$$
$$1309 = 1000(1 + i)^{36}$$
$$1.309 = (1 + i)^{36}$$
$$i = 0.75\% \text{ (per month)}$$

$$r = im = 0.75 \times 12 = 9\%$$

The answer is b.

3-32

The multistate Powerball Lottery, worth $182 million, was won by a single individual who had purchased five tickets at $1 each. The winner was given two choices: receive 26 payments of $7 million each, with the first payment to be made now and the rest to be made at the end of each of the next 25 years, or receive a single lump-sum payment now that would be equivalent to the 26 payments of $7 million each. If the state uses an interest rate of 4% per year, the amount of the lump sum payment is closest to

a. $109,355,000
b. $111,881,000
c. $116,354,000
d. $182,000,000

Solution

$P = 7,000,000 + 7,000,000(P/F, 4\%, 25)$
$= \$116,354,000$

The answer is c.

3-33
John Buck opens a savings account by depositing $1000. The account pays 6% simple interest. After 3 years John makes another deposit, this time for $2000. The amount in the account when John withdraws the money 8 years after the first deposit is nearest to

a. $3180
b. $4080
c. $4270
d. $4520

Solution

F with simple interest $= P + P(i)(n)$
$F = 1000 + 1000(0.06)(8) \leftarrow$ Initial deposit remains in the account for the full 8 years
$\quad + 2000 + 2000(0.06)(5) \leftarrow$ Second deposit remains in the account for 5 years
$F = \$4080$

The answer is b.

3-34
The future worth (in Year 8) of $10,000 deposited at the end of Year 3 plus $10,000 deposited at the end of Year 5, and $10,000 deposited at the end of Year 8 at an interest rate of 12% per year is closest to

a. $32,100
b. $39,300
c. $41,670
d. $46,200

Solution

$F = 10,000(F/P, 12\%, 5) + 10,000(F/P, 12\%, 3) + 10,000$
$= \$41,670$

The answer is c.

3-35

Money invested at 6%, compounded monthly will triple in approximately how many months?

a. 19
b. 57
c. 113
d. 221

Solution

$i = 6/12 = \frac{1}{2}\%$

Let $F = 3$ and $P = 1$
$F = P(1 + i)^n$
$3 = 1(1 + 0.005)^n$

$3 = 1.005^n$ $n = \frac{\ln 3}{\ln 1.005} = 220.27$

The answer is d.

3-36

A woman deposited $10,000 into an account at her credit union. The money was left on deposit for 10 years. During the first 5 years the woman earned 9% interest, compounded monthly. The credit union then changed its interest policy; as a result, in the second 5 years the woman earned 6% interest, compounded quarterly.

a. How much money was in the account at the end of the 10 years?
b. Calculate the rate of return that the woman received.

Solution

a. At the end of 5 years:
$F = 10,000 \ (F/P, \frac{3}{4}\%, 60)^* = \$15,660.00$ $^* \ i = 9/12 = \frac{3}{4}\%$ $n = (12)(5) = 60$
At the end of 10 years:
$F = 15,660(F/P, 1\frac{1}{2}\%, 20)^{**} = \$21,094.02$ $^{**} \ i = 6/4 = 1\frac{1}{2}\%$ $n = (4)(5) = 20$

b. $10,000(F/P, i, 10) = 21,094.02$
        $(F/P, i, 10) = 2.1094$

Try $i = 7\%$ $(F/P, 7\%, 10) = 1.967$
Try $i = 8\%$ $(F/P, 8\%, 10) = 2.159$

$7\% < i < 8\%$ Therefore interpolate:

$i = 7.75\%$

Chapter 4

Equivalence For Repeated Cash Flow

4-1

A young engineer wishes to buy a house but can afford monthly payments of only $500. Thirty-year loans are available at 6% interest compounded monthly. If she can make a $5000 down payment, what is the price of the most expensive house that she can afford to purchase?

Solution

$i = 6/12 = \frac{1}{2}\%$ $n = 30 \times 12 = 360$

$P* = 500(P/A, \frac{1}{2}\%, 360) = 83,396.00$
$P = 83,396.00 + 5000$
$P = \$88,396$

4-2

A person borrows $15,000 at an interest rate of 6%, compounded monthly to be paid off with payments of $456.33.

a. What is the length of the loan in years?
b. What is the <u>total</u> amount that would be required at the end of the twelfth month to payoff the entire loan balance?

Solution

a. $P = A(P/A, i\%, n)$
       $15,000 = 456.33(P/A, \frac{1}{2}\%, n)$
   $(P/A, \frac{1}{2}\%, n) = 15,000/456.33$
                $= 32.871$

From the $\frac{1}{2}\%$ interest table, $n = 36$ months $= 6$ years.

b. $456.33 + 456.33(P/A, \frac{1}{2}\%, 24) = \$10,752.50$

4-3

A $50,000 loan with a nominal interest rate of 6% is to be repaid over 30 years with payments of $299.77. The borrower wants to know how many payments, $N*$, he will have to make until he owes only half of the amount he borrowed initially.

Solution

The outstanding principal is equal to the present worth of the remaining payments when the payments are discounted at the loan's effective interest rate.

Therefore, let N' be the remaining payments.

$$\frac{1}{2}(50,000) = 299.77(P/A, \frac{1}{2}\%, N')$$
$$(P/A, \frac{1}{2}\%, N') = 83.397$$
$$N' = 108.30 \approx 108 \qquad \text{From } i = \frac{1}{2}\% \text{ table}$$

So, $N^* = 360 - N' = 252$ payments

4-4

While in college, Ellen received $40,000 in student loans at 8% interest. She will graduate in June and is expected to begin repaying the loans in either 5 or 10 equal annual payments. Compute her yearly payments for both repayment plans.

Solution

5 Years	10 Years
$A = P(A/P, i, n)$	$A = P(A/P, i, n)$
$= 40,000(A/P, 8\%, 5)$	$= 40,000(A/P, 8\%, 10)$
$= \$10,020.00$	$= \$5,960.00$

4-5

Given:

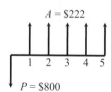

$A = \$222$

$P = \$800$

Find: $i\%$.

Solution

$$P = A(P/A, i\%, 5)$$
$$800 = 222(P/A, i\%, 5)$$
$$(P/A, i\%, 5) = 800/222$$
$$= 3.6$$

From the interest tables, $i = 12\%$.

4-6

J.D. Homeowner has just bought a house with a 20-year, 9%, $70,000 mortgage on which he is paying $629.81 per month.

a. If J.D. sells the house after 10 years, how much must he pay the bank to completely pay off the mortgage at the time of the 120th payment?
b. How much of the first $629.81 payment on the loan is interest?

Solution

    a. $P = 120^{th}$ payment + PW of remaining 120 payments
          = 629.81 + 629.81(P/A, ¾%, 120)
          = $49,718.46

    b. $70,000 × 0.0075 = $525

4-7

How much will accumulate in an Individual Retirement Account (IRA) in 15 years if $5000 is deposited in the account at the end of each quarter during that time? The account earns 8% interest, compounded quarterly. What is the effective interest rate?

Solution

    $i = 8/4 = 2\%$ $n = 4 \times 15 = 60$

    $F = 5000\ (F/A, 2\%, 60) = \$570,255$

    Effective interest rate $= (1 + 0.02)^4 - 1 = 8.24\%$

4-8

Suppose you wanted to buy a $180,000 house. You have $20,000 cash to use as the down payment. The bank offers to lend you the remainder at 6% nominal interest. The term of the loan is 20 years. Compute your monthly loan payment.

Solution

    Amount of loan: $180,000 − $20,000 = $160,000

    $i = 6/12 = \frac{1}{2}\%$ per month $n = 12 \times 20 = 240$

    $A = 160,000(A/P, \frac{1}{2}\%, 240) = \$1145.60$ per month

4-9

To offset the cost of buying a $120,000 house, James and Lexie borrowed $25,000 from their parents at 6% nominal interest, compounded monthly. The loan from their parents is to be paid off in 5 years in equal monthly payments. The couple has saved $12,500. Their total down payment is therefore $25,000 + 12,500 = $37,500. The balance will be mortgaged at 9% nominal interest, compounded monthly for 30 years. Find the combined monthly payment that the couple will be making for the first 5 years.

Solution

Payment to parents:

$25,000(A/P, ½%, 60) = \$482.50$

Borrowed from bank: $120,000 – 37,500 = \$82,500$

Payment to bank:

$82,500(A/P, ¾%, 360) = \$664.13$

Therefore, monthly payments are $482.50 + 664.13 = \$1,146.63$.

4-10

If $15,000 is deposited into a savings account that pays 4% interest compounded quarterly, how much can be withdrawn each quarter for 5 years?

Solution

$A = 15,000(A/P, 1\%, 20)$
$= \$831.00$ per quarter

4-11

How much will Thomas accumulate in a bank account that pays 5% annual interest compounded quarterly if he deposits $800 at the end of each quarter for 7 years?

Solution

$F = 800(F/A, 1.25\%, 28)$
$= \$25,824.00$

4-12

A consumer purchased new furniture by borrowing $1500 using the store's credit plan, which charges 18% compounded monthly.

a. What are the monthly payments if the loan is to be repaid in 3 years?
b. How much of the first payment is interest?
c. How much does the consumer still owe just after making the 20th payment?

Solution

a. $A = 1500(A/P, 1\frac{1}{2}\%, 36)$
    $= \$54.30$ per month

b. Interest payment = Principal × Interest rate
    Interest payment = $1,500 \times 0.015$
    $= \$22.50$

c. $P = 54.30(P/A, 1\frac{1}{2}\%, 16)$
    $= \$767.31$

4-13

A company borrowed $20,000 at 8% interest. The loan was repaid according to the following schedule. Find X, the amount that will pay off the loan at the end of Year 5.

Year	Amount
1	$4000
2	4000
3	4000
4	4000
5	X

Solution

$20,000 = 4000(P/A, 8\%, 4) + X(P/F, 8\%, 5)$
$6752 = X(0.6806)$
$X = 6752/0.6806$
$= \$9920.66$

4-14

The local loan shark has loaned you $1000. The interest rate you must pay is 20%, compounded monthly. The loan will be repaid by making 24 equal monthly payments. What is the amount of each monthly payment?

Solution

$i = 20/12 = 1\frac{2}{3}\%$

$A = 1000(A/P, 1\frac{2}{3}\%, 24)$

There is no $1\frac{2}{3}\%$ compound interest table readily available. Therefore the capital recovery factor must be calculated.

$(A/P, 1.666\%, 24) = [0.01666(1.01666)^{24}]/[(1.01666)^{24} - 1] = 0.050892$

$A = 1000(0.050892) = \$50.90$

4-15

Find the uniform annual equivalent for the following cash flow diagram if $i = 10\%$. Use the appropriate gradient and uniform series factors.

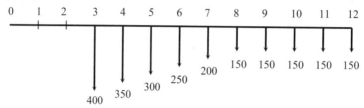

Solution

$$P^1 = [400(P/A, 10\%, 6) - 50(P/G, 10\%, 6)](P/F, 10\%, 2) = \$1039.45$$

$$P^2 = [150(P/A, 10\%, 4)](P/F, 10\%, 8) = \$221.82$$

$$P = 1039.45 + 221.82 = \$1261.27$$

$$A = 1261.27(A/P, 10\%, 12) = \$185.15$$

4-16

You need to borrow $10,000, and the following two alternatives are available at different banks. Alternative A: pay $2571 at the end of each year for 5 years, starting at the end of the first year (5 payments in total) and Alternative B: pay $207.58 at the end of each month, for 5 years, starting at the end of the first month (60 payments in total). On the basis of the interest rate being charged in each case, which alternative should you choose?

Solution

Alternative A:

$$10,000 = 2571(P/A, i, 5)$$
$$(P/A, i, 5) = 10,000/2571$$
$$= 3.890$$

From the interest tables, $i \approx 9\%$.

Alternative B:

$$10,000 = 207.58(P/A, i, 60)$$
$$(P/A, i, 60) = 10,000/ 207.58$$
$$= 48.174$$

From the interest tables, $i = 0.75\%$.

The effective interest rate is $(1 + 0.0075)^{12} - 1 = 9.38\%$.

Therefore, choose the first alternative.

4-17

Using a credit card, Ben Spendthrift has just purchased a new stereo system for $975 and will be making payments of $45 per month. If the interest rate is 18% compounded monthly, how long will it take to completely pay off the stereo?

Solution

$i = 18/12 = 1\frac{1}{2}\%$

$975 = 45(P/A, 1\frac{1}{2}\%, n)$
$(P/A, 1\frac{1}{2}\%, n) = 975/45$
$\qquad = 21.667$

From the $1\frac{1}{2}\%$ table, n is between 26 and 27 months. The loan will not be completely paid off after 26 months. Therefore, the payment in the 27th month will be smaller.

4-18

The accumulated savings of an engineer on the verge of retirement, amounting to $100,000, are in an account paying 6% compounded quarterly. The engineer wishes to withdraw $6000 each quarter. For how long can she withdraw the full amount?

Solution

$i = 6/4 = 1\frac{1}{2}\%$

$6000 = 100,000(A/P, 1\frac{1}{2}\%, n)$
$(A/P, 1\frac{1}{2}\%, n) = 0.0600$

From the $1\frac{1}{2}\%$ table, $n = 19$ quarters or $4\frac{3}{4}$ years.

Note: This leaves some money in the account, but not enough for a full $6000 withdrawal.

4-19

Explain in one or two sentences why $(A/P, i\%, \infty) = i$.

Solution

To have an infinitely long annuity (A) series, the principal (present sum P) must never be reduced. For this to occur, only the interest earned each period may be removed. To remove more than the interest earned would decrease the original P, and less interest would be available in the next period.

4-20

If $3000 is deposited into an account paying $13\frac{1}{2}\%$ interest, how much can be withdrawn each year indefinitely?

Solution

$(A/P, i, \infty) = i$

$A = Pi$

$A = 3000 \times 0.135 = \$405$

4-21

A grandfather gave his grandchild a 10th birthday present of $100. The child's parents talked him into putting this gift into a bank account so that when he had grandchildren of his own, he could give them similar gifts. If the child in fact lets this account grow for 50 years, and the account then contains $100,000, what was the interest rate of the account?

a.   14.0%
b.   14.8%
c.   15.8%
d.   15.0%

Solution

$\$100,000 = \$100(1 + i)^{50}$
$i = 14.8\%$

The answer is b.

4-22

The annual cost to maintain a cemetery plot is $75. If interest is 6%, how much must be set aside to pay for perpetual maintenance?

a. $1150
b. $1200
c. $1250
d. $1300

Solution

$P = 75(P/A, 6\%, \infty)$
$= 75(1/0.06)$
$= \$1250$

The answer is c.

4-23

Henry Fuller has agreed to purchase a used automobile for $6500. He wishes to limit his monthly payment to $200 for a period of 2 years. What down payment must he make to complete the purchase if the interest rate on the loan will be 9%?

Solution

$$P = P' + A(P/A, \tfrac{3}{4}\%, 24)$$
$$6500 = P' + 200(21.889)$$
$$P' = 6500 - 4377.80$$
$$= \$2122.20 \leftarrow \text{down payment}$$

4-24

A bank is offering a loan of $20,000 with an interest rate of 12%, payable with monthly payments over a 4-year period.

a. Calculate the monthly payment required to repay the loan.
b. This bank also charges a loan fee of 4% of the amount of the loan, payable at the time of the closing of the loan (that is, at the time the borrower receives the money). What effective interest rate is the bank charging?

Solution

a. The monthly payments:

$$i = 12/12 = 1\%, \qquad n = 12 \times 4 = 48$$

$$20{,}000(A/P, 1\%, 48) = \$526$$

b. Actual money received $= P = 20{,}000 - 0.04(20{,}000) = \$19{,}200$

$A = \$526$ based on $20,000

Recalling that $A = P(A/P, i, n)$
$$526 = 19{,}200(A/P, i, 48)$$
$$(A/P, i, 48) = 526/19{,}200$$
$$= 0.02739$$

For $i = 1\frac{1}{4}\%$, the A/P factor at $n = 48 = 0.0278$

For $i = 1\%$, the A/P factor at $n = 48 = 0.0263$

By interpolation, $i \approx 1 + \frac{1}{4}[(0.0263 - 0.02739)/(0.0263 - 0.0278)]$
$$i \approx 1.1817\%$$

Therefore, $i_{\text{eff}} = (1 + 0.011817)^{12} - 1 = 0.1514 = 15.14\%$.

4-25

The annual worth of a quarterly lease payment of $500 at 8% interest is nearest to

a. $2061
b. $2102
c. $2123
d. $2253

Solution

Lease payments are beginning-of-period cash flows.

First find the present worth of the quarterly payments at $8/4 = 2\%$.

$P = 500 + 500(P/A, 2\%, 3) = \$1941.95$

$A = 1941.95(1 + 0.02)^4$
     $= \$2102$

The answer is b.

4-26

Find the present equivalent of the following cash flow diagram if $i = 18\%$.

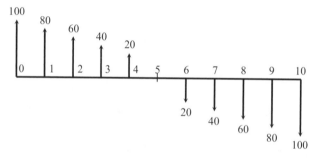

Solution

$P = 100 + 80(P/A, 18\%, 10) - 20(P/G, 18\%, 10) = \$172.48$

4-27

To start business, ECON ENGINEERING has just borrowed $500,000 at 6%, compounded quarterly, which will be repaid by quarterly payments of $50,000 each, with the first payment due in one year. How many quarters after the money is borrowed will the loan be fully paid off?

Solution

$i = 6/4 = 1\frac{1}{2}\%$

$500,000 = 50,000(P/A, 1\frac{1}{2}\%, n)(P/F, 1\frac{1}{2}\%, 3)$
$(P/A, 1\frac{1}{2}\%, n) = 500,000/[50,000(0.9563)]$
                  $= 10.46$

From the $1\frac{1}{2}\%$ table, $n = 12$ payments plus 3 quarters without payments equals 15 quarters before loan is fully paid off.

4-28

The first payment on a 30-year mortgage of $100,000 at a 6% interest rate was made on September 1, 1999. What amount of interest was paid for the 12 monthly payments of 2002?

Solution

Monthly payment $A = 100,000(A/P, \frac{1}{2}\%, 360) = \$599.55$

Interest periods remaining Jan. 1, 2002 = 331
Jan. 1, 2003 = 319

$P' = 599.55(P/A, \frac{1}{2}\%, 331) = 599.55(161.624)$ $= 96,901.67$
$P'' = 599.55(P/A, \frac{1}{2}\%, 319) = 599.55(159.257)$ $= 95,482.53$
Interest $= 599.55(12) - (96,901.67 - 95,482.53) = \$5775.46$

4-29

Holloman Hops has budgeted $300,000 per year to pay for labor over the next 5 years. If the company expects the cost of labor to increase by $10,000 each year, and the interest rate is 10%, what is the expected cost of the labor in the first year?

Solution

$A' = \$300,000$
$A' = A + 10,000(A/G, 10\%, 5)$
$300,000 = A + 10,000(1.81)$
$A = \$281,900$ first-year labor cost

4-30

For the cash flow shown, determine the value of G that will make the future worth at the end of Year 6 equal to $8000 at an interest rate of 12% per year.

Year	0	1	2	3	4	5	6
Cash Flow	0	600	$600 + G$	$600 + 2G$	$600 + 3G$	$600 + 4G$	$600 + 5G$

Solution

$P = 8000(P/F, 12\%, 6)$
$= 8000(0.5066)$
$= \$4052.80$

$4052.80 = 600(P/A, 12\%, 6) + G(P/G, 12\%, 6)$
$4052.80 = 600(4.111) + G(8.930)$
$G = \$177.63$

4-31

Big John Sipes, owner of Sipes's Sipping Shine, has decided to replace the distillation machine his company now uses. After some research, he finds an acceptable distiller that costs $62,500. The current machine has approximately 1200 lb of copper tubing that can be salvaged and sold for $4.75/lb to use as a down payment on the new machine. The remaining components of the distillation machine can be sold as scrap for $3000. This amount will also be used to pay for the replacement equipment. The remaining money will be obtained through a 10-year mortgage with quarterly payments at an interest rate of 8%. Determine the quarterly payment required to pay off the mortgage. Also determine the effective interest rate on the loan.

Solution

$$i = 8/4 = 2\% \qquad n = 4 \times 10 = 40$$

$$P = 62{,}500 - (1{,}200 \times 4.75) - 3000 = 53{,}800$$

$$A = 53{,}800(A/P, 2\%, 40)$$

$$= 53{,}800(0.0366)$$

$$= \$1969$$

$$i_{\text{eff}} = (1 + 0.02)^4 - 1 = 8.24\%$$

4-32

Ray Witmer, an engineering professor at UTM, is preparing to retire to his farm and care for his cats and dogs. During his many years at UTM he invested well and has a balance of $1,098,000 in his retirement fund. How long will he be able to withdraw $100,000 per year, beginning today, if his account earns interest at a rate of 4% per year?

Solution

$$A = \$100{,}000 \qquad P = 1{,}098{,}000 - 100{,}000^* = \$998{,}000 \qquad \text{*First withdrawal is today.}$$

$$100{,}000 = 998{,}000(A/P, 4\%, n)$$
$$(A/P, 4\%, n) = 100{,}000/998{,}000$$
$$(A/P, 4\%, n) = 0.1002$$

From the $i = 4\%$ table, $n = 13$ additional years of withdrawals, 14 total years of withdrawals.

4-33

Abby W. deposits $75 per month into an account paying 9% interest for 2 years, to be used to purchase a car. The car she selects costs more than the amount in the account. She agrees to pay $125 per month for 2 more years at 12% interest, and also uses a gift from her uncle of $375 as part of the down payment. What is the cost of the car to the nearest dollar?

Solution

$i = 9/12 = \frac{3}{4}\%$ $n = 12 \times 2 = 24$

$F = 75(F/A, \frac{3}{4}\%, 24)$
   $= 75(26.189)$
   $= \$1964.18 \leftarrow$ Amount in account

$i = 12/12 = 1\%$ $n = 12 \times 2 = 24$

$P = 125(P/A, 1\%, 24)$
   $= 125(21.243)$
   $= \$2655.38 \leftarrow$ Amount repaid by loan

Total $= 1964.18 + 2655.38 + 375$
      $= \$4994.56 = \$4995 \leftarrow$ Cost of automobile

4-34

The amount required to establish an endowment to provide an annual scholarship of $20,000 requires a deposit into an account paying 8% is nearest to

a. $1600
b. $25,000
c. $250,000
d. $500,000

Solution

$P = 20,000(P/A, 8\%, \infty)$
$P = 20,000(1/.08)$
$P = \$250,000$

The answer is c.

4-35

Abby Motors offers to sell customers used automobiles with $400 down and payments for 3 years of $215 per month. If the interest rate charged to its customers is 12%, the cost of the automobile is nearest to

a. $1760
b. $2160
c. $6475
d. $6875

Solution

$i = 12/12 = 1\%$ $\qquad n = 12 \times 3 = 36$

$P = 400 + 215(P/A, 1\%, 36)$
$\quad = \$6873.01$

The answer is d.

4-36

A tractor is bought for $125,000. What is the required payment per year to completely pay off the tractor in 20 years, assuming an interest rate of 6%?

a. $1150
b. $5550
c. $10,900
d. $12,750

Solution

$A = 125,000(A/P, 6\%, 20)$
$\quad = \$10,900$

The answer is c.

4-37

Using the tables for uniform gradients, solve for the future value at the end of year 7 if $i = 10\%$.

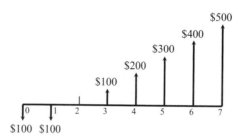

Solution

$PV = 100(P/G, 10\%, 7) - 100(P/A, 10\%, 7) - 100$
$\quad = \$689.50$

$FV = 689.5(F/P, 10\%, 7)$
$\quad = \$1343.84$

4-38

Jason W. bought a Mercedes when he came to UTM as an engineering student. The Mercedes was purchased by taking a loan that was to be paid off in 20 equal, quarterly payments. The interest rate on the loan was 12%. Four years later, after Jason made his 16th payment, he got married (no more dating!) and sold the Mercedes to his buddy Houston S. Houston made arrangements with Jason's bank to refinance the loan and to pay Jason's unpaid balance by making 16 equal, quarterly payments at the same interest rate that Jason was paying. Houston flunked out of UTM (too many dates!) $3\frac{1}{4}$ years later, after having made his 13th payment; he then sold the car to Jeff M. Jeff paid the bank $2000 cash (he had a good summer job!) to pay the loan balance. How much had Jason borrowed to buy the new Mercedes?

Solution

$i = 12/4 = 3\%$

Jason W.

$A = P(A/P, 3\%, 20)$
$A = P(0.0672)$ Quarterly payment for Jason

Jason owes

$P = 0.0672P(P/A, 3\%, 4)$ Present worth of four remaining payments
$\quad = 0.0672P(3.717)$
$\quad = 0.2498P$

Houston S.

$A = 0.2498P(A/P, 3\%, 16)$ Quarterly payment for Houston
$\quad = 0.2498P(0.0796)$
$\quad = 0.0199P$

Jeff M.

$P = 0.0199P(P/A, 3\%, 3)$ Present worth of three remaining payments
$\quad = 0.0199P(2.829)$
$\quad = 0.0563P$

Set final payment equal to present worth of remaining payments:

$2000 = 0.0562P$

$P = \$35,556.75$

4-39

A mortgage of $50,000 for 30 years, with monthly payments at 6% interest is contemplated. At the last moment, you receive news of a $25,000 gift from your parents to be applied to the principal. Leaving the monthly payments the same, what amount of time will now be required to pay off the mortgage, and what is the amount of the last payment? (Assume that any residual partial payment amount is added to the last payment.)

Solution

$i = 6/12 = \frac{1}{2}\%$ $n = 12 \times 30 = 360$ periods

$A = 50,000(A/P, \frac{1}{2}\%, 360)$
   $= \$299.77$ monthly payment

Note: For a more accurate answer, a factor of $1/(P/A)$ was used.

After reduction of P to 25,000,

$25,000 = 299.77(P/A, \frac{1}{2}\%, n)$
$(P/A, \frac{1}{2}\%, n) = 83.40$

Try $n = 104$ periods: $P/A = 80.942$
Try $n = 120$ periods: $P/A = 90.074$

By interpolation, $n = 108.31$ periods $= 9.03$ years.

At 9 years (108 periods): $P = 299.77(P/A, \frac{1}{2}\%, 108)$
                           $= 299.77(83.2934)$
                           $= \$24,968.87$

Residual $= 25,000 - 24,968.87 = \$31.13$

Last payment = Value of residual at time of last payment + Last payment
              $= 31.13(F/P, \frac{1}{2}\%, 108) + 299.77$
              $= \$353.12$

4-40

A person would like to retire 10 years from now. He currently has $32,000 in savings, and he plans to deposit $300 per month, starting next month, in a special retirement plan. The $32,000 is earning 8% interest, while the monthly deposits will pay him 6% nominal annual interest. Once he retires, he will deposit the total of the two sums of money into an account that he expects will earn a 4% annual interest rate. Assuming that he will only spend the interest he earns, how much will he collect in annual interest, starting in Year 11?

Solution

Savings:

$F = 32,000(F/P, 8\%, 10) = \$69,086$

Monthly deposits:

$i = 6/12 = \frac{1}{2}\%$ $n = 12 \times 10 = 120$

$F = 300(F/A, \frac{1}{2}\%, 120) = \$49,164$

The total amount on deposit at the end of Year 10 is

$F_T = 69,086 + 49,164 = \$118,250$

The interest to collect per year $= 118,250 \times 0.04 = \$4730$

Chapter 5

Present Worth Analysis

5-1

Emma and her husband decide to buy $1000 worth of utility stocks beginning one year from now. Since they expect their salaries to increase, they will increase their purchases by $200 per year for the next 9 years. What would the present worth of all the stocks be if they yield a uniform dividend rate of 10% throughout the investment period and the price per share remains constant?

Solution

PW of the base amount ($1000) is: $1000(P/A, 10\%, 10) = \$6144.57$

PW of the gradient is: $200(P/G, 10\%, 10) = \$4578.27$

Total PW $= 6144.57 + 4578.27 = \$10,722.84$

5-2

It takes $10,000 to put on the local art festival each year. Immediately *before* this year's festival, the sponsoring committee determined that it had $60,000 in an account paying 8% interest. *After* this year, how many more festivals can be sponsored without raising more money? Think carefully!

Solution

$60,000 - 10,000 = 10,000(P/A, 8\%, n)$
$\quad (P/A, 8\%, n) = 50,000/10,000$
$\qquad\qquad = 5$

From the $i = 8\%$ table, $n = 6$.

Thus 6 is the number of festivals after this year's. There will be some money left over but not enough to pay for a 7th year.

5-3

A tax refund expected one year from now has a present worth of $3000 if $i = 6\%$. What is its present worth if $i = 10\%$?

Solution

Let x = refund value when received at the end of Year 1 = 3000(F/P, 6%, 1);

PW   = $x(P/F$, 10%, 1)

Therefore, the PW if i = 10% = 3000(F/P, 6%, 1)(P/F, 10%, 1) = $2890.94,

5-4

The winner of a sweepstakes prize is given the choice of a one-time payment of $1,000,000 or a guaranteed $80,000 per year for 20 years. If the value of money is 5%, which option should the winner choose?

Solution

Option 1: P = $1,000,000

Option 2: P = 80,000(P/A, 5%, 20) = $996,960

Choose Option 1: take the $1,000,000 now.

5-5

A tunnel to transport water through the Lubbock mountain range initially cost $1,000,000 and has expected maintenance costs that will occur in a 6-year cycle as shown.

End of Year:	1	2	3	4	5	6
Maintenance:	$35,000	$35,000	$35,000	$45,000	$45,000	$60,000

The capitalized cost at 8% interest is nearest to

a. $1,003,300
b. $1,518,400
c. $1,191,700
d. $13,018,350

Solution

Capitalized cost = PW of cost for an infinite time period.

First compute the equivalent annual cost (EAC) of the maintenance.

EAC = 35,000 + [10,000(F/A, 8%, 3) + 15,000](A/F, 8%, 6) = $41,468.80

For $n = \infty$, $P = A/I$

Capitalized cost = 1,000,000 + (41,468.80/0.08) = $1,518,360

The answer is b.

5-6

An engineer is considering buying a life insurance policy for his family. He currently owes $77,500, and he would like his family to have an annual available income of $35,000 indefinitely (that is, to ensure that the original capital does not decrease, the annual interest should amount to $35,000).

a. If the engineer assumes that any money from the insurance policy can be invested in an account paying a guaranteed 4% annual interest, how much life insurance should he buy?

b. If he now assumes that the money can be invested at 7% annual interest, how much life insurance should he buy?

Solution

  a.   4% interest $n = \infty$

$$A = Pi \quad \text{or} \quad P = A/i = 35,000/0.04 = 875,000$$

Total life insurance $= 77,500 + 875,000 = \$952,500$

  b.   7% interest $n = \infty$

$$P = A/i = 35,000/0.07 = 500,000$$

Total life insurance $= 77,500 + 500,000 = \$577,500$

5-7

Investment in a crane is expected to produce profit from its rental of $15,000 during the first year of service. The profit is expected to decrease by $2500 each year thereafter. At the end of 6 years, assume that the salvage value is zero. At 12% interest, the present worth of the profits is nearest to

a. $39,350
b. $45,675
c. $51,400
d. $61,675

Solution

$$P = 15,000(P/A, 12\%, 6) - 2500(P/G, 12\%, 6) = \$39,340$$

The answer is a.

5-8

The annual income from an apartment house is $20,000. The annual expense is estimated to be $2000. If the apartment house can be sold for $100,000 at the end of 10 years, how much should you be willing to pay for it now, with required return of 10%?

Solution

$$P = (A_{\text{INCOME}} - A_{\text{EXPENSE}})(P/A, 10\%, 10) + F_{\text{SALE}}(P/F, 10\%, 10)$$
$$= (20,000 - 2,000)(P/A, 10\%, 10) + 100,000(P/F, 10\%, 10)$$
$$= \$149,160$$

5-9

A scholarship is to be established that will pay $200 per quarter at the beginning of fall, winter, and spring quarters. It is estimated that a fund for this purpose will earn 10% interest, compounded quarterly. What lump sum at the beginning of summer quarter, when deposited, will assure that the scholarship may be continued into perpetuity?

Solution

$$i = 10/4 = 2\frac{1}{2}\%$$

$$P = 200(P/A, 2\frac{1}{2}\%, 3) = \$571.20$$
$$A' = 571.20(A/P, 2\frac{1}{2}\%, 4) = \$151.82$$

For $n = \infty$

$$P' = A'/i = 151.82/0.025 = \$6073 \text{ deposit}$$

5-10

Your company has been presented with an opportunity to invest in a project. The facts on the project are as tabulated.

Investment required	$60,000,000
Salvage value after 10 years	0
Gross income	20,000,000
Annual operating costs:	
Labor	2,500,000
Materials, licenses, insurance, etc.*	1,000,000
Fuel and other costs	1,500,000
Maintenance costs	500,000
*Beginning-of-period cash flow	

The project is expected to operate as shown for 10 years. If management expects to make 15% on its investments before taxes, would you recommend this project?

Solution

$$PW = -60,000,000 + [20,000,000 - 4,500,000 - 1,000,000(F/P, 15\%, 1)](P/A, 15\%, 10)$$
$$= \$12,022,650$$

Accept the project because it has a positive NPW.

5-11

Find the present worth of the following cash flow diagram if $i = 8\%$.

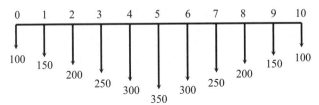

Solution

$P = 100 + 150(P/A, 8\%, 5) + 50(P/G, 8\%, 5)$
$\quad + [300(P/A, 8\%, 5) - 50(P/G, 8\%, 5)](P/F, 8\%, 5)$
$\quad = \$1631.97$

5-12

A couple wants to begin saving money for their child's education. They estimate that $10,000 will be needed on the child's 18th birthday, $12,000 on the 19th birthday, $14,000 on the 20th birthday, and $16,000 on the 21st birthday. Assume an 8% interest rate with only annual compounding. The couple is considering two methods of setting aside the needed money.

a.   How much money would have to be deposited into the account on the child's first birthday to accumulate enough money to cover the estimated college expenses? (*Note*: A child's "first birthday" is celebrated one year after the child is born.)

b.   What uniform annual amount would the couple have to deposit each year on the child's first through seventeenth birthdays to accumulate enough money to cover the estimated college expenses?

Solution

a.

note: year 0 corresponds to
         child's first birthday

```
0  2  4  6  8  10  12  14  16                    10K  12  14K  16K
|_____|            18    20
|                                                                                
P                                               F
```

Let F = the the number of dollars needed at the beginning of Year 16
$\quad = 10,000(P/A, 8\%, 4) + 2000(P/G, 8\%, 4)$
$\quad = 42,420$

The amount needed today: $P = 42,420(P/F, 8\%, 16) = \$12,382.40$

b.

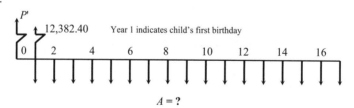

$P' = 12,382.40(P/F, 8\%, 1) = \$11,464.86$

$A = 11,464.86(A/P, 8\%, 17) = \$1,256.55$

5-13

Assume that you borrowed \$50,000 at an interest rate of 1% per month, to be repaid in uniform monthly payments for 30 years. How much of the 163rd payment would be interest, and how much would be principal?

Solution

In general, the interest paid on a loan at time t is determined by multiplying the effective interest rate times the outstanding principal just after the preceding payment at time $t - 1$.

To find the interest paid at time $t = 163$, (call it I_{163}) first find the outstanding principal at time $t = 162$ (call it P_{162}).

This can be done by computing the future worth at time $t = 162$ of the amount borrowed, minus the future worth of 162 payments. Alternately, compute the present worth, at time 162, of the 198 payments remaining.

The uniform payments are $50,000(A/P, 1\%, 360) = \$514.31$. Therefore,

$P_{162} = 50,000(F/P, 1\%, 162) - 514.31(F/A, 1\%, 162) = 514.31(P/A, 1\%, 198) = \$44,259.78$

The interest $I_{163} = 0.01(44,259.78) = \$442.59$
The principal in the payment is $514.31 - 442.59 = \$71.72$.

5-14

A municipality is seeking a new tourist attraction, and the town council has voted to budget \$500,000 for the project. A survey shows that an interesting cave can be enlarged and developed for a contract price of \$400,000. The proposed attraction is expected to have an infinite life. The estimated annual expenses of operation total \$50,000. The price per ticket is to be based on an average of 12,000 visitors per year. If money is worth 8%, what should be the price of each ticket?

Solution

If the $100,000 cash, left over after developing the cave, is invested at 8%, it will yield a perpetual annual income of $8000. This $8000 can be put toward the expenses ($50,000 a year). The balance of the expenses can be raised through ticket sales, making the price per ticket:

Ticket price = $42,000/12,000 tickets = $3.50

Alternate solution:

$$PW_{COST} = PW_{BENEFIT}$$
$$400,000 + (50,000)/0.08 = 500,000 + T/0.08$$
$$400,000 + 625,000 = 500,000 + T/0.08$$
$$T = 525,000(0.08)$$
$$= 42,000$$

Ticket price = $42,000/12,000 tickets = $3.50.

5-15

Sarah Bishop, having become a very successful engineer, wishes to start an endowment at UTM that will provide scholarships of $10,000 per year to four deserving engineering students beginning in Year 6 and continuing indefinitely. If the university earns 10% per year on endowments funds, the amount Sarah must donate now is closest to

a. $225,470
b. $248,360
c. $273,200
d. $293,820

Solution

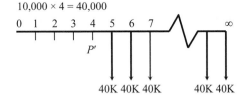

Amount needed at end of Year 4 $P' = 40,000(P/A, 10\%, \infty)$
$$= 40,000(1/0.1)$$
$$= 400,000$$
Amount needed today $P = 400,000(P/F, 10\%, 4)$
$$= \$273,200$$

The answer is c.

5-16

A local car wash charges $3 per wash, or one can opt to pay $12.98 for 5 washes, payable in advance with the first wash. If you normally washed your car once a month, and your cost of money is 1% compounded monthly, would the option be worthwhile?

Solution

$$NPV_{Pay\ for\ 5} = -\$12.98$$

$$NPV_{Pay/Wash} = -3.00 - 3.00(P/A, 1\%, 4)$$
$$= -\$14.71$$

Therefore, the "pay for 5" option is the more economical.

5-17

A project has a first cost of $14,000, uniform annual benefits of $2400, and a salvage value of $3000 at the end of its 10-year useful life. What is its net present worth at an interest rate of 12%?

Solution

$$PW = -14,000 + 2400(P/A, 20\%, 10) + 3000(P/F, 20\%, 10) = \$526$$

5-18

McClain, Edwards, Shiver, and Smith (MESS) LLC is considering the purchase of new automated cleaning equipment. The industrial engineer for the company, David "the Dirtman" R., has been asked to calculate the present worth of the two best alternatives based on the following data.

	Mess Away	Quick Clean
First cost	$65,000	$78,000
Annual savings	20,000	24,000
Annual operating costs	4,000	2,750
Scheduled maintenance	$1500 at the end of 3rd year	$3000 at the end of 3rd year
Annual insurance*	2,000	2,200
Salvage value	10% of first cost	12.5% of first cost
Useful life	5 years	5 years

* Assume beginning-of-period payments.

David is so busy cleaning his office he has asked you to help with the work. Determine which equipment should be purchased, given an interest rate of 8%.

Solution

Mess Away

Year		
0	First cost	(65,000)
1–5	Annual net savings: 16,000(*P/A*, 8%, 5)	63,888
0–4	Annual insurance: 2000 + 2000(*P/A*, 8%, 4)	(8,624)
3	Scheduled maintenance: 1500(*P/F*, 8%, 3)	(1,191)
5	Salvage value: 6500(*P/F*, 8%, 5)	4,424
		$(6,503)

Quick Clean

Year		
0	First cost	(78,000)
1–5	Annual net savings: 21,250(*P/A*, 8%, 5)	84,851
0–4	Annual insurance: 2200 + 2200(*P/A*, 8%, 4)	(9,486)
3	Scheduled maintenance: 3000(*P/F*, 8%, 3)	(2,381)
5	Salvage value: 10,000(*P/F*, 8%, 5)	6,806
		$ 1,790

Choose Quick Clean.

5-19
Mary Ann requires approximately 30 pounds of bananas each month, January through June, and 35 pounds of bananas each month, July through December, to make banana cream pies for her cast-away friends the Skipper, Gilligan, the Professor, Ginger, and the Millionaire and his Wife (the Howells). Bananas can be bought at a local market for 40 cents/lb. If Mary Ann's cost of money is 3%, approximately how much should she set aside at the beginning of each year to pay for the bananas?

a. $149.50
b. $150.50
c. $152.50
d. $153.50

Solution

Cost of bananas January– June $30 \times 0.40 = \$12$
                July–December $35 \times 0.40 = \$14$

$i = 3/12 = \frac{1}{4}\%$

$P = 12(P/A, \frac{1}{4}\%, 6) + 14(P/A, \frac{1}{4}\%, 6)(P/F, \frac{1}{4}\%, 6)$
    $= \$153.41$

The answer is d.

5-20

A project has a first cost of $10,000, net annual benefits of $2000, and a salvage value of $3000 at the end of its 10-year useful life. The project will be replaced identically at the end of 10 years, and again at the end of 20 years. What is the present worth of the entire 30 years of service, given an interest rate of 10%?

Solution

PW of 10 years $= -10,000 + 2000(P/A, 10\%, 10) + 3000(P/F, 10\%, 10) = \$3445.76$

PW of 30 years $= 3445.76[1 + (P/F, 10\%, 10) + (P/F, 10\%, 20)] = \$5286.45$

Alternate solution:

PW of 30 years $= -10,000[1 + (P/F, 10\%, 10) + (P/F, 10\%, 20)] + 2000(P/A, 10\%, 30)$
$\qquad\qquad + 3000[(P/F, 10\%, 10) + (P/F, 10\%, 20) + (P/F, 10\%, 30)]$
$\qquad = \$5286.45$

5-21

The present worth of costs for a $5000 investment with a complex cash flow diagram is $5265. What is the capitalized cost if the project has a useful life of 12 years, and the MARR is 18%?

Solution

Capitalized cost $= 5265(A/P, 18\%, 12)(P/A, 18\%, \infty) = \$6102$

5-22

A used car dealer tells you that if you put $1500 down on a particular car, your payments will be $190.93 per month for 4 years at a nominal interest rate of 18%. Assuming monthly compounding, what is the cost to you of the car?

Solution

$A \quad = \$190.93$ per period $\qquad i = 18/12 = 1\frac{1}{2}\% \qquad n = 12 \times 4 = 48$

$P \quad = 1500 + 190.93(P/A, 1\frac{1}{2}\%, 48)$
$\qquad = \$8000$

5-23

If the current interest rate on bonds of a certain type is 10%, compounded semiannually, what should be the market price of a 14% bond having a $1000 face value? The bond will mature (pay its face value) 6½ years from today, and the next interest payment to the bondholder will be due in 6 months.

Solution

Semiannual interest payment = 0.07(1000) = $70

PV = $70(P/A, 5%, 13) + $1000(P/F, 5%, 13) = $1187.90

5-24

What is the price of a 3-year savings certificate worth $5000 three years from now, at 12% interest, compounded continuously?

Solution

$$P = Fe^{-rn} = \$5000e^{-(0.12)3} = 5000e^{-0.36} = \$3488.50$$

5-25

What is the present worth of a cash flow that decreases uniformly, by $20 per year, from $400 in Year 11 to $220 in Year 20, if i equals 10%?

Solution

PW = [400(P/A, 10%, 10) – 20(P/G, 10%, 10)](P/F, 10%, 10)
    = $770.91

5-26

A farmer must borrow $20,000 to purchase a tractor. The bank has offered the following choice of payment plans, each determined by using an interest rate of 8%. If the farmer's minimum attractive rate of return (MARR) is 15%, which plan should he choose?

Plan A: $5010 per year for 5 years
Plan B: $2956 per year for 4 years plus $15,000 at end of 5 years
Plan C: Nothing for 2 years, then $9048 per year for 3 years

Solution

PWC_A = 5010(P/A, 15%, 5) = $16,794

PWC_B = 2956(P/A, 15%, 4) + 15,000(P/F, 15%, 5) = $15,897

PWC_C = 9048(P/A, 15%, 3)(P/F, 15%, 2) = $15,618

Plan C is lowest-cost plan.

5-27

A resident will give money to his town to purchase a statue honoring the town founders and will pay to maintain the work at a cost of $500 per year forever. If an interest rate of 10% is used, and the resident gives a total of $15,000; how much can be paid for the statue?

Solution

$$\text{Capitalized cost} = 15,000 = P + 500(P/A, 10\%, \infty)$$
$$P = 15,000 - 500(1/0.1)$$
$$= \$10,000$$

5-28

A project being considered by the XYZ Company will have $100,000 in construction costs in each of the first 3 years of the project. Income of $100,000 will begin flowing in Year 4 and will continue through Year 10. The net present worth at 4% of the project is approximately

a. $184,841
b. $188,513
c. $251,089
d. $256,078

Solution

$$P = -100,000(P/A, 4\%, 3) + 100,000(P/A, 4\%, 7)(P/F, 4\%, 3)$$
$$= \$256,077.80$$

The answer is d.

5-29

Corns Squeezings, Inc., is considering the purchase of new mashing equipment. The CEO of the company, Dollar Signs Dallas, has requested that you provide the net present value for the equipment being considered. The relevant data for the new equipment are as follows:

First cost	$125,000	
Annual income	10,000	
Annual operating costs	8,000	(first year and increasing by $750 per year)
Property taxes	5% of first cost	(payable at the end of each year)
Salvage value	8% of first cost	

CSI has a minimum attractive rate of return (MARR) of 4%, and the equipment is has an expected useful life of 6 years.

Solution

Year		
0	First cost	(125,000)
1–6	Annual income: 10,000(P/A, 4%, 6)	52,420
1–6	Annual costs: 8000(P/A, 4%, 6) + 750(P/G, 4%, 6)	(51,316)
1–6	Taxes: 6250(P/A, 4%, 6)	(32,763)
6	Salvage value: 10,000(P/F, 4%, 6)	7,903
		NPV $(148,756)

5-30
Dolphin, Inc. trains mine-seeking dolphins in a 5-mine tank. The company is considering purchasing a new tank for $750,000; realistic dummy mines cost $105,000 apiece. The U.S. Navy will pay $105,000 for each dolphin trained, and the new tank would allow the company to train 3 dolphins per year. The tank will last 10 years and will cost $50,000 per year to maintain. If the MARR equals 5%, what is the net present value?

Solution

$$NPV = -\text{Cost} - \text{Cost of mines} - \text{Annual maintenance}(P/A, 5\%, 10) + \text{Income}(P/A, 5\%, 10)$$
$$= -750,000 - 250,000(5) - 50,000(P/A, 5\%, 10) + 105,000(3)(P/A, 5\%, 10)$$
$$= \$46,330$$

5-31
Using a 10% interest rate, determine which alternative, if any, should be selected, based on net present worth.

Alternative	*A*	*B*
First cost	$5300	$10,700
Uniform annual benefit	1800	2,100
Useful life	4 years	8 years

Solution

Alternative *A*:

$$NPW = 1800(P/A, 10\%, 8) - 5300 - 5300(P/F, 10\%, 4)$$
$$= \$683.10$$

Alternative *B*:

$$NPW = 2100(P/A, 10\%, 8) - 10,700$$
$$= \$503.50$$

Select Alternative *A*.

5-32

Three purchase plans are available for a new car.

  Plan *A*: $5000 cash immediately
  Plan *B*: $1500 down and 36 monthly payments of $116.25
  Plan *C*: $1000 down and 48 monthly payments of $120.50

If a customer expects to keep the car for 5 years, and her cost of money is 18% compounded monthly, which payment plan should she choose?

Solution

Note that in all cases the car is kept for 5 years; that is the common analysis period.

$i = 18/12 = 1\frac{1}{2}\%$

$PW_A = \$5000$

$PW_B = 1500 + 116.25(P/A, 1\frac{1}{2}\%, 36) = \$4715.59$

$PW_C = 1000 + 120.50(P/A, 1\frac{1}{2}\%, 48) = \$5102.18$

Therefore, Plan *B* is the best plan.

5-33

Given the following three mutually exclusive alternatives, and assuming that $i = 10\%$,

	Alternative		
	A	*B*	*C*
Initial cost	$50	$30	$40
Annual benefits	15	10	12
Useful life, in years	5	5	5

which alternative, if any, is preferable?

Solution

$PW_A = -50 + 15(P/A, 10\%, 5) = \$6.87$

$PW_B = -30 + 10(P/A, 10\%, 5) = \$7.91$

$PW_C = -40 + 12(P/A, 10\%, 5) = \$5.49$

Choose Alternative *C*.

5-34

Consider two investments:

1. Invest $1000 and receive $110 at the end of each month for the next 10 months.
2. Invest $1200 and receive $130 at the end of each month for the next 10 months.

If this were your money, and you wanted to earn at least 12% interest on your investment, which investment, if either, would you choose? What nominal interest rate do you earn on the investment you choose? Solve by present worth analysis.

Solution

$i = 12/12 = 1\%$

Alternative 1:   NPW $= 110(P/A, 1\%, 10) - 1000 = \$41.81$
Alternative 2:   NPW $= 130(P/A, 1\%, 10) - 1200 = \$31.23$

Choose Alternative 1 → Maximum NPW.

Nominal interest: NPW $= 0 = -1000 + 110(P/A, i\%, 10)$
$\qquad (P/A, i\%, 10) = 9.1$

From the interest tables, $i \cong 1.75\%$.

Nominal interest $= 1.75\% \times 12$ months $= 21\%$.

5-35

A manufacturing firm has a minimum attractive rate of return (MARR) of 12% on new investments. What uniform annual benefit would Investment B have to generate to make it preferable to Investment A?

Year	Investment A	Investment B
0	−$60,000	−$45,000
1–6	+15,000	?

Solution

NPW of $A = -60,000 + 15,000(P/A, 12\%, 6)$
$\qquad = \$1665$

NPW of $B \geq 1665 = -45,000 + A(P/A, 12\%, 6)$
$\qquad\qquad \therefore A = \$11,351$

Annual benefit $> \$11,351$ per year

5-36

Projects A and B have first costs of $6500 and $17,000, respectively. Project A has net annual benefits of $2000 during each year of its 5-year useful life, after which it can be replaced identically.

Project B has net annual benefits of $3000 during each year of its 10-year life. Use present worth analysis, and an interest rate of 10%, to determine which project to select.

Solution

$PW_A = -6500[1 + (P/F, 10\%, 5)] + 2000(P/A, 10\%, 10) = \$1754.15$

$PW_B = -17,000 + 3000(P/A, 10\%, 10) = \$1435.00$

Select Project A because of its higher present worth.

5-37

The lining of a chemical tank in a certain manufacturing operation is replaced every 5 years at a cost of $5000. A new type of lining is now available that would last 10 years, but it costs $9000. The manufacturer's tank needs a new lining now, and the company intends to use the tank for 40 years, replacing linings when necessary. Compute the present worth of costs of 40 years of service for the 5-year and 10-year linings if $i = 10\%$.

Solution

PW   5-year lining:

$PW = [5000(A/P, 10\%, 5)](P/A, 10\%, 40) = \$12,898.50$

PW   10-year lining:

$PW = [9000(A/P, 10\%, 10)](P/A, 10\%, 40) = \$14,319.39$

5-38

Be-low Mining, Inc., is trying to decide whether it should purchase or lease new earthmoving equipment. If purchased, the equipment will cost $175,000 and is expected to be used 6 years, at which time it can be sold for $72,000. At the midpoint of its life (Year 3), an overhaul costing $20,000 must be performed. The equipment can be leased for $30,000 per year. Be-low will not be responsible for the midlife over haul if the equipment is leased. If the equipment is purchased, it will be leased to other mining companies whenever possible; this is expected to yield revenues of $15,000 per year. The annual operating cost regardless of the decision will be approximately equal. What would you recommend if the MARR is 6%?

Solution

Lease:

(Recall that lease payments are beginning-of-period cash flows.)

$$P = -30,000 - 30,000(P/A, 6\%, 5)$$
$$= -\$156,360$$

Buy:

$$P = -175,000 + 72,000(P/F, 6\%, 6) - 20,000(P/F, 6\%, 3) + 15,000(P/A, 6\%, 6)$$
$$= -\$67,277$$

5-39

The city council wants the municipal engineer to evaluate three alternatives for supplementing the city water supply. The first alternative is to continue deep-well pumping at an annual cost of $10,500. The second alternative is to install an 18-inch pipeline from a surface reservoir. First cost is $25,000 and annual pumping cost is $7000.

The third alternative is to install a 24-inch pipeline from the reservoir at a first cost of $34,000 and annual pumping cost of $5000. The life of each alternative is 20 years. For the second and third alternatives, salvage value is 10% of first cost. With interest at 8%, which alternative should the engineer recommend? Use present worth analysis.

Solution

Fixed output, therefore minimize cost.

Year	Deep Well	18-in. Pipeline	24-in. Pipeline
0		−25,000	−34,000
1–20	−10,500	−7,000	−5,000
20		+2,500	+3,400

Deep Well: PWC $= -10,500(P/A, 8\%, 20) = -\$103,089$

18-in. Pipeline: PW of cost $= -25,000 - 7000(P/A, 8\%, 20) + 2500(P/F, 8\%, 20) = -\$93,190$

24-in. Pipeline: PW of cost $= -34,000 - 5000(P/A, 8\%, 20) + 3400(P/F, 8\%, 20) = -\$82,361$

Choose the 24-inch pipeline.

5-40

A magazine subscription is $12 annually payable in advance; a 3-year subscription costs $28. If the value of money is 12%, which is the better choice?

Solution

$$PW_{\text{3-year Subscription}} = 12 + 12(P/A, 12\%, 2) = 12 + 12(1.69) = 32.28$$

Choose the 3-year subscription because $28 < $32.28.

5-41

Two alternatives are being considered for recovering aluminum from garbage. The first has a capital cost of $100,000 and a first-year maintenance cost of $15,000, with maintenance increasing by $500 per year for each year after the first.

The second has a capital cost of $120,000 and a first-year maintenance cost of $3000, with maintenance increasing by $1000 per year after the first.

Revenues from the sale of aluminum are $20,000 in the first year, increasing $2000 per year for each year after the first. The life of both alternatives is 10 years. There is no salvage value. The before-tax MARR is 10%. Use present worth analysis to determine which alternative is preferred.

Solution

Alternative 1:

$$NPW = -100,000 + 15,000(P/A, 10\%, 10) + 500(P/G, 10\%, 10) = \$3620.50$$

Alternative 2:

$$NPW = -120,000 + 17,000(P/A, 10\%, 10) + 1000(P/G, 10\%, 10) = \$7356.00$$

Choose Alternative 2 $\rightarrow$ maximum NPW.

5-42

As a temporary measure, before a plant expansion is approved and completed, a brewing company is deciding between two used filling machines: the Kram and the Zanni.

a. The Kram filler has an initial cost of $85,000; the estimated annual maintenance is $8000.

b. The Zanni filler has a purchase price of $42,000, with annual maintenance costs of $8000.

The Kram filler has a higher efficiency than the Zanni, and it is expected that savings would amount to $4000 per year if the Kram filler were installed. It is anticipated that the filling machine will not be needed after 5 years, and at that time, the salvage value for the Kram filler would be $25,000, while the Zanni would have little or no value.

Assuming a minimum attractive rate of return (MARR) of 10%, which filling machine should be purchased?

Solution

Fixed output; therefore, minimize costs.

Kram:
  NPW $= 25,000(P/F, 10\%, 5) - 85,000 - 4000(P/A, 10\%, 5)$
      $= -84,641.5$ (or a PWC of $84,641.50)

Zanni:
  NPW $= -42,000 - 8000(P/A, 10\%, 5)$
      $= -72,328$ (or a PWC of $72,328)

Therefore choose the Zanni filler.

5-43
Two technologies are currently available for the manufacture of an important and expensive food and drug additive.

Laboratory *A* is willing to release the exclusive right to manufacture the additive in this country for $50,000 payable immediately, and a $40,000 payment each year for the next 10 years. The production costs are $1.23 per unit of product.

Laboratory *B* is also willing to release similar manufacturing rights, specifying the following schedule of payments:

> on the closing of the contract, $10,000
> from Years 1 to 5, at the end of each year, a payment of $25,000 each
> from Years 6 to 10, also at the end of each year, a payment of $20,000

The production costs are $1.37 per unit of product.

Neither lab is to receive any money after 10 years for this contract. It is anticipated there will be an annual production of 100,000 items for the next 10 years. On the basis of analyses and trials, the products of *A* and *B* are practically identical in quality. Assuming a MARR of 12%, which lab should be chosen?

Solution

Laboratory *A*:   The annual production cost $= 1.23 \times 100K = \$123K$

  PWC $= 50,000 + [40,000 + 123,000](P/A, 12\%, 10) = \$970,950$

Laboratory *B*:   The annual production cost $= 1.37 \times 100K = \$137K$

  PWC $= 10,000 + [25,000 + 137,000](P/A, 12\%, 5)$
      $+ [20,000 + 137,000](P/A, 12\%, 5)(P/F, 12\%, 5) = \$915,150$

Therefore, choose Laboratory *B*.

5-44

An engineering analysis by net present worth (NPW) is to be made for the purchase of two devices, A and B. If an 8% interest rate is used, recommend the device to be purchased.

	Cost	Uniform Annual Benefit	Salvage	Useful Life
Device A	$600	$100	$250	5 years
Device B	700	100	180	10 years

Solution

Device A:

$$\text{NPW} = 100(P/A, 8\%, 10) + 250(P/F, 8\%, 10) - 600 - [600 - 250](P/F, 8\%, 5) = -\$51.41$$

Device B:

$$\text{NPW} = 100(P/A, 8\%, 10) + 180(P/F, 8\%, 10) - 700 = \$54.38$$

Select Device B.

5-45

Cheap Motors Manufacturing must replace one of its tow motors. The NPW of Alternative A is $-\$5,876$; for Alternative B it is $-\$7547$, and for Alternative C, $-\$3409$. Alternatives A and B are expected to last for 12 years, and Alternative C is expected to last for 6 years. If Cheap's MARR is 4%. the alternative that should be chosen is

a. A
b. B
c. C
d. No alternative should be chosen; all NPW values are negative.

Solution

A 12-year analysis period is necessary.

$$\text{NPW}_{A12} = -\$5876$$

$$\text{NPW}_{B12} = -\$7547$$

$$\text{NPW}_{C12} = -3409 + 3409(P/F, 4\%, 6)$$
$$= -\$6103$$

An alternative must be chosen, minimize the PW of costs; therefore, the answer is a.

5-46

A firm is considering the purchase of a new machine to increase the output of an existing production process. Of all the machines considered, management has narrowed the field to the machines represented by the following cash flows.

Machine	Initial Investment	Annual Operating Income
1	$ 50,000	$22,815
2	60,000	25,995
3	75,000	32,116
4	80,000	34,371
3	100,000	42,485

If each of these machines provides the same service for 3 years and the minimum attractive rate of return is 12%, which machine should be selected?

Solution

Maximize the PW.

Machine	Initial Investment	Operating Income (*P/A*, 12%, 3)	NPW
1	$ –50,000	+ 22,815(2.402)	= $4802
2	–60,000	+ 25,995(2.402)	= $2440
3	–75,000	+ 32,116(2.402)	= $2143
4	–80,000	+ 34,371(2.402)	= $2559
5	–100,000	+ 42,485(2.402)	= $2049

Select Machine 1.

5-47

A company decides that it <u>must</u> provide repair service for the equipment it sells. Based on the following, which alternative for providing repair service should be selected?

Alternative	NPW
A	–$9241
B	–6657
C	–8945

Solution

None of the alternatives look desirable; but since one must be chosen (the do-nothing alternative is not available), choose the one that maximizes NPW (in this case, minimizes net present costs). Thus the best of the three alternatives is *B*.

5-48

The following data are associated with three grape-crushing machines under consideration by Rabbit Ridge Wineries LLC.

	Smart Crush	Super Crush	Savage Crush
First cost	$52,000	$63,000	$105,000
O & M costs	15,000	9,000	12,000
Annual benefits	38,000	31,000	37,000
Salvage value	13,000	19,000	22,000
Useful life	4 years	6 years	12 years

If Rabbit Ridge uses a MARR of 12%, which alternative, if any, should be chosen?

Solution

A 12-year analysis period is necessary.

Smart Crush:

$NPW_4 = -52,000 + 23,000(P/A, 12\%, 4) + 13,000(P/F, 12\%, 4)$
  $= \$26,113$

$NPW_{12} = 26,113 + 26,113(P/F, 12\%, 4) + 26,113(P/F, 12\%, 8)$
  $= \$53,255$

Super Crush:

$NPW_6 = -63,000 + 22,000(P/A, 12\%, 6) + 19,000(P/F, 12\%, 6)$
  $= \$37,067$

$NPW_{12} = 37,067 + 37,067(P/F, 12\%, 6)$
  $= \$55,845$

Savage Crush:

$NPW_{12} = -105,000 + 25,000(P/A, 12\%, 12) + 22,000(P/F, 12\%, 12)$
  $= \$54,497$

To maximize NPW, choose Super Crush.

Chapter 6

Annual Cash Flow Analysis

6-1

Deere Construction just purchased a new track hoe attachment costing $12,500. The CFO, John, expects the implement will be used for 5 years, at which time its salvage value is estimated to be $4000. Maintenance costs are estimated at $0 the first year, increasing by $100 each year thereafter. If a 12% interest rate is used, what is the equivalent uniform annual cost of the implement?

a. $2925
b. $2975
c. $3015
d. $3115

Solution

$$EUAC = 12,500(A/P, 12\%, 5) - 4000(A/F, 12\%, 5) + 100(A/G, 12\%, 5)$$
$$= \$3015.40$$

The answer is c.

6-2

The survey firm of Myers, Anderson, and Pope (MAP) LLP is considering the purchase of a piece of new GPS equipment. Data concerning the alternative under consideration are as follows.

First cost	$28,000
Annual income	7,000
Annual costs	2,500
Recalibration at end of Year 4	4,000
Salvage value	2,800

If the equipment has a life of 8 years and MAP's minimum attractive rate of return (MARR) is 5%, what is the annual worth of the equipment?

Solution

$$EUAC = 28,000(A/P, 5\%, 8) - 4500 - 4000(P/F, 5\%, 4)(A/P, 5\%, 8) - 2800(A/F, 5\%, 8)$$
$$= -\$47.63$$

6-3

Ronald McDonald decides to install a fuel storage system for his farm that will save him an estimated 6.5 cents/gallon on his fuel cost. He uses an estimated 20,000 gallons/year on his farm. Initial cost of the system is $10,000, and the annual maintenance the first year is $25, increasing by $25 each year thereafter. After a period of 10 years the estimated salvage is $3000. If money is worth 12%, is the new system a wise investment?

Solution

$\text{EUAC} = 10,000(A/P, 12\%, 10) + 25 + 25(A/G, 12\%, 10)$
$\qquad = \$1884.63$

$\text{EUAB} = 20,000(0.065) + 3000(A/F, 12\%, 10) = \$1471.00$

$\text{EUAW} = -\$413.63 \therefore$ not a wise investment

6-4

The incomes for a business for 5 years are as follows: $8250, $12,600, $9,750, $11,400, and $14,500. If the value of money is 12%, what is the equivalent uniform annual benefit for the 5-year period?

Solution

$\text{PW} = 8250(P/F, 12\%, 1) + 12,600(P/F, 12\%, 2) + 9750(P/F, 12\%, 3)$
$\qquad + 11,400(P/F, 12\%, 4) + 14,500(P/F, 12\%, 5)$
$\qquad = \$39,823$

$\text{EUAB} = 39,823(A/P, 12\%, 5) = \$11,047$

6-5

Morton and Moore LLC (M^2) is trying to decide between two machines that are necessary in its manufacturing facility. If M^2 has a minimum attractive rate of return (MARR) of 15%, which of the following machines should be chosen?

	Machine A	Machine B
First cost	$45,000	$24,000
Annual operating costs	31,000	35,000
Overhaul in Years 2 and 4	—	6,000
Overhaul in Year 5	12,000	—
Salvage value	10,000	8,000
Useful life	8 years	6 years

Solution

$$EUAC_A = -45{,}000(A/P, 15\%, 8) - 31{,}000 - 12{,}000(P/F, 15\%, 5)(A/P, 15\%, 8)$$
$$+ 10{,}000(A/F, 15\%, 8)$$
$$= -\$41{,}632$$

$$EUAC_B = -24{,}000(A/P, 15\%, 6) - 35{,}000 - 6000[(P/F, 15\%, 2)$$
$$+ (P/F, 15\%, 4)](A/P, 15\%, 6) + 8000(A/F, 15\%, 6)$$
$$= -\$42{,}532$$

Minimize EUAC; therefore, choose Machine A.

6-6

The state engineer estimates that the cost of a canal is $680 million. The legislative analyst estimates the equivalent annual cost of the investment for the canal to be $20.4 million. If the analyst expects the canal to last indefinitely, what interest rate is he using to compute the equivalent annual cost (EAC)? If the canal lasts only 50 years, and the analyst continues to believe that the EAC will be $20.4 million, what interest rate is he assuming?

Solution

a. $A = P(A/P, i\%, n)$
  For $n = \infty$, $(A/P, i\%, \infty) = i$
  $A = P(i)$
  $i = A/P = \dfrac{20.4}{680} = 0.03$ or $i = 3\%$

b. $A = P\,(A/P, i\%, 50)$
  $(A/P, i\%, 50) = \dfrac{20.4}{680} = 0.03$

  Searching interest tables at $n = 50$, we find $i = 1.75\%$.

6-7

What uniform annual payment for 12 years is equivalent to receiving all the following?

  $ 3,000   at the end of each year for 12 years
  20,000 today
   4,000 at the end of 6 years
    800 at the end of each year forever
  10,000 at the end of 15 years

Use an 8% interest rate.

Solution

$A_1 = \$3000$

$A_2 = 20{,}000(A/P, 8\%, 12) = \$2654$

$A_3 = 4000(P/F, 8\%, 6)(A/P, 8\%, 12) = \$334.51$

$A_4 = (800/0.08)(A/P, 8\%, 12) = \$1327$

$A_5 = 10{,}000(P/F, 8\%, 15)(A/P, 8\%, 12) = \$418.27$

$$\sum_{i=1}^{n} Ai = 3000 + 2654 + 334.51 + 1327 + 418.27 = \$7733.78$$

6-8

For the cash flow diagram shown, which of the following equations properly calculates the uniform equivalent?

a. $A = 100(A/P, i, 3) + 100(A/F, i, 3)$

b. $A = 100(A/P, i, 15)$

c. $A = 100(A/P, i, 15) + 100(A/F, i, 3)$

d. $A = 100(A/F, i, 3) + 100(A/F, i, 15)$

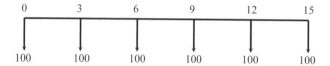

Solution

The answer is c.

6-9

A project has a first cost of $75,000, operating and maintenance costs of $10,000 during each year of its 8-year life, and a $15,000 salvage value. If the interest rate is 12%, what is its equivalent uniform annual cost (EUAC)?

Solution

$\text{EUAC} = 75{,}000(A/P, 12\%, 8) + 10{,}000 - 15{,}000(A/F, 12\%, 8) = \$23{,}878$

6-10

A foundation supports an annual campus seminar by using the earnings of a $50,000 gift. It is felt that 10% interest will be realized for 10 years but that plans should be made to anticipate an interest rate of 6% after that time. What uniform annual payment may be established from the beginning, to fund the seminar at the same level into infinity?

Solution

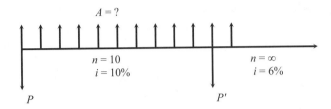

Assume first seminar occurs at time of deposit.

$$P' = A/i = A/0.06$$

$$P = A + A(P/A, 10\%, 10) + P'(P/F, 10\%, 10)$$
$$50,000 = A + 6.145A + (A/.06)0.3855$$
$$13.57A = 50,000$$
$$A = \$3,684.60$$

6-11
A project requires an initial investment of $10,000 and returns benefits of $6000 at the end of every fifth year thereafter. If the minimum attractive rate of return (MARR) is 10%, the equivalent uniform annual worth is closest to

a. −$17.20
b. −$1,600
c. −$5,000
d. −$8,410

Solution

Year:	0	5	10	15	20	25, ...	... ∞
Cash Flow ($):	−10,000	6000	6000	6000	6000	6000	6000

$$\text{EUAW} = 6000(A/F, 10\%, 5) - 10,000(A/P, 10\%, \infty)$$
$$= -\$17.20$$

The answer is a.

6-12

At an interest rate of 10% per year, the perpetual equivalent annual cost of $70,000 now, $100,000 at the end of Year 6, and $10,000 per year from the end of Year 10 through infinity is closest to:

a. $16,510
b. $24,200
c. $31,500
d. $37,630

Solution

$$P = 70,000 + 100,000(P/F, 10\%, 6) + 10,000(P/A, 10\%, \infty)(P/F, 10\%, 10)$$
$$= \$165,110$$

$$A = 165,110(A/P, 10\%, \infty)$$
$$= \$16,511$$

The answer is a.

6-13

A recent engineering graduate makes a donation of $20,000 now and will pay $375 per month for 10 years to endow a scholarship. If interest is 9%, what annual amount can be awarded? Assume that the first scholarship will be bestowed at the end of the first year after full funding.

Solution

$$P = 20,000 + 375(P/A, \tfrac{3}{4}\%, 120)$$
$$= 49,603.25$$
$$A = Pi$$
$$= 49,603.25(0.09)$$
$$= \$4464.29 \text{ scholarship}$$

6-14

Given

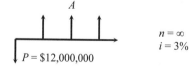

$n = \infty$
$i = 3\%$

$P = \$12,000,000$

Find: A

Solution

$$A = Pi$$
$$= 12,000,000(0.03)$$
$$= \$360,000$$

6-15

A land surveyor just starting in private practice needs a van to carry crew and equipment. He can lease a used van for $8000 per year, paid at the beginning of each year, in which case maintenance is provided. Alternatively, he can buy a used van for $12,000 and pay for maintenance himself. He expects to keep the van for 3 years, at which time he would sell it for an anticipated $3500. Given a MARR of 10%, what is the most the surveyor should pay for uniform annual maintenance to make it worthwhile to buy the van instead of leasing it?

Solution

Lease:
$$\text{EUAC} = 6500(F/P, 10\%, 1) = 6500(1.10) = \$7150$$

Buy:
$$\text{EUAC} = 16,000(A/P, 10\%, 3) + M - 3000(A/F, 10\%, 3)$$

Setting equal and solving for M yields

$$7150 = 6433.60 + M - 906.30$$
$$M = \$1622.70$$

6-16

The first cost of a fairly large flood control dam is expected to be $5 million. The maintenance cost will be $60,000 per year, and a $100,000 outlay will be required every 5 years. At 10%, the EUAC of the dam project is closest to:

a. $576,380
b. $591,580
c. $630,150
d. $691,460

Solution

$$\text{EUAC} = 5,000,000(A/P, 10\%, \infty) + 60,000 + 100,000(A/F, 10\%, 5)$$
$$= \$576,380$$

The answer is a.

6-17

A rich folk singer has donated $500,000 to endow a university professorial chair in Bohemian Studies. If the money is invested at 8.5%, how much can be withdrawn each year, ad infinitum, to pay the Professor of B.S.?

Solution

$$A = 500,000(A/P, 8.5\%, \infty) = 500,000(0.085) = \$42,500$$

6-18

Assuming monthly payments, which would be the better financing plan on the same $19,000 car?

Plan *a*:. 6% interest on the full amount for 48 months
Plan *b*:. a $2500 rebate (discount) and 12% interest on the remaining amount for 48 months

Solution

Plan a. $A = 19,000(A/P, \frac{1}{2}\%, 48) = \$446.50/\text{mo}$.

Plan b. $A = 16,500(A/P, 1\%, 48) = \$433.95/\text{mo}$.

Choose Plan *b*.

6-19

The town of Dry Hole needs an additional supply of water from Duck Creek. The town engineer has selected two plans for comparison. The gravity plan would divert water at a point 10 miles up Duck Creek and carry it through a pipeline by gravity to the town. A system using a pumping station would divert water at a point closer to town and pump it into the town. The pumping plant would be built in two stages, with 75% of its capacity installed initially and the remaining 25% installed 10 years later. The engineer has assumed that each plan will last 40 years and be worthless at the end of its life. Use the following data and an interest rate of 8% to find the maximum that should be paid for the gravity plan.

	Gravity	Pumping
Initial investment	$??????	$1,800,000
Completion cost in 10th year		350,000
Annual operating and maintenance costs	$10,000	$25,000
Annual power costs:		
Average costs the first 10 years	0	$ 50,000
Average costs the next 30 years	0	$100,000

Solution

Gravity:
   $\text{EUAC} = X(A/P, 8\%, 40) -10,000$
         $= 0.0839X - 10,000$

Pumping:
   $\text{EUAC} = 1,800,000(A/P, 8\%, 40) + 350,000(P/F, 8\%, 10)(A/P, 8\%, 40) + 25,000$
           $+ [50,000(P/A, 8\%, 10) + 100,000(P/A, 8\%,30)(P/F, 8\%,10)](A/P, 8\%, 40)$
        $= \$261,521$

Setting the two alternatives equal yields

   $0.0839X - 10,000 = 261,521$
            $X = \$2,997,867$

6-20

Twenty-five thousand dollars is deposited in a bank trust account that pays 9% interest, compounded semiannually. Equal annual withdrawals are to be made from the account, beginning one year from now and continuing forever. Calculate the maximum amount of W, the annual withdrawal.

Solution

$i = 9/2 = 4\frac{1}{2}\%$

$A = Pi = 25,000(0.045) = 1125$ per semiannual period

$W = 1125(F/A, 4\frac{1}{2}\%, 2) = \$2300.63$

6-21

Smith, LYons, Carson, and Kirk (SLYCK) Inc. is considering the purchase of new petroleum processing equipment. Following are the relevant data for the alternatives under consideration.

First cost	$278,750
Annual income	$125/barrel of processed petroleum
Annual operating costs	$25,500 the first year increasing $2,000 each year thereafter
Annual property taxes	8% of first cost
Annual insurance	4% of first cost payable at the beginning of each year
Salvage value	15% of first cost
Useful life	10 years

SLYCK's minimum attractive rate of return is 4%. Determine the number of barrels per year of petroleum that must be processed to justify purchasing the new equipment.

Solution

Year		
0	First cost 278,750(A/P, 4%, 10)	(34,369.88)
1–10	Income 125(X)	125(X)
1–10	Costs 25,500 + 2000(A/G, 4%, 10)	(33,854.00)
1–10	Taxes 0.08(278,750)	(22,300.00)
0–9	Insurance 0.04(278,750)(F/P, 4%, 1)	(11,596.00)
10	Salvage value 0.15(278,750)(A/F, 4%,10)	3,482.98
		0

$0 = -34,369.88 - 33,854.00 - 22,300.00 - 11,596.00 + 3,482.98 + 125(X)$

$X = 789.09$ barrels

6-22

If the interest rate is 10% and compounding is semiannual, what series of equal annual transactions is equivalent to the following series of semiannual transactions? The first of the equal annual transactions is to occur at the end of the second year and the last at the end of the fourth year.

Time (year)	0		1		2		3		4		5	5½
Period	0	1	2	3	4	5	6	7	8	9	10	11
Cash flow	$0	600	500	400	300	200	100	300	500	700	900	1100

Solution

$i = 10/2 = 5\%$

$P = 600(P/A, 5\%, 5) - 100(P/G, 5\%, 5) + [100(P/A, 5\%, 6) + 200(P/G, 5\%, 6)](P/F, 5\%, 5)$
    $= 4046.80$

Effective $i = (1 + 0.10/2)^2 - 1 = 10.25\%$

Sum at end of Year 1: $F = 4046.80(F/P, 10.25\%, 1) = 4461.60$

Equal annual payments: $A = 4461.60(A/P, 10.25\%, 3) = \$1802.04$

6-23

A tractor costs $12,500 and will be used for 5 years, at which time its estimated salvage value will be $4000. Maintenance costs are estimated to be $100 for the first year, increasing by $100 each year thereafter. If $i = 12\%$, what is the equivalent uniform annual cost (EUAC) for the tractor?

Solution

EUAC $= 12,500(A/P, 12\%, 5) + 100 + 100(A/G, 12\%, 5) - 4,000(A/F, 12\%, 5)$
       $= \$3115.40$

6-24

If in the last week of February 2006 Ellen won $250,000 and invested it by March 1, 2006, in a "sure thing" that paid 8% interest, compounded annually, what uniform annual amount can she withdraw on the first of March for 15 years starting in 2012?

Solution

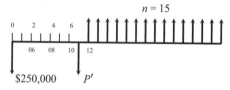

$P' = 250,000(F/P, 8\%, 7) = \$428,500$
$A = 250,000(F/P, 8\%, 7)(A/P, 8\%, 15) = \$50,048.80$

6-25

A machine having a first cost of $20,000 is expected to save $1500 in the first year of operation, and the savings should increase by $200 every year until (and including) the 9th year; thereafter, the savings will decrease by $150 until (and including) the 16th year. Using equivalent uniform annual worth, is this machine economical? Assume a MARR of 10%.

Solution

There are a number of possible solutions.
Here's one:

EUAW $= -20,000(A/P, 10\%, 16) + [1500(P/A, 10\%, 9) + 200(P/G, 10\%, 9)](A/P, 10\%, 16)$
$\qquad + [2950(P/A, 10\%, 7) - 150(P/G, 10\%, 7)](P/F, 10\%, 9)(A/P, 10\%, 16)$
$\qquad = -\$280.94$; the machine is not economical

6-26

Calculate the equivalent uniform annual cost of the following schedule of payments.

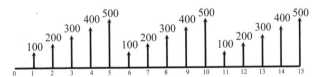

Solution

Since payments repeat every 5 years, analyze for 5 years only.

$A = 100 + 100(A/G, 8\%, 5) = \$284.60$

6-27

The initial cost of a van is $12,800; its salvage value after 4 years will be $5500. Maintenance is estimated to be a uniform gradient amount of $120 per year (with no maintenance costs the first year), and the operation cost is estimated to be 36 cents/mile for 400 miles/month. If money is worth 12%, what is the approximate equivalent uniform annual cost (EUAC) for the van, expressed as a monthly cost?

Solution

EUAC $= 12,800(A/P, 12\%, 5) + 120(A/G, 12\%, 5) + 0.36(400)(12) - (5500)(A/F, 12\%, 5)$
$\qquad = 4626/12$
$\qquad = \$385.50/$month

6-28
The uniform equivalent of the cash flow diagram shown is given by which one of the following answers?

a. $50(A/G, i, 8)$
b. $50(A/G, i, 9)$
c. $50(A/G, i, 10)$
d. $50(A/G, i, 9)(F/A, i, 9)(A/F, i, 10)$

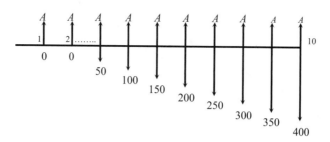

Solution

Note these two concepts:
    1. The G series is 9 periods long
    2. The uniform equivalent is 10 periods long

The answer is d.

6-29
Granny Gums has established a scholarship at the Martin College of Dentistry. She will make deposits into an endowment account that pays 12% per year based on the following schedule.

Year:	0	1	2	3	4	5	6
Deposit amount ($):	100	90	80	70	60	50	40

If the first scholarship is to be awarded one year after the first deposit is made and thereafter the award will be given indefinitely, what is the scholarship amount?

a. $33.68
b. $45.68
c. $68.26
d. $92.58

Solution

First find the present worth of the gradient deposits.

$P = 100 + 90(P/A, 12\%, 6) - 10(P/G, 12\%, 6)$
  $= \$380.69$

$A = 380.69(A/P, 12\%, \infty)$
  $= 380.69(.12)$
  $= \$45.68$

The answer is b.

6-30

A proposed steel bridge has an indefinite life. The initial cost of the bridge is $3,750,000, and annual maintenance costs are estimated to be $25,000. The bridge deck will be resurfaced every 10 years for $900,000, and anticorrosion paint will be applied every 5 years for $250,000. If the interest rate is 8%, what is the EAC?

If 650,000 axles will cross the bridge each year, what approximate toll per axle should be charged? Give your answer to the nearest nickel.

Solution

$\text{EUAC} = 3,750,000(A/P, 8\%, \infty) + 900,000(A/F, 8\%, 10) + 250,000(A/F, 8\%, 5) + 25,000$
     $= \$429,725$

$\text{Toll} = 429,725/650,000$
    $= 0.6611$
    $\approx 70\text{¢ per axle}$

6-31

The Tennessee Department of Highways is trying to decide whether it should "hot-patch" a short stretch of an existing highway or resurface it. If the hot-patch method is chosen, approximately 500 cubic meters of material would be required at a cost of $800/cubic meter (in place). If hot-patched, the shoulders will have to be improved at the same time at a cost of $24,000. The shoulders must be maintained at a cost of $3000 every 2 years. The annual cost of routine maintenance on the patched road is estimated to be $6000.

Alternatively, the state can resurface the road at a cost of $500,000. If maintained properly, at a cost of $2000 per year beginning in the second year, the surface will last for 10 years. The shoulders would require reworking at the end of the fifth year at a cost of $15,000. Regardless of the method selected, the road will be completely rebuilt in 10 years. At an interest rate of 9%, which alternative should be chosen?

Solution

Hot-Patch:

$$\text{EUAC} = 500(800)(A/P, 9\%, 10) + 24,000(A/P, 9\%, 10)$$
$$+ 3,000(A/F, 9\%, 2)(P/A, 9\%, 8)(A/P, 9\%, 10) + 6000$$
$$= \$73,297$$

Resurface:

$$\text{EUAC} = 500,000(A/P, 9\%, 10) + 15,000(P/F, 9\%, 5)(A/P, 9\%, 10)$$
$$+ 2000(P/A, 9\%, 9)(P/F, 9\%, 1)(A/P, 9\%, 10)$$
$$= \$81,133$$

Minimize EUAC; choose the hot-patch alternative.

6-32

A college has been willed $100,000 to establish a permanent scholarship. If funds are invested at 6% and all funds earned are disbursed yearly, what will be the value of the scholarship in the sixth year of operation?

Solution

$A = Pi = 100,000(0.06) = \$6000$ for any year

6-33

The annual worth of a quarterly lease payment of $500 at 8% interest is nearest to

a. $2061
b. $2102
c. $2253
d. $2433

Solution

Recall that lease payments are made at beginning of period.

$i = 8/4 = 2\%$ $n = 4$

$A = 500(F/P, 2\%, 1)(F/A, 2\%, 4)$
  $= \$2102.22$

Alternate solution:

$A = [500 + 500(P/A, 2\%, 3)](F/P, 2\%, 4)$
  $= \$2101.24$

The answer is b.

6-34

Dorf Motors Manufacturing must replace one of its tow motors. The net present cost of Alternative A is $8956; Alternative B is $5531, and Alternative C is $4078. Alternative A is expected to last for 12 years; Alternative B has an expected life of 7 years; and Alternative C is expected to last for 5 years. If Dorf's MARR is 5%, the alternative that should be chosen is

a. A
b. B
c. C
d. No alternative should be chosen; all economic measures are negative.

Solution

Annual worth analysis is appropriate because of the different useful lives.

$EUAC_A = 8956(A/P, 5\%, 12)$
         $= \$1010.23$

$EUAC_B = 8956(A/P, 5\%, 7)$
         $= \$955.76$

$EUAC_C = 8956(A/P, 5\%, 5)$
         $= \$942.02$

Minimize EUAC; therefore, the answer is c.

6-35

Johnny on the Job portable toilets must purchase new portable toilets that will be rented to construction companies for job site use. The toilet model the company is considering costs $275/unit. The company plans to purchase 50 toilets. Each month the service and upkeep for the toilets is estimated to cost $8.75/unit. Every 6 months the toilets must undergo cleaning and sanitizing that is contracted to cost $250 for all 50 toilets. The cleaning and sanitizing must also be performed before the company can dispose of the units, which will have a salvage value of $50/toilet. JOJ wishes to make $5/unit in addition to covering all costs. If the MARR for JOJ is 6%, how much should be charged (to the nearest $) per toilet per month for rental? Assume that all toilets are rented and can be used for 2 years.

Solution

$i = 6/12 = \frac{1}{2}\%$ $n = 12 \times 2 = 24$

$EUMC = 275(50)(A/P, \frac{1}{2}\%, 24) + 8.75(50) + 250(A/F, \frac{1}{2}\%, 6) - 50(50)(A/F, \frac{1}{2}\%, 24)$
       $= \$989.53$

Cost per unit $= 989.53/50$
              $= 19.79$
Profit $+ \underline{\ 5.00}$
              $\$24.79 \rightarrow$ Rent for $25/unit

6-36
Data for tractors A and B are listed. With interest of 12%, and based on equivalent uniform annual cost (EUAC), which tractor should be selected?

	A	B
First cost	$30,000	$36,000
Annual maintenance	1,500	2,000
Salvage value	5,000	8,000
Useful life	6 years	6 years

Solution

EUAC = $P(A/P, i\%, n) - S(A/F, i\%, n)$ + Other costs

Tractor A:

EUAC = $30,000(A/P, 12\%, 6) - 5000(A/F, 12\%, 6) + 1500$
$\quad = \$8180$

Tractor B:

EUAC = $36,000(A/P, 12\%, 6) - 8000(A/F, 12\%, 6) + 2000$
$\quad = \$9770$

Since the criterion is a minimized EUAC, select tractor A.

6-37
According to the manufacturers' literature, the costs of running automatic grape peelers, if maintained according to the instruction manuals, are as follows.

	Slippery	Grater
First cost	$500	$300
Maintenance	$100 at end	Year 1 $ 0
	of Years 2,	2 50
	4, 6, and 8	3 75
		4 00
		5 125
Useful life	10 years	5 years

Which alternative is preferred if MARR = 15%?

Solution

Slippery:

EUAC = [500 + 100(A/F, 15%, 2)(P/A, 15%, 8)](A/P, 15%, 10)
          = $141.24

Grater:

EUAC = [300 + 25(P/G, 15%, 5) + 25(P/A, 15%, 4)(P/F, 15%, 1)](A/P, 15%, 5)
          = $151.07

Therefore, choose Slippery with lower EUAC.

6-38
A semiconductor manufacturer has been ordered by the city to stop discharging acidic waste liquids into the city sewer system. Your analysis shows that the company should select one of the following three systems.

| | Installed | Annual | |
System	Cost	Operating Cost	Salvage Value
CleanH$_2$O	$30,000	$6000	$ 2,000
AcidFree	35,000	5000	5,000
Evergreen	80,000	1000	40,000

If the system is expected to be used for 20 years and to last that long, as well, and money is worth 8%, which system should be purchased?

Solution

CleanH$_2$O: EUAC = 6000 + 30,000(A/P, 8%, 20) – 2000(A/F, 8%, 20)
                          = $9013

AcidFree: EUAC = 5000 + 35,000(A/P, 8%, 20) – 5000(A/F, 8%, 20)
                          = $8456

Evergreen: EUAC = 1000 + 80,000(A/P, 8%, 20) – 40,000(A/F, 8%, 20)
                          = $8276

Purchase the system with the lowest EUAC, Evergreen.

6-39

The following alternatives describe possible projects for the use of a vacant lot. In each case the project cost includes the purchase price of the land.

	Parking Lot	Gas Station
Investment cost	$50,000	$100,000
Annual income	35,000	85,000
Annual operating expenses	25,000	$70,000 in Year 1, then increasing by 1000/yr
Salvage value	10,000	10,000
Useful life	5 years	10 years

a. If the minimum attractive rate of return (MARR) equals 18%, what should be done with the land?

b. Is it possible that the decision would be different if the MARR were higher than 18%? Why or why not? (No calculations necessary.)

Solution

a. $EUAW_{P.L.} = (35,000 - 25,000) - 50,000(A/P, 18\%, 5) + 10,000(A/F, 18\%, 5) = -\$4592$

$EUAW_{G.S.} = (85,000 - 70,000) - 100,000(A/P, 18\%, 10) + 10,000(A/F, 18\%, 10) - 1000(A/G, 18\%, 10) = -\$10,019$

Since both EUAWs are negative, leave the lot vacant.

b. No. Higher MARR favors lower-cost projects, and the lowest-cost project (do nothing) has already been chosen.

6-40

Given the following information about possible investments being considered by the ABC Block Company, what is the best choice at a minimum attractive rate of return (MARR) of 10%?

	A	*B*
Investment cost	$5000	$8000
Annual benefits	1200	800
Useful life	5 years	15 years

Solution

Since the useful lives are different, use equivalent annual worth analysis.

$EUAW_A = 1200 - 5000(A/P, 10\%, 5) = -\$119.00$

$EUAW_B = 800 - 8000(A/P, 10\%, 15) = -\$252.00$

Choose the do-nothing alternative.

6-41

You are considering purchasing the Press-o-Matic or Steam-It-Out model automatic ironing system to allow you to handle more dry cleaning business. Both machines have the same cost, $5000. The Press-o-Matic will generate a positive cash flow of $1300 per year for 5 years and then be of no service or salvage value. The Steam-It-Out will generate a positive cash flow of $800 per year for 10 years and then be of no service or salvage value. You plan to be in the dry cleaning business for the next 10 years. How would you invest the $5000 you have in your hand if you feel the time value of money is worth the same as your high-interest bank account offers, which is

a. 8%?
b. 12%?

Solution

  a, Press EUAW $= 1300 - 5000(A/P, 8\%, 5) = \$47.50$
      Steam EUAW $= 800 - 5000(A/P, 8\%, 10) = \$55.00$

    Choose the higher EUAW, Steam-It-Out.

  b. Press EUAW $= 1300 - 5000(A/P, 12\%, 5) = -\$87.00$
      Steam EUAW $= 800 - 5000(A/P, 12\%, 10) = -\$85.00$

    Choose neither option because both have a negative annual worth.

6-42

Data for Machines X and Y are listed. With an interest rate of 8%, and based upon equivalent uniform annual cost (EUAC), which machine should be selected?

	X	Y
First cost	$5000	$10,000
Annual maintenance	500	200
Salvage value	600	1,000
Useful life	5 years	15 years

Solution

Machine *X*:

EUAC = 5000(*A/P*, 8%, 5) – 600(*A/F*, 8%, 5) + 500 = $1650.20

Machine *Y*:

EUAC = 10,000(*A/P*, 8%, 15) – 1000(*A/F*, 8%, 15) + 200 = $1331.20

Decision criterion is minimize EUAC; therefore, choose *Y*.

6-43

Consider Projects *A* and *B*. Which project would you approve if a project must be selected? The expected period of service is 15 years, and the interest rate is 10%.

	Project *A*	Project *B*
Initial cost	$50,000	$75,000
Annual operating costs	15,000	10,000
Annual repair costs	5,000	3,000
Salvage value	5,000	10,000

Solution

Project *A*:

EUAC$_A$ = 50,000(*A/P*, 10%, 15) + 20,000 – 5000(*A/F*, 10%, 15) = $26,417.50

Project *B*:

EUAC$_B$ = 75,000(*A/P*, 10%, 15) + 13,000 – 10,000(*A/F*, 10%, 15) = $22,547.50

Choose the least cost: Project *B*.

6-44

Assuming a 10% interest rate, determine which alternative should be selected.

	A	*B*
First cost	$5300	$10,700
Uniform annual benefit	1800	2,100
Salvage value	0	200
Useful life	4 years	8 years

Solution

Alternative *A*:

EUAW $= 5300(A/P, 10\%, 4) - 1800$
$= \$127.85$

Alternative *B*:

EUAW $= 10,700(A/P, 10\%, 8) + 200(A/F, 10\%, 8) - 2100$
$= \$112.30$

Choose alternative *A*.

6-45

A company must decide whether to buy Machine *A* or Machine *B*. After 5 years, Machine *A* will be replaced with another *A*.

	Machine *A*	Machine *B*
First cost	$10,000	$20,000
Annual maintenance	1,000	0
Salvage value	10,000	10,000
Useful life	5 years	10 years

With the minimum attractive rate of return (MARR) = 10%, which machine should be purchased?

Solution

$\text{EUAW}_A = -10,000(A/P, 10\%, 5) - 1000 + 10,000(A/F, 10\%, 5) = -\$2000$

$\text{EUAW}_B = -20,000(A/P, 10\%, 10) + 10,000(A/F, 10\%, 10) = -\$2627$

Therefore, Machine *A* should be purchased.

6-46

The construction costs and annual maintenance costs of two alternatives for a canal are given. Use equivalent uniform annual cost (EUAC) analysis to decide which alternative you would recommend. Assume 7% interest and infinite life. What is the capitalized cost of maintenance for the alternative you choose?

	Alternative *A*	Alternative *B*
Construction cost	$25,000,000	$50,000,000
Annual maintenance costs	3,500,000	2,000,000

Solution

a.   Alternative A: EUAC $= A + Pi = 3.5\text{M} + 25\text{M}(0.07) = \$5,250,000$
      Alternative B: EUAC $= A + Pi = 2.0\text{M} + 50\text{M}(0.07) = \$5,500,000$

      Fixed output $\therefore$ minimize cost; choose A.

b. $P = A/i = 3,500,000/0.07 = \$50,000,000$

6-47

The manager of Cats-N-The-Pond, Inc. is trying to decide between two alternative designs for an aquacultural facility. Both facilities produce the same number of fish for sale. The first alternative costs $250,000 to build and has a first-year operating cost of $110,000. Operating costs are estimated to increase by $10,000 per year for each year after the first.

The second alternative costs $450,000 to build and has a first-year operating cost of $40,000 per year, escalating at $5000 per year for each year after the first. The estimated life of both plants is 10 years, and each has a salvage value that is 10% of construction cost.

Assume an 8% interest rate. Use equivalent uniform annual cost (EUAC) analysis to determine, which alternative should be selected.

Solution

	Alternative 1	Alternative 2
First cost	$250,000	$450,000
Uniform annual costs	110,000	40,000
Gradient	10,000	5,000
Salvage value	25,000	45,000

Alternative 1:   EUAC $= 250,000(A/P, 8\%, 10) - 25,000(A/F, 8\%, 10) + 110,000$
                       $+ 10,000(A/G, 8\%, 10)$
                       $= \$184,235$

Alternative 2:   EUAC $= 450,000(A/P, 8\%, 10) - 45,000(A/F, 8\%, 10) + 40,000$
                       $+ 5000(A/G, 8\%, 10)$
                       $= \$123,300$

Fixed output (same amount of fish for sale) $\therefore$ minimize EUAC.

Choose Alternative 2.

6-48

The plant engineer of a major food processing corporation is evaluating alternatives to supply electricity to the plant. He will pay $3 million for electricity purchased from the local utility at the end of the first year and estimates that this cost will increase thereafter at $300,000 per year. He desires to know if he should build a 4000-kilowatt power plant. His operating costs (other than fuel) for such a power plant are estimated to be $130,000 per year. He is considering two alternative fuels:

a.   Wood: Installed cost of the power plant is $1200/kW. Fuel consumption is 30,000 tons per year. Fuel cost for the first year is $20/ton and is estimated to increase at a rate of $2/ton for each year after the first. No salvage value.

b.   Oil: Installed cost is $1000/kW. Fuel consumption is 46,000 barrels per year. Fuel cost is $34 per barrel for the first year and is estimated to increase at $1/barrel per year for each year after the first. No salvage value.

If interest is 12%, and the analysis period is 10 years, which alternative should the engineer choose? Solve the problem by equivalent uniform annual cost analysis (EUAC).

Solution

	Do Nothing	Wood	Oil
First cost	0	$4000 \times 1200 = 4,800,000$	$4000 \times 1000 = 4,000,000$
Annual oper. costs	0	130,000	130,000
Annual energy costs	3,000,000	$30,000 \times 20 = 600,000$	$46,000 \times 34 = 1,564,000$
Gradient	300,000	$30,000 \times 2 = 60,000$	$46,000 \times 1 = 46,000$

Do Nothing:

$\quad$ EUAC = 3000K + 300K(A/G, 12%, 10) = $4,075,500

Wood:

$\quad$ EUAC = 4800K(A/P, 12%, 10) + 130K + 600K + 60K(A/G, 12%, 10) = $1,794,700

Oil:

$\quad$ EUAC = 4000K(A/P, 12%, 10) + 130K + 1564K + 46K(A/G, 12%, 10) = $2,566,190

Minimize EUAC; choose wood.

6-49

Two alternatives are being considered by a food processor for the warehousing and distribution of its canned products in a sales region. These canned products come in standard cartons of 24 cans per carton. The two alternatives are as follows.

Alternative *A*:   To have its own distribution system. The administrative costs are estimated at $43,000 per year, and other general operating expenses are calculated at $0.009 per carton. A warehouse will have to be purchased, at a cost of $300,000.

Alternative *B*:   To sign an agreement with an independent distribution company that is asking a payment of $0.10 per carton distributed.

Assume a study period of 10 years and that the warehouse can be sold at the end of this period for $200,000.

   a. Which alternative should be chosen, if management expects that the number of cartons to be distributed will be 600,000 per year?

   b. Find the minimum number of cartons per year that will make the alternative of having a distribution system (Alt. *A*) more profitable than to sign an agreement with the distribution company (Alt. *B*).

Solution

   a. For 600,000 cartons/year

   Alternative *A*:

   Capital expenses = $300,000(A/P, 10\%, 10) - 200,000(A/F, 10\%, 10) = \$36,270$

Annual Costs:	Administration		$43,000
	Operating expenses	$0.009 \times 600,000$	5,400
		=	
	Capital expenses		36,270
		Total =	$84,670

   ∴ Total annual costs = $84,670.

   Alternative *B*:

   Total annual costs = $0.10 \times 600,000 = \$60,000$

   ∴ Sign an agreement for Alternative *B*.

b.   Let M = number of cartons/year.

The EUAC for Alternative B (agreement) = $EUAC_{AGREEMENT}$ = 0.10M

The EUAC for Alternative A (own system) = $EUAC_{OWN}$ = 43,000 + 0.009M + 36,270

We want $EUAC_{OWN} < EUAC_{AGREEMENT}$

$$43,000 + 0.009M + 36,270 < 0.10M$$
$$79,270 < (0.10 - 0.009)M$$
$$79,270/0.091 < M$$
$$871,099 < M$$

∴ Owning the distribution system is more profitable for 871,100 or more cartons/year.

6-50

Two alternative investments are being considered. What is the minimum uniform annual benefit that will make Investment B preferable to Investment A? Assume that interest is 10%.

Year	A	B
0	–$500	–$700
1–5	+150	?

Solution

$EUAW_A = EUAW_B$

$$-500(A/P, 10\%, 5) + 150 = -700(A/P, 10\%, 5) + X$$
$$X = \$202.76$$

6-51

Consider two investments:

1.   Invest $1000 and receive $110 at the end of each month for the next 10 months.

2.   Invest $1200 and receive $130 at the end of each month for the next 10 months.

If this were your money, and you wanted to earn at least 12% interest on it, which investment would you make, if any? Solve the problem by annual cash flow analysis.

Solution

Alternative 1:   EUAW = EUAB – EUAC = $110 - 1000(A/P, 1\%, 10) = \$4.40$
Alternative 2:   EUAW = EUAB – EUAC = $130 - 1200(A/P, 1\%, 10) = \$3.28$

Maximum EUAW; therefore, choose Alternative 1.

6-52

An airport expansion that is expected to be used indefinitely is under way at Jackson Hole Metro Airport. Land acquisition and major earthworks that will last as long as the airport is used are expected to cost $600 million. Terminal construction that will last 20 years is budgeted at $200 million. (Assume that the terminal is to be identically replaced every 20 years.) Runway construction will cost $150 million. The runways will also be used indefinitely, with repaving required every 10 years at a cost of $10 million. The operating and maintenance costs are estimated to be $15 million per year. What is the annual cost of the project if $i = 5\%$ and the airport will be used indefinitely?

Solution

$$\text{EUAC} = 600(A/P, 5\%, \infty) + 200(A/P, 5\%, 20) + 150(A/P, 5\%, \infty) + 10(A/F, 5\%, 10) + 15$$
$$= \$69,335,000$$

6-53

Green County is planning to construct a bridge across the south branch of Carey Creek to facilitate traffic flow though Clouser Canyon. The first cost for the bridge will be $9,500,000. Annual maintenance and repairs the first year of operation, estimated to be $10,000, are expected to increase by $1000 each year thereafter. In addition to regular maintenance, every 5 years the road way will be resurfaced at a cost of $750,000, and the structure must be painted every 3 years at a cost of $100,000. If Green County uses 5% as its cost of money and the bridge is expected to last for 20 years, what is the EUAC?

Solution

$$\text{EUAC} = 9,500,000(A/P, 5\%, 20) + [10,000 + 1000(A/G, 5\%, 20)]$$
$$+ 750,000(A/F, 5\%, 5)(P/A, 5\%, 15)(A/P, 5\%, 20)$$
$$+ 100,000(A/F, 5\%, 3)(P/A, 5\%, 18)(A/P, 5\%, 20)$$
$$= \$922,551$$

Chapter 7

Rate of Return Analysis

7-1

Andrew T. invested $15,000 in a high-yield account. At the end of 30 years he closed the account and received $539,250. Compute the effective interest rate he received on the account.

Solution

Recall that $F = P(1 + i)^n$

$$539{,}250 = 15{,}000(1 + i)^{30} \Rightarrow 539{,}250/15{,}000 = (1 + i)^{30}$$
$$35.95 = (1 + i)^{30}$$
$$\sqrt[30]{35.95} = 1 + i$$
$$1.1268 = 1 + i$$
$$.1268 = i$$
$$i = 12.68\%$$

7-2

The heat loss through the exterior walls of a processing plant is expected to cost the owner $3000 next year. A salesman from Superfiber, Inc. claims he can reduce the heat loss by 80% with the installation of $15,000 worth of Superfiber now. If the cost of heat loss rises by $200 per year, after next year (gradient), and the owner plans to keep the building 10 more years, what is his rate of return, neglecting depreciation and taxes?

Solution

NPW = 0 at the rate of return

Try 12%:
$$NPW = -15{,}000 + 0.8(3000)(P/A, 12\%, 10) + 0.8(200)(P/G, 12\%, 10)$$
$$= \$1800.64$$
Try 15%:
$$NPW = -\$237.76$$

By interpolation, $i = 14.7\%$.

7-3

Does the following project have a positive or negative rate of return? Show how this is known to be true.

Investment cost	$2500
Net benefits	300 in Year 1, increasing by $200 per year
Salvage value	50
Useful life	4 years

Solution

Year	Benefits	
1	300	Total benefits obtained are less than the investment,
2	500	so the "return" on the investment is negative.
3	700	
4	900	
4	50	
	Total = $2450 < Cost	

7-4

At what interest rate would $1000 at the end of 2010 be equivalent to $2000 at the end of 2017?

Solution

$$(1 + i)^7 = 2$$
$$i = (2)^{1/7} - 1 = 0.1041 = 10.41\%$$

7-5

A painting, purchased one month ago for $1000, has just been sold for $1700. What nominal annual rate of return did the seller receive on her investment?

Solution

$$i = 7000/1000 = 70\% \qquad r = 70 \times 12 = 840\%$$

7-6

Find the rate of return for a $10,000 investment that will pay $1000 per year for 20 years.

Solution

$$10,000 = 1000(P/A, i\%, 20)$$
$$(P/A, i\%, 20) = 10$$

From interest tables: $7\% < i < 8\%$ $\qquad \therefore$ interpolate: $i = 7.77\%$

7-7

Some time ago a young engineer obtained a mortgage at a 12% interest rate, for a total of $52,000. She has to pay 240 more monthly payments of $534.88 each. As interest rates are going down, she inquires about the conditions under which she could refinance the mortgage. If the bank charges an origination fee of 2% of the amount to be financed, and if the bank and the engineer agree that the fee will be paid by combining the fee with the refinanced mortgage, what percentage rate would make refinancing her mortgage attractive, if the new mortgage terms require 120 payments?

Solution

The amount to be refinanced:

$i = 12/12 = 1\%$

a.   PW of 240 monthly payments left $= 534.88(P/A, 1\%, 240)$
$= \$48,577.27$

b.   New loan fee (2%) $= 48,577.27(0.02) = \$971.55$

$\Rightarrow$ Total amount to refinance $= 48,577.27 + 971.55 = \$49,548.82$

The new monthly payments are: $A_{NEW} = 49,548.82(A/P, i, 120)$
The current payments are: $A_{OLD} = 534.88$

We want $A_{NEW} < A_{OLD}$.

Substituting $\Rightarrow 49,548.82(A/P, i, 120) < 534.88$
$(A/P, i, 120) < 534.88/49,548.82 = 0.0108$

For $i = \frac{1}{4}\%$: $(A/P, \frac{1}{4}\%, 120) = 0.00966$
For $i = \frac{1}{2}\%$: $(A/P, \frac{1}{2}\%, 120) = 0.0111$

$\frac{1}{4}\% < i < \frac{1}{2}\%$ $\therefore$ interpolate

$i = 0.4479\%$

This corresponds to a nominal annual percentage rate of $12 \times 0.4479 = 5.375\%$.
Therefore, the engineer must wait until interest rates are less than 5.375%.

7-8

Your company has been presented with an opportunity to invest in a project that is summarized as follows.

Investment required	$60,000,000
Annual gross income	14,000,000
Annual operating costs	5,500,000
Salvage value after 10 years	0

The project is expected to operate as shown for 10 years. If your management expects to make 10% on its investments before taxes, would you recommend this project?

Solution

$$\text{Net income} = 14,000,000 - 5,500,000)$$
$$= \$8,500,000$$

NPW = 0 at the rate of return

$$0 = -60,000,000 + 8,500,000(P/A, i, 10)$$
$$(P/A, i, 10) = 60/8.5$$
$$= 7.0588$$

At 6%: $P/A = 7.360$
At 7%: $P/A = 7.024$

$6\% < i < 7\%$ ∴ interpolate

$i = 6.9\%$

IRR < 10 % ∴ Do not recommend project.

7-9

Consider the following investment in a piece of land.

Purchase price	$10,000
Annual maintenance	100
Expected sale price after 5 years	20,000

Determine:

   a.   A trial value for i
   b.   The rate of return (to 1/100 percent)
   c.   The lowest sale price the investor should accept if she wishes to earn a return of 10% after keeping the land for 10 years

Solution

a. $(F/P, i\%, 5) = 20,000/10,000$
$$= 2$$

Searching interest tables, where $n = 5$:

$$i = 15\ \%$$

b. $NPW = -10,000 - 100(P/A, i\%, 5) + 20,000(P/F, i\%, 5) = 0$

Try $i = 15\%$: $= -391.2$
Try $i = 12\%$: $= +987.5$

$15\% < i < 12\%$ $\therefore$ interpolate

$i = 14.15\ \%$

c. $NFW = 0 = -10,000(F/P, 10\%, 10) - 100(F/A, 10\%, 10) + Sale\ price$

Sale price = \$27,534

7-10
Calculate the rate of return of the following cash flow with accuracy to the nearest 1/10 percent.

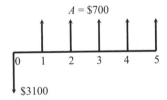

Solution

$NPW = 0$ at the rate of return

$$0 = -3,100 + 700(P/A, i, 5)$$
$(P/A, i, 5) = 4.4286$

$(P/A, 4\%, 5) = 4.452$
$(P/A, 4\frac{1}{2}\%, 5) = 4.390$

$4\% < i < 4\frac{1}{2}\%$ $\therefore$ interpolate

$i = 4.2\%$

7-11

An investment that cost $1000 is sold 5 years later for $1261. What is the nominal rate of return on the investment, given that interest was compounded annually?

Solution

$$F = P(F/P, i\%, 5)$$
$$1261 = 1000 \ (F/P, i\%, 5)$$
$$(F/P, i\%, 5) = 1261/1000$$
$$= 1.2610$$

$$(F/P, 4\frac{1}{2}\%, 5) = 1.246$$
$$(F/P, 5\%, 5) = 1.276$$

$4\frac{1}{2}\% < i < 5\%$ ∴ interpolate

$i = 4.75\%$

7-12

Lexie C. made an initial investment of $5000 in a trading account with a stock brokerage house. After a period of 17 months, the value of the account had increased to $6400. Assuming that there were no additions or withdrawals from the account, what was the nominal annual interest rate earned on the initial investment?

Solution

$$F = P(F/P, i, 17)$$
$$F/P = 6400/5000$$
$$= 1.28$$

$$(1 + i)^{17} = 1.28$$
$$1 + i = (1.28)^{1/17}$$
$$i = 0.0146$$

Annual interest rate $= 1.46 \times 12 = 17.52\%$.

7-13

Whiplash Airbags has been presented the investment opportunity summarized as follows.

Year	0	1	2	3	4	5	6	7	8
Cash flow (1000s)	$(440)	20	40	60	80	100	120	140	160

Determine the IRR for the proposed investment.

Solution

NPW = 0 at the rate of return

Try 8%:
$$NPW = 440{,}000 + 20{,}000(P/A, 8\%, 8) + 20{,}000(P/G, 8\%, 8)$$
$$= \$31{,}060$$

Try 10%:
$$NPW = -\$12{,}720$$

By interpolation, $i = 9.42\%$.

7-14
You have a choice of $2000 now or $250 now with $80 a month for 2 years. What interest rate will make these choices comparable?

Solution

$$2000 = 250 + 80(P/A, i, 24)$$
$$P/A = 21.875$$

At 1%: $P/A = 21.243$
At ¾%: $P/A = 21.889$

$¾\% < i < 1\%$ ∴ interpolate

$i = 0.7554\%$ per month, or 9.07% per year

7-15
Stock in Joe's Billiards, Inc. can be purchased for $14.26 per share; dividends are paid each quarter at a rate of $0.16 per share. Determine the effective i if, after 4 years, the stock is sold for $21.36 per share.

Solution

¼ Year		3%	3½%
0	Cost	−14.26	−14.26
1–16	Dividends 0.16(P/A, $i\%$, 16)	+2.01	+1.93
16	Sale 21.36(P/F, $i\%$, 16)	+13.31	+12.32
	NPW =	$1.06	−$0.01

$i = 3\frac{1}{2}$ per quarter

$i_{eff} = (1 + 0.035)^4 - 1$
$= 14.75\%$

7-16

A 9.25% coupon bond issued by Gurley Gears LLC is purchased January 1, 2011, and matures December 31, 2019. The purchase price is $1079 and interest is paid semiannually. If the face value of the bond is $1000, determine the effective internal rate of return.

Solution

$n = 2 \times 9 = 18$ ½-year periods

½ Year		4%
0	First cost	−1079.00
1–18	Interest 46.25(P/A, i%, 18)	+585.48
18	Maturity 1000(P/F, i%, 18)	+493.60
	NPW =	$0.08

$$IRR = (1 + 0.04)^2 - 1$$
$$= 8.16\%$$

7-17

Sain and Lewis Investment Management (SLIM), Inc. is considering the purchase of a number of bonds to be issued by Southeast Airlines. The bonds have a face value of $10,000 and a face rate of 7.5% payable annually. The bonds will mature 10 years after they are issued. The issue price is expected to be $8750. Determine the yield to maturity (IRR) for the bonds. If SLIM Inc. requires at least a 10% return on all investments, should the firm invest in the bonds?

Solution

Year		10%	9%
0	First cost	−8750.00	−8750.00
1–10	Interest 750(P/A, i%, 10)	+4608.75	+4813.50
10	Maturity 10,000(P/F, i% n)	+3855.00	+4224.00
	NPW =	−$286.25	$287.50

9% < IRR < 10% ∴ interpolate

$i = 9.5\% \Rightarrow$ Do not invest.

7-18

A bond with a face value of $1500 can be purchased for $800. The bond will mature 5 years from now, and the bond dividend rate is 12%. Dividends are paid every 3 months. What effective interest rate would an investor receive if she purchased the bond?

Solution

NPW = 0 at IRR

Try 7%:
$$NPW = -800 + 45(P/A, 7\%, 20) + 1500(P/F, 7\%, 20)$$
$$= \$64.33$$

Try 8%:
$$NPW = -800 + 45(P/A, 8\%, 20) + 1500(P/F, 8\%, 20)$$
$$= -\$36.44$$

$7\% < i < 8\%$ ∴ interpolate

$i = 7.64\%$ per quarter

Effective interest rate $= (1 + 0.07638)^4 - 1 = 0.3423 = 34.23\%$

7-19
One share of Milton Hotels, Inc. stock is currently selling for $20.75. A dividend of 35¢ per share is paid semiannually. The stock has increased in price by 5% annually for the last several years. Assuming that the stock continues to increase in price at the same rate and that the dividend amount does not increase, what is the IRR if an investor sells the stock after 4 years?

a.   4.00%
b.   5.00%
c.   8.00%
d.   8.25%

Solution

Projected resale value $= 1.05^4(20.75) = \$25.22$

NPW = 0 at IRR

Try 4%:
$$NPW = -20.75 + 0.35(P/A, 4\%, 8) + 25.22(P/F, 4\%, 8)$$
$$= \$0.04$$

Try 4½%:
$$NPW = -20.75 + 0.35(P/A, 4\frac{1}{2}\%, 8) + 25.22(P/F, 4\frac{1}{2}\%, 8)$$
$$= -\$0.70$$

$4\% < i < 4\frac{1}{2}\%$ ∴ interpolate

$i = 4.03\%$ per period

Effective interest rate $= (1 + 0.00403)^2 - 1 = 8.22\%$

The answer is d.

7-20

An investment of $350,000 is made, followed by income of $200,000 each year for 3 years. There is no residual value at the end of 3-year period. The IRR of the investment is nearest to

a. 15.3%
b. 32.7%
c. 41.7%
d. 57.1%

Solution

NPW = 0 at IRR

$$0 = -350,000 + 200,000(P/A, i\%, 3)$$
$$(P/A, i\%, 3) = 350,000/200,000$$
$$= 1.75$$

At 30%: $P/A = 1.816$
At 35%: $P/A = 1.696$

The answer is b.

7-21

Tri-State Tire is considering the purchase of new inflation equipment for its Martin operation. From the following cash flows associated with the new equipment, determine the IRR.

Year	Cash Flow
0	$(2000)
1	1000
2	750
3	500
4	250
5	0
6	–250

Solution

NPW = 0 at IRR

Try 7%:
$$NPW = -2,000 + 1000(P/A, 7\%, 6) - 250(P/G, 7\%, 6)$$
$$= \$20.51$$

Try 8%:
$$NPW = -2,000 + 1000(P/A, 8\%, 6) - 250(P/G, 8\%, 6)$$
$$NPW = -\$7.35$$

$7\% < i < 8\%$ $\therefore$ interpolate

$i = 7.73\%$

Chapter 7A

Difficulties Solving for an Interest Rate

7A-1

How many positive rates of return does the following cash flow have?

Year	Cash Flow
0	−$50,000
1	+25,000
2	+25,000
3	0
4	−50,000
5	+25,000
6	+25,000
7	+25,000

Solution

Year	Accumulated Cash Flow	
0	−$50,000	3 sign changes in cash flow
1	−25,000	
2	0	Cash Flow Rule of Signs: There may be as many
3	0	as 3 positive RORs.
4	−50,000	
5	−25,000	Accumulated Cash Flow: $A_7 \neq 0$, and one sign
6	0	change in accumulated cash flow; therefore, one
7	$+25,000 = A_7$	positive rate of return.

Note: Also check to see if there is any external investment during project life.

7A-2

Consider the following cash flow generated by an investment opportunity presented to Insane Airlines.

Year	Cash Flow
0	$-800,000
1	-150,000
2	250,000
3	-100,000
4	400,000
5–10	250,000

If external investments yield 4%, determine the rate of return on the internal investment.

Solution

Year	Cash Flow	Transformed Cash Flow		NPW @ 12%	NPW @ 15%
0	-$800,000		-800,000	-800,000	-800,000
1	-150,000		-150,000	-133,935	-130,440
2	+250,000	− 9,6154(1.04)↓	+153,846	122,646	116,323
3	-100,000	+ 100,000	0	0	0
4	+400,000		+400,000	254,200	228,720
5–10	+250,000		+250,000	653,135	540,923
				96,046	−44,474

By interpolation, the rate of return is 14.05%.

7A-3

Determine the internal rate of return for the following cash flows, assuming that the external investment rate is 5%.

Year	Cash Flow
0	-$1000
1	250
2	-250
3–5	250

Solution

Year	Cash Flow	Transformed Cash Flow		NPW @ 8%	NPW @ 9%
0	-$1000		-$1000	-$1000	-$1000
1	250	− 238.10(1.05)↓	11.90	11.02	10.92
2	-250	+ 250	0	0	0
3–5	450		450	994.23	958.73
				5.25	−30.35

By interpolation, the rate of return is 8.15%.

Chapter 8

Choosing the Best Alternative

8-1

Sugar-N-Spice, a cookie factory, needs a new cookie cutter machine. They have narrowed their choices to the following machines.

	A	B	C
Cost	$18,000	$25,000	$15,000
Annual net savings	1,055	2,125	1,020
IRR	7%	9%	8%

Each machine has a 25-year useful life with no salvage value. If the MARR for Sugar-N-Spice is 10%, which piece of equipment should be chosen?

Solution

Incremental analysis is required for IRR.

NPW = 0 at IRR

IRR_{B-A}
$$0 = [-5,000 - (-18,000)] + (2125 - 1055)(P/A, i\%, 25)$$
$(P/A, i\%, 25) = 7000/1070$
$$= 6.5421 \qquad\qquad 12\% < IRR < 15\% \quad \therefore \text{ Choose most expensive: } B$$

IRR_{B-C}
$$0 = [-25,000 - (-15,000)] + (2125 - 1020)(P/A, i\%, 25)$$
$(P/A, i\%, 25) = 10,000/1070$
$$= 6.5421 \qquad\qquad 8\% < IRR < 9\% \quad \therefore \text{ Choose least expensive: } C$$

8-2

Hayes, Angle, Reed, and Davis (HARD), a local concrete finishing company, is considering investing in newer, more productive curb-forming equipment. Data concerning the three best alternatives are as follows.

	A	B	C
Initial investment	$50,000	$22,000	$15,000
Annual net income	5,093	2,077	1,643
Computed IRR	8%	7%	9%

Each alternative has a 20-year useful life with no salvage value. If the MARR for HARD is 7%, which alternative should be chosen?

Solution

Incremental analysis is required for IRR.

NPW = 0 at IRR

IRR_{A-B}
$$0 = [-50,000 - (-22,000)] + (5093 - 2077)(P/A, i\%, 20)$$
$$(P/A, i\%, 20) = 28,000/3016$$
$$= 9.284 \qquad 8\% < IRR < 9\% \qquad \therefore \text{ Choose most expensive: } A$$

IRR_{A-C}
$$0 = [-50,000 - (-15,000)] + (5093 - 1643)(P/A, i\%, 20)$$
$$(P/A, i\%, 20) = 35,000/3450$$
$$= 10.145 \qquad 7\% < IRR < 8\% \qquad \therefore \text{ Choose most expensive: } A$$

8-3

Barber Brewing is considering investing in one of the following opportunities.

	A	B	C	D
First cost	$100.00	$130.00	$200.00	$330.00
Annual income	100.00	90.78	160.00	164.55
Annual cost	73.62	52.00	112.52	73.00

Each alternative has a 5-year useful life. Use net present worth to prepare a choice table.

Solution

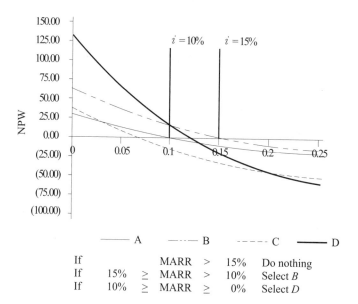

If			MARR	>	15%	Do nothing
If	15%	$\geq$	MARR	>	10%	Select B
If	10%	$\geq$	MARR	$\geq$	0%	Select D

8-4

Abby W. is considering investing in one of the following investment projects.

	A	B	C	D	E
First cost	$100.00	$130.00	$200.00	$330.00	$000.00
Annual income	150.00	130.78	185.00	184.55	00.00
Annual cost	123.62	92.00	137.52	93.00	00.00

Each alternative has a 5-year useful life. If Abby requires at least an 8% return on her investments, which alternative should she select?

Solution

NPW = 0 at IRR.

$0 = -$First cost + Net income $(P/A, i\%, n)$ Therefore $(P/A, i\%, n) =$ First cost/net income.

IRR$_A$	$P/A = 100/26.38 = 3.791$	IRR = 10%	
IRR$_B$	$P/A = 130/38.78 = 3.352$	IRR = 15%	
IRR$_C$	$P/A = 200/47.48 = 4.212$	IRR = 6%	Eliminate, does not meet MARR
IRR$_D$	$P/A = 330/91.55 = 3.605$	IRR = 12%	
IRR$_E$		IRR = 0%	Eliminate, does not meet MARR

Incremental analysis required.

IRR$_{D-B}$ $P/A = 200/52.77 = 3.790$ IRR = 10%   ∴ Choose most expensive: D

IRR$_{D-A}$ $P/A = 230/65.17 = 3.529$ 12% < IRR < 15%   ∴ Choose most expensive: D

8-5

Two mutually exclusive investment projects have been presented to your company. Project A's rate of return is 6%, and Project B's rate of return is 8%. The cost of Project A is less than the cost of Project B. Incremental analysis yields a rate of return of 4%. If both alternatives have the same useful life and the MARR is 5%, which project should be chosen?

a. A
b. B
c.   Neither
d.   Both

Solution

Since ROR$_{B-A}$ < MARR, choose the least expensive.

The answer is a.

8-6

E and A Construction must replace a piece of heavy earthmoving equipment. Cat and Volvo are the two best alternatives. Both alternatives are expected to last 6 years. If E and A has a minimum attractive rate of return (MARR) of 11%, which alternative should be chosen? Use IRR analysis.

	Cat	Volvo
First cost	$15,000	$22,500
Annual operating cost	3,000	1,500
Salvage value	2,000	4,000

Solution

$IRR_{Volvo-Cat}$

NPW = 0 at the rate of return

Try 10%:

$$NPW = -7500 + 1500(P/A, 10\%, 6) + 2000(P/F, 10\%, 6)$$
$$= \$161.50$$

Try 12%:

$$NPW = -\$320.30$$

$10\% < IRR < 12\%$ ∴ interpolate: $IRR = 10.67\% < 11\%$

Therefore choose the least expensive: Cat.

8-6

Horizon Wireless must rebuild a cell tower recently destroyed by a tornado. A tower made of normal steel (NS) will cost $30,000 to construct and should last 15 years. Maintenance will cost $1000 per year. If corrosion-resistant steel (CRS) is used, the tower will cost $36,000 to build, but the annual maintenance cost will be reduced to $250 per year. Determine the IRR of building the corrosion-resistant tower. If Horizon requires a return of 9% on its capital projects, which tower should be chosen?

Solution

$$NPW_{NS} = -30,000 - 1000(P/A, i\%, 15)$$
$$NPW_{CRS} = -36,000 - 250(P/A, i\%, 15)$$

$$-30,000 - 1000(P/A, i\%, 15) = -36,000 - 250(P/A, i\%, 15)$$
$$6000 - 750(P/A, i\%, 15) = 0$$
$$(P/A, i\%, 15) = 8.000$$

At 9%: $P/A = 8.061$
At 10%: $P/A = 7.606$

$9\% < i < 10\%$ ∴ interpolate: $i = 9.13\%$ ∴ Use corrosion-resistant steel (the more expensive alternative) to build the tower.

Chapter 9

Other Analysis Techniques

FUTURE WORTH

9-1
Lucky Lindy has just won $20,000 and wants to invest it for 12 years. There are three plans available to her.

a.   A savings account that pays 3¾% per year, compounded daily.

b.   A money market certificate that pays 6¾% per year, compounded semiannually.

c.   An investment account that, based on past experience, is likely to pay 8½% per year.

If Lindy did not withdraw any interest, how much would be in each of the three investment plans at the end of 12 years?

Solution

a. $F = P(1 + i)^n$

$$i_{eff} = \left(1 + \frac{r}{m}\right)^m - 1 = \left(1 + \frac{0.0375}{365}\right)^{365} - 1 = 3.82\%$$

$$FW = \$20,000(1 + .0382)^{12} = \$31,361.89$$

b. $i_{eff} \left(1 + \dfrac{0.0675}{2}\right)^2 - 1 = 6.86\%$

$$FW = \$20,000(1 + 0.0686)^{12} = \$44,341.67$$

c. $FW = \$20,000(1 + 0.115)^{12} = \$73,846.24$

Choose Plan C, since this plan yields the highest return at the end of 12 years.

9-2
Be-Low Mining Inc. must purchase a new coring machine that costs $30,000 and is expected to last 12 years, with a salvage value of $3000. The annual operating expenses are expected to be $9000 the first year, increasing by $200 each year thereafter. The annual income is expected to be $12,000 per year. If Be-Low's MARR is 10%, determine the NFW of the machine purchase.

Solution

$$NFW = -30,000(F/A, 10\%, 12) - [9000 + 200(A/G, 10\%, 12)](F/A, 10\%, 12)$$
$$+ 12,000(F/A, 10\%, 12) + 3000$$
$$= \$-45,754$$

9-3

The future worth of 20 quarterly lease payments of $500 at an interest rate of 8% is nearest to

a. $8176
b. $8339
c. $12,149
d. $12,392

Solution

$$FW = [500 + 500(P/A, 2\%, 19)](F/P, 2\%, 20)$$
$$= \$12,391.75$$

Alternate solution:

$$FW = [500(F/P, 2\%, 1)](F/A, 2\% \ 20)$$
$$= \$12,391.47$$

The answer is d.

9-4

A new automobile offers free maintenance during the first year of ownership. The maintenance costs the second year are estimated to be $100, increasing by $100 each year thereafter. Assume that you are planning on owning the automobile 5 years and that your cost of money is 8%. The future worth of the maintenance costs is nearest to

a. $683
b. $737
c. $1083
d. $1324

Solution

$$FW = 100(P/G, 8\%, 5)(F/P, 8\%, 5)$$
$$= \$1083$$

The answer is c.

9-5

Zill, Anderson, and Pope (ZAP) Bug Killers, Inc. recently purchased new electrical shock equipment guaranteed to kill any flying insect. The equipment cost $16,250 and has a useful life of 4 years. Each year the equipment will result in income of $5500. The costs incurred to operate the machine are estimated to be $500 the first year, increasing by $250 year thereafter. When the equipment is disposed of, it is expected to have a value of $800. If ZAP's MARR is 8%, what is the net future worth of the equipment? Was the purchase a wise investment?

Solution

$$NFW = -16,250(F/P, 8\%, 4) + [5000 - 250(A/G, 8\%, 4)](F/A, 8\%, 4) + 800$$
$$= -\$351.61 \rightarrow \text{Not a wise investment.}$$

9-6

Tuff Nuts, Inc. must buy a new nut-cracking machine. The industrial engineer has collected the following information concerning the apparent best alternative. Calculate the future worth of the alternative if the MARR is 6%.

First cost	$250,000
Annual benefits	73,000 the first year, decreasing by $1200 each year thereafter
Annual O & M costs	28,000 the first year, increasing by $1600 each year thereafter
Salvage value	42,000
Useful life	6 years

Solution

$$NFW = -250,000(F/P, 6\%, 6) + [45,000 - 2800(A/G, 6\%, 6)](F/A, 6\%, 6) + 42,000$$
$$= -\$44,380$$

9-7

An engineer is considering the purchase of a new set of batteries for a tractor. Given the cost, annual benefit, useful life, and $i = 12\%$. Conduct a net future worth (NFW) analysis to decide which alternative to purchase.

	A	*B*
Cost	$150	$90
Annual benefit	40	40
Useful life	6 years	3 years

Solution

Alternative *A*:

$$NFW = 40(F/A, 12\%, 6) - 150(F/P, 12\%, 6) = \$28.5$$

Alternative B:

NFW = $40(F/A, 12\%, 6) - 90(F/P, 12\%, 6) - 90(F/P, 12\%, 3) = \$20.49$

Choose Alternative A, largest NFW.

9-8

The following investment opportunities have been presented to Sigman Signals, Inc. Use future worth analysis and a MARR of 6% to determine which, if either, alternative should be selected.

	A	B
First cost	$22,000	$30,000
Annual benefits	6,000	10,000
Annual cost	1,000	3,500
Midlife overhaul	4,000	7,500
Salvage value	3,000	8,000
Useful life	6 years	6 years

Solution

Investment A:
NFW = $-22,000(F/P, 6\%, 6) + 5000(F/A, 6\%, 6) + 4000(F/P, 6\%, 3) + 3000$
       = $\$1893$

Investment B:
NFW = $-30,000(F/P, 6\%, 6) + 10,000(F/A, 6\%, 6) + 7500(F/P, 6\%, 3) + 8000$
       = $\$1835$

Choose Investment A, highest NFW.

BENEFIT/COST RATIO

9-9

Rash, Riley, Reed, and Rogers Consulting has a contract to design a major highway project that will provide service from Memphis to Tunica, Mississippi. R^4 has been requested to provide an estimated B/C ratio for the project, summarized as follows.

Initial cost	$20,750,000
Right-of-way maintenance	550,000
Resurfacing (every 8 years)	10% of first cost
Shoulder grading and rework (every 6 years)	750,000
Average number of road users per year	2,950,000
Average time savings value per road user	$2

Determine the B/C ratio if $i = 8\%$.

Solution

$$AW_{BENEFITS} = 2,950,000 \times \$2 = \$5,840,000$$
$$AW_{COSTS} = 20,750,000(A/P, 8\%, \infty) + 550,000 + 0.10(20,750,000)(A/F, 8\%, 8)$$
$$+ 750,000(A/F, 8\%, 6) = \$2,507,275$$

$$B/C = \frac{AW_{BENEFITS}}{AW_{COSTS}} = \frac{5,840,000}{2,507,275} = 2.33$$

9-10
A proposed bridge on the interstate highway system is being considered at the cost of $2 million. It is expected that the bridge will last 20 years. Construction costs will be paid by the federal and state governments. Operation and maintenance costs are estimated to be $180,000 per year. Benefits to the public are estimated to be $900,000 per year. The building of the bridge will result in an estimated cost of $250,000 per year to the general public. The project requires a 10% return. Determine the B/C ratio for the project. State any assumptions made about benefits or costs.

Solution

$250,000 cost to general public is disbenefit.

$$AW_{BENEFITS} = 900,000 - 250,000 = \$650,000$$
$$AW_{COSTS} = 2,000,000(A/P, 10\%, 20) + 180,000 = \$415,000$$

$$B/C = \frac{AW_{BENEFITS}}{AW_{COSTS}} = \frac{650,000}{415,000} = 1.57$$

9-11
The town of Podunk is considering building a new downtown parking lot. The land will cost $25,000, and the construction cost of the lot is estimated to be $150,000. Each year, costs associated with the lot are estimated to be $17,500. The income from the lot is estimated to be $18,000 the first year, increasing by $3500 each year for the 12-year expected life of the lot. Determine the B/C ratio if Podunk uses a cost of money of 4%.

Solution

$$PW_{BENEFITS} = 18,000(P/A, 4\%, 12) + 3500(P/G, 4\%, 12) = \$334,298$$
$$PW_{COSTS} = 175,000 + 17,500(P/A, 4\%, 12) = 339,238$$

$$B/C = \frac{PW_{BENEFITS}}{PW_{COSTS}} = \frac{334,298}{339,238} = 0.99$$

9-12

Tires-R-Us is considering the purchase of new tire-balancing equipment. The machine, which will cost $12,699, will result in annual savings of $1500 with a salvage value at the end of 12 years of $250. For a MARR of 6%, use B/C analysis to determine whether the equipment should be purchased.

Solution

$$PW_{BENEFITS} = \$1,500(P/A, 6\%, 12) + \$250(P/F, 6\%, 12) = \$12,700.25$$
$$PW_{COSTS} = \$12,699$$

$$B/C = 12,700/12,699 = 1.00$$

Conclusion: Yes, the machine should be purchased.

9-13

Dunkin City wants to build a new bypass between two major roads that will cut travel time for commuters. The road will cost $14,000,000 and save 17,500 people $100/year on gas. The road will need to be resurfaced every year at a cost of $7500. The road is expected to be used for 20 years. Use B/C analysis to determine whether Dunkin City should build the road. The cost of money is 8%.

Solution

$$PW_{COSTS} = 14,000,000 + 250,000(P/A, 8\%, 20) = \$16,454,500$$
$$PW_{BENEFITS} = (17,500)(100)(P/A, 8\%, 20) = \$17,181,500$$

$$B/C = 17,181,500/16,454,500 = 1.04$$

Conclusion: Yes, Dunkin City should build the bypass.

PAYBACK PERIOD

9-14

For calculating payback period, when is the following formula valid?

$$Payback\ period = \frac{First\ Cost}{Annual\ Benefits}$$

Solution

    a. When there is a single cost occurring at time zero (first cost).
    b. When Annual Benefits = <u>Net</u> Annual Benefits after any annual costs have been subtracted.
    c. When Net Annual Benefits are <u>uniform.</u>

9-15

Is the following statement true or false?

If two investors are considering the same project, the payback period will be longer for the investor with the higher minimum attractive rate of return (MARR).

Solution

Since payback period is generally the time to recover the investment, and ignores the MARR, it will be the same for both investors. The statement is false.

9-16

What is the payback period for a project with the following characteristics, given a minimum attractive rate of return (MARR) of 10%?

First cost	$20,000
Annual benefits	8,000
Annual maintenance	2,000 in Year 1, then increasing by $500 per year
Salvage value	2,000
Useful life	10 years

Solution

Payback occurs when the sum of <u>net</u> annual benefits is equal to the first cost. Time value of money is ignored.

Year	Benefits	–	Costs	=	Net Benefits	Total Net Benefits
1	8000	–	2000	=	6000	6,000
2	8000	–	2500	=	5500	11,500
3	8000	–	3000	=	5000	16,500
4	8000	–	3500	=	4500	21,000 > 20,000

Payback period = 4 years (actually a little less).

9-17

Determine the payback period (to the nearest year) for the following project if the MARR is 10%.

First cost	$10,000
Annual maintenance	500 in Year 1, increasing by $200 per year
Annual income	3,000
Salvage value	4,000
Useful life	10 years

Solution

Year	Net Income	Sum
1	2500	2500
2	2300	4800
3	2100	6900
4	1900	8800
5	1700	10,500 > 10,000

Payback period = 5 years.

9-18

Determine the payback period (to the nearest year) for the following project.

Investment cost	$22,000
Annual maintenance costs	1,000
Annual benefits	6,000
Overhaul costs	7,000 every 4 years
Salvage value	2,500
Useful life	12 years
MARR	10%

Solution

Year	Σ Costs	Σ Benefits	
0	22,000	—	
1	23,000	6,000	
2	24,000	12,000	
3	25,000	18,000	
4	33,000	24,000	
5	34,000	30,000	
6	35,000	36,000	← Payback

Payback period = 6 years.

9-19
A cannery is considering different modifications to some of their can fillers in two plants that have substantially different types of equipment. These modifications will allow better control and efficiency of the lines. The required investments amount to $135,000 in Plant A and $212,000 for Plant B. The expected benefits (which depend on the number and types of cans to be filled each year) are as follows.

Year	Plant A Benefits	Plant B Benefits
1	$ 73,000	$ 52,000
2	73,000	85,000
3	80,000	135,000
4	80,000	135,000
5	80,000	135,000

a.   Assuming that MARR = 10%, which alternative is should be chosen?
b.   Which alternative should be chosen based on payback period?

Solution

a. May be solved in various ways. Using NPW method

$$NPW_A = -135K + 73K(P/A, 10\%, 2) + 80K(P/A, 10\%, 3)(P/F, 10\%, 2)$$
$$= \$156,148.50$$

$$NPW_B = -212K + 52K(P/F, 10\%, 1) + 85K(P/F, 10\%, 2)$$
$$+ 135K(P/A, 10\%, 3)(P/F, 10\%, 2)$$
$$= \$182,976.80$$

Therefore, modifications to Plant B are more profitable.

b.

Year	Plant A Benefits	Cumulative Benefits	Plant B Benefits	Cumulative Benefits
1	73,000	73,000	52,000	52,000
2	73,000	146,000*	85,000	137,000
3	80,000	226,000	135,000	272,000**

*The PBP of A is less than 2 years   **The PBP of B is less than 3 years
(1.85 years)   (2.55 years)

Based on payback, Alternative A has the shortest payback period and should be chosen.

9-20

In this problem the minimum attractive rate of return is 10%. Three proposals are being considered.

Proposal *A*
A = $1000

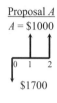

$1700

Proposal *B*
A = $1000

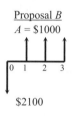

$2100

Proposal *C*
A = $1000

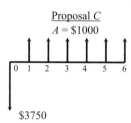

$3750

a. Which proposal would you choose using future value analysis?
b. How many years for payback for each alternative?

Solution

a. Proposal *A*: EUAB = 1000 − 1700(*A*/*P*, 10%, 2)
    = $20.50

Proposal *B*: EUAB = 1000 − 2100(*A*/*P*, 10%, 3)
= $155.60

Proposal *C*: EUAB = 1000 − 3750(*A*/*P*, 10%, 6)
= $139.00

Proposal *A*: FW = 20.50(*F*/*A*, 10%, 6) = $ 158.20

Proposal *B*: FW = 155.60(*F*/*A*, 10%, 6) = $1200.60

Proposal *C*: FW = 139.00(*F*/*A*, 10%, 6) = $1072.50

Choose highest FW: Proposal *B*.

b. Proposal *A*: $\dfrac{1700}{1000}$ = 1.7 years

Proposal *B* $\dfrac{2100}{1000}$ = 2.1 years

Proposal *C* $\dfrac{3750}{1000}$ = 3.75 years

BREAKEVEN

9-21

A machine that produces a certain piece must be turned off by the operator after each item is completed. The machine "coasts" for 15 seconds after being turned off, preventing the operator from removing the piece too quickly before beginning work on the next item. An engineer has suggested installing a brake that would reduce the coasting time to 3 seconds.

The machine produces 50,000 pieces a year. The time to produce one piece is 1 minute 45 seconds, excluding coasting time. The operator earns $8 an hour, and other direct costs for operating the machine are $4 an hour. The brake will require servicing every 500 hours of operation. It will take the operator 30 minutes to perform the necessary maintenance, and parts and material will cost $44. The brake is expected to last for 7500 hours of operation (with proper maintenance). It will have no salvage value.

How much could be spent for the brake if the MARR is 10%?

Solution

$$\text{Annual cost without the brake} = 50,000 \left(\frac{2}{60} \right) (12) = \$20,000$$

$$\text{Annual cost with the brake} \quad = 50,000 \left(\frac{1.8}{60} \right) (12) = \$18,000$$

$$\text{Maintenance} = \left[\frac{\left(50,000 \left(\frac{1.8}{60} \right) \right)}{500} \right] \left(0.5(12 + 44) \right) = \$150$$

$$\text{Brake will last:} \quad \frac{7500}{\left(\frac{5000(1.8)}{60} \right)} = 5 \text{ years}$$

$$\text{Maximum amount} = (20,000 - 18,150)(P/A, 10\%, 5) = \$7013.35$$

9-22

A proposed building may be roofed in either galvanized steel sheet (S) or composition roofing (C). The composition roof costs $20,000 and must be replaced every 5 years at the same cost. The steel roof costs $28,000 but the useful life is unknown. Neither roof has any salvage value, nor is maintenance needed. If the minimum attractive rate of return (MARR) equals 15%, what minimum life must the steel roof have to make it the better alternative? (Report to the nearest whole year; don't bother interpolating.)

Solution

$$EAC_S = EAC_C$$

$$28{,}000(A/P, 15\%, n) = 20{,}000(A/P, 15\%, 5)$$
$$28{,}000(A/P, 15\%, n) = 5.966$$

$$(A/P, 15\%, n) = 0.2131$$

$$(A/P, 15\%, 8) = 0.2229$$
$$(A/P, 15\%, 9) = 0.2096 \qquad \rightarrow \quad n = 9$$

9-23

A road can be paved with either asphalt or concrete. Concrete costs $15,000/km and lasts for 20 years. What is the maximum that should be spent on asphalt, which lasts only 10 years? The annual maintenance costs are $500/km for both pavements. The cost of money = 12%.

Solution

Maintenance doesn't affect the answer because it is the same for both. However, there is nothing wrong with including it.

$$15{,}000(A/P, 12\%, 20) = P_{ASPHALT}(A/P, 12\%, 10)$$
$$15{,}000(0.1339) = P_{ASPHALT}(0.1770)$$
$$P_{ASPHALT} = \$11{,}347$$

9-24

What is the breakeven capital cost for Project B in comparison to Project A if interest equals 10%?

Year	A	B
0	−1000	?
1–5	+300	+200

Solution

$$\text{NPW of } A = -1000 + 300\,(P/A, 10\%, 5)$$
$$= \$137.30$$

$$\text{NPW of } B = \text{NPW of } A$$
$$137.3 = P_B + 200(P/A, 10, 5)$$
$$P_B = -\$620.90$$

9-25

What is the smallest acceptable annual income from a project that has a $70,000 investment cost and a $70,000 salvage value if the life is 15 years and the minimum attractive rate of return (MARR) is 20%?

Solution

Income $= 70,000(A/P, 20\%, 15) - 70,000(A/F, 20\%, 15)$
$= 70,000[(A/P, 20\%, 15) - (A/F, 20\%, 15)]$
$= \$14,000$

9-26

A car rental agency has a contract with a garage for major repair service (as specified in the contract) for $450 per car, every 6 months. Management estimates that for $150,000, amortized at 8% interest for 20 years, and a salvage value of $60,000, the company could have its own facility, doing its own car repairs at a cost of $200 per car, every 6 months. Ignoring taxes and other economic factors, what is the minimum number of cars needed to make the change feasible?

Solution

Let N = number of autos needed

$450N = 150,000(A/P, 4\%, 40) + 60,000(A/F, 4\%, 40) - 200N$
$250N = 6945$
$N = 27.78$, or 28 autos needed

9-27

The annual income from an apartment house is $20,000. The annual expense is estimated to be $2000. If the apartment house can be bought today for $149,000, what is the breakeven resale price in 10 years, with 10% considered to be suitable interest rate?

Solution

$P = (A_{\text{INCOME}} - A_{\text{EXPENSES}})(P/A, i\%, n) + F_{\text{RESALE}}(P/F, i\%, n)$
$149,000 = (20,000 - 2000)(P/A, 10\%, 10) + F_{\text{RESALE}}(P/F, 10\%, 10)$
$149,000 = 18,000(6.145) + F_{\text{RESALE}}(0.3855)$
$F_{\text{RESALE}} = \$99,584.95$

9-28

A machine, costing $2000 to buy and $300 per year to operate, will produce savings of $650 per year for 8 years. If the interest rate is 10%, what is the minimum salvage value that would make the machine an attractive investment?

Solution

$$NPW\ 0 = -2000 + 350(P/A, 10\%, 8) + SV(P/F, 10\%, 8)$$
$$0 = -132.75 + 0.4665SV$$
$$SV = \$284.57$$

9-29

The PARC Company can purchase gizmos to be used in building whatsits for $90 each. PARC can manufacture their own gizmos for $7000 per year overhead cost plus $25 direct cost for each gizmo, provided they purchase a gizmo maker for $100,000. PARC expects to make whatsits using gizmos for 10 years. The gizmo maker should have a salvage value of $20,000 after 10 years. PARC uses 12% as its minimum attractive rate of return. At what annual production rate N should PARC make its own gizmos?

Solution

Equivalent cost solution:

EAC_{BUY} $= \$90N$

EAC_{MAKE} $= 100,000(A/P, 12\%, 10) + 7000 + 25N - 20,000(A/F, 12\%, 10)$
              $= 23,560 + 25N$

For breakeven:

$EAC_{BUY} = EAC_{MAKE}$
$$90N = 23,560 + 25N$$
$$N = 362.5$$

This indicates that the gizmos should be bought if 362 or fewer are to be used per year and made if 363 or more will be used per year.

9-30

Assume that you need to buy new automobile tires and are considering purchasing either the Econo-Ride, which costs $33.95 per tire, or the Road King, which costs $65.50. Both tires are alike except that the Road King is more durable and will last longer. Regardless of which tire is purchased, balancing and installation costs are $1.50 per tire. The salesman says the Econo-Ride will last 20,000 miles. Assume a minimum attractive rate of return (MARR) of 6% and that you drive 10,000 miles per year.

a. How many miles would the Road King have to last to make you indifferent in your choice?
b. The salesman says the Road King will be on sale next week. If he also says the tire will last 30,000 miles, what would the sale price have to be to make you indifferent in your choice?

Solution

a. $4(1.5 + 33.95)(A/P, 6\%, \frac{20,000}{10,000}) = 4(1.5 + 65.50)(A/P, 6\%, N)$

$$(A/P, 6\%, N) = 0.28859$$

From tables, $N = 4$, or 40,000 miles.

b. $4(1.5 + 33.95)(A/P, 6\%, \frac{20,000}{10,000}) = 4(1.5 + P)(A/P, 6\%, \frac{30,000}{10,000})$

$$P = \$50.18$$

9-31

Oliver Douglas decides to install a fuel storage system for his farm that will save him an estimated 6.5 cents/gallon on his fuel cost. Initial cost of the system is $10,000, and the annual maintenance is $25 the first year, increasing by $25 each year thereafter. After a period of 10 years the estimated salvage is $3000. If money is worth 12%, what, approximately, is the breakeven quantity of fuel?

a.   12,600 gallons
b.   20,250 gallons
c.   26,400 gallons
d.   29,200 gallons

Solution

$$EAC = 10,000(A/P, 12\%, 10) + 3000(A/F, 12\%, 10) + 25 + 25(A/G, 12\%, 10)$$
$$= \$1713.63$$

$$EAB = gallons(0.065) = \$G(0.065)$$

$$0 = -1713.63 + G(0.065)$$
$$G = 26,364 \text{ gallons}$$

The answer is c.

9-32

A soft drink company has researched the possibility of marketing a new low-calorie beverage, in a study region. The expected profits depend largely on the sales volume, and there is some uncertainty about the precision of the sales-forecast figures. The estimated investment is $173,000, while the anticipated profits are $49,500 per year for the next 6 years. If the company's minimum attractive rate of return (MARR) is 15%, and it is estimated that in the worst case the profits will be reduced to $40,000 per year, is the decision to invest sensitive to the uncertainty of the sales forecast? What is the minimum volume of sales for the project to breakeven, if there is a profit of $6.70 per unit volume?

Solution

a. For an annual profit of $49,500
    NPW = 49,500(P/A, 15%, 6) – 173,000
    = +14,308 (attractive)

b. For an annual profit of $40,000
    NPW = 40,000(P/A, 15%, 6) – 173,000
    = –21,640 (not attractive)

Therefore, the decision is sensitive to the expected variations in sales or profits.

The breakeven: NPW = 0

NPW = 0 = X(P/A, 15%, 6) – 173,000, where X = minimum amount of profit ($)

$X = \frac{173,000}{(P/A, 15\%, 6)} = \$45,718.82$

in volume units = $\frac{\$45,718.82}{\$6.70/\text{unit}}$ = 6824 volume units

9-33

Given the following:

$AW_A = -23,000(A/P, 10, 10) + 4000(A/F, 10, 10) – 3000 – 3X$
$AW_B = -8000(A/P, 10, 4) – 2000 – 6X$

For these two AW relations, the breakeven point X in miles per year is nearest to

a. 655
b. 1130
c. 1224
d. 1590

Solution

Setting $AW_A = AW_B$: $-6491 – 3X = -4524 – 6X$
$-1967 = 3X$
$X = 655.67$

9-34

ABC Manufacturing has a minimum attractive rate of return (MARR) of 12% on new investments. What uniform annual benefit would Investment *B* have to generate to make it preferable to Investment *A*?

Year	Investment *A*	Investment *B*
0	–$60,000	–$45,000
1–6	+15,000	?

Solution

NPW of A = $-60 + 15(P/A, 12\%, 6)$ = 1.665   NPW of $B \geq 1.665 = -45 + B(P/A, 12\%, 6)$

$\therefore B = 11,351$

$B > \$11,351$ per year

9-35

Over the next 6 years, investment in a crane is expected to produce profit from its rental as shown. Assume that the salvage value is zero. Assuming 12% interest, what is the breakeven cost of the crane?

Year	Profit
1	$15,000
2	12,500
3	10,000
4	7,500
5	5,000
6	2,500

Solution

PW_{PROFIT} = $15,000(P/A, 12\%, 6) - 2500(P/G, 12\%, 6)$ = \$39,340
$Cost_{BE}$ = \$39,340

9-36

The government has ordered management of a coal-burning power plant to install a $5 million pollution abatement device to remove sulfur that is currently being emitted into the air. The sulfur will be removed by allowing the plant's exhaust to pass through a filter. The filtration system requires the presence of a certain chemical that costs $1000 per kilogram. Studies have been conducted that show that the number of units of sulfur that may be recovered annually from the exhaust is equal to 100 times the square root of the number of kilograms of the chemical used in the filtration system.

Therefore:

$$(\text{units of sulfur}) = 100 \times (\text{kg of chemical})^{\frac{1}{2}}$$

Each unit of sulfur that is removed may then be sold by the power plant to chemical supply companies for $300. The filtration system and chemical have an expected life of 20 years, after which time the chemical will have a resale value of $500 per kilogram, while the filtration system itself will have no resale value.

Use a before-tax MARR of 10% to find the optimal amount of the chemical that should be purchased by the power plant.

Solution

Let X = number of kg of chemical purchased

Net annual cost (X) = (Purchase cost of pollution abatement device)$(A/P, 10\%, 20)$
+ (Chemical purchase cost)$(A/P, 10\%, 20)$
– (Salvage value of chemical)$(A/P, 10\%, 20)$
– (Annual sale value of sulfur)

Net annual cost (X) = $(5,000,000)(A/P, 10\%, 20) + (1000X)(A/P, 10\%, 20)$
$- (500X)(A/F, 10\%, 20) - (300)(100\sqrt{X})$
$= 587.5 + 108.75X - 30,000\sqrt{X}$

To minimize cost, differentiate net annual cost (X) and set = 0:

$$\frac{d\text{NAC}(X)}{dX} = 108.75 - \frac{30,000}{\sqrt[2]{X}} = 0$$

$$\frac{1}{\sqrt[2]{X}} = \frac{108.75}{30,000} \Rightarrow \sqrt{X} = \frac{30,000}{2(108.75)} = 137.931$$

$X = 137.931^2 = 19,024.97$

Check for maximum or minimum: $\dfrac{d^2\text{NAC}(X)}{dX^2} = \dfrac{7,500}{\sqrt{X^3}} > 0$ for $X > 0$

9-37
To produce an item in-house, equipment costing $250,000 must be purchased. It will have a life of 4 years and an annual cost of $80,000; each unit will cost $40 to manufacture. Buying the item externally will cost $100 per unit. At $i = 12\%$, determine the breakeven production number.

Solution

Buy = $-100X$

Make = $-250,000(A/P, 12\%, 4) - 80,000 - 40X$
$= -82,300 - 80,000 - 40X$
$= -162,300 - 40X$

Setting Buy and Make equal: $-100X = -162,300 - 40X$
$60X = -162,300$
$X = 2705$ units

9-38

Data for two drill presses under consideration by B&R Gears are listed. Assuming an interest rate of 12%, what salvage value of Press B will make the two alternatives equal?

	A	B
First cost	$30,000	$36,000
Annual maintenance	1,500	2,000
Salvage value	5,000	?
Useful life	6 years	6 years

Solution

$$EAC = P(A/P, i\%, n) - SV(A/F, i\%, n) + \text{Other costs}$$

Drill press A

$$EAC = 30,000(A/P, 12\%, 6) - 5000(A/F, 12\%, 6) + 1500$$
$$= \$8180$$

Drill press B

$$EAC = 36,000(A/P, 12\%, 6) - SV(A/F, 12\%, 6) + 2000$$
$$= \$10,755.20 - SV(0.1232)$$

Setting the two EACs equal: $8180 = 10,755.20 - SV(0.1232)$
$$SV = \$20,903$$

9-39

Joyce, Adams, and Mays (JAM) Inc. is considering the purchase of new fruit processing equipment. The relevant data for the alternative under consideration are as follows.

First cost	$78,750
Annual income	$25/ton of processed fruit
Annual operating costs	$5500 the first year, increasing $800 each year thereafter
Annual property taxes	8% of first cost
Annual insurance	4% of first cost, payable at the beginning of each year
Salvage value	15% of first cost + $1000
Useful life	10 years

JAM's MARR is 4%. Determine the number of tons of fruit that must be processed annually to justify purchasing the machine.

Solution

NPV = 0 at breakeven.

$0 = -78,750 + 25(X)(P/A, 4\%, 10) - [5500(P/A, 4\%, 10) + 800(P/G, 4\%, 10)]$
$\quad - 0.08(78,750)(P/A, 4\%, 10) - [0.04(78,750) + 0.04(78,750)(P/A, 4\%, 9)]$
$\quad + (0.15(78,750) + 1\,A000)(P/F, 4\%, 10)$
$0 = -219,478 + 202.78X$
$X = 1082.35$ tons

9-40
Dolphin, Inc. trains mine-seeking dolphins in a 5-mine tank. The company is considering purchasing a new tank for $750,000, along with realistic dummy mines that cost $250,000 apiece. The new tank will allow the company to train 3 dolphins per year and will last 10 years, costing $50,000 per year to maintain. If Dolphin's MARR is 5%, how much must the company receive (per dolphin) from the U.S. Navy to breakeven?

Solution

NPV = −Cost − Cost of mines − Annual maintenance(P/A, 5%, 10) + Income(P/A, 5%, 10)
$\quad = -750,000 - 250,000(5) - 50,000(P/A, 5\%, 10) + 3(X)(P/A, 5\%, 10)$
$\quad X = \$103,000$

9-41
The Tennessee Department of Highways is trying to decide whether it should "hot-patch" a short stretch of an existing highway or resurface it. If the hot-patch method is chosen, approximately 300 cubic meters of material would be required at a cost of $600/cubic meter (in place). The shoulders would have to be improved at the same time, at a cost of $24,000. These shoulder improvements must be redone every 2 years (assume the same cost). The annual cost of routine maintenance on the patched road is estimated to be $5000. Alternatively, the state can resurface the road. This surface will last 10 years if maintained properly at a cost of $2000 per year. The shoulders would require reworking at the end of the fifth year at a cost of $5000. Regardless of the method selected, the road will be completely rebuilt in 10 years. At an interest rate of 8%, what is the maximum amount that should be paid for resurfacing the road?

Solution

Hot-Patch
$\quad$ EUAC $= [300(600) + 24,000](A/P, 8\%, 10)$
$\qquad\qquad + 24,000(A/F, 8\%, 2)(P/A, 8\%, 8)(A/P, 8\%, 10) + 5000$
$\qquad = \$45,277$

Resurface
$\quad$ EUAC $= X(A/P, 8\%, 10) + 5000(P/F, 8\%, 5)(P/A, 8\%, 10) + 2000$
$\qquad = 0.1490X - 2507$
$\qquad X = \$287,047$

Chapter 10

Uncertainty
in
Future Events

10-1

Tee-to-Green Golf, Inc. is considering the purchase of new automated club assembly equipment. The industrial engineer for TGG thinks that she has determined the "best' choice. However she is uncertain how to evaluate the equipment because of questions concerning the actual annual savings and salvage value at the end of the expected life. The equipment will cost $500,000 and is expected to last for 8 years. The engineer has the following information concerning the savings and salvage value estimates and the projected probabilities.

	$p = .20$	$p = .50$	$p = .25$	$p = .05$
Savings per year	$65,000	$82,000	$90,000	$105,000
Salvage value	40,000	55,000	65,000	75,000

Determine the NPW if TGG's MARR is 6%.

Solution

E(Savings) = .2(65,000) + .5(82,000) + .25(90,000) + .05(105,000) = $81,750

E(Salvage) = .2(40,000) + .5(55,000) + .25(65,000) + .05(75,000) = $55,500

NPW = −500,000 + 81,750(P/A, 6%, 8) + 55,500(P/F, 6%, 8)
    = $42,489

10-2

Acme Insurance offers an insurance policy that pays $1000 in reimbursement for luggage lost on a cruise. Historically the company pays this amount in 1 out of every 200 policies it sells. What is the minimum amount Acme must charge for such a policy if the company's goal is to make at least $10 dollars per policy?

Solution

The probability that a loss occurs is $\dfrac{1}{200}$ = .005

The expected loss to the company is therefore .005(1000) = $5

To make a profit of $10 from each policy sold, Acme must charge $15 per policy.

10-3

Consolidated Edison Power is evaluating the construction of a new electric generation facility. The two choices are a coal-burning plant (CB) and a gaseous diffusion (GD) plant. The CB plant will cost $150 per megawatt to construct, and the GD plant will cost $300 per megawatt. Owing to uncertainties concerning fuel availability and the impact of future regulations related to air and water quality, the useful life of each plant is unknown, but the following probability estimates have been made.

	Probability	
Useful Life (years)	CB Plant	GD Plant
10	.10	.05
20	.50	.25
30	.30	.50
40	.10	.20

a. Determine the expected life of each plant.
b. Based on the ratio of construction cost per megawatt to expected life, which plant would you recommend that Con Ed build?

Solution

  a. Expected life

   Coal burning = .10(10) + .50(20) + .30(30) + .10(40) = 24 years

   Gaseous diffusion = .05(10) + .25(20) + .50(30) + .20(40) = 28.5 years

  b. Ratios

   Coal burning = 150/24 = $6.25 per megawatt per year

   Gaseous diffusion = 300/28.5 = $10.53 per megawatt per year

   Recommend the coal-burning plant.

10-4

Crush Cola Company must purchase a bottle-capping machine. The following is known about the machine and about possible cash flows.

	$p = .30$	$p = .50$	$p = .20$
First cost	$40,000	$40,000	$40,000
Annual savings	2,000	3,500	5,000
Annual costs	7,000	5,000	4,000
Actual salvage value	4,000	5,000	6,500

The machine is expected to have a useful life of 10 years. Crush has a MARR of 6%. Determine the NPW of the machine.

Solution

E(Saving/Costs) $= (2000 - 7000)(.30) + (3500 - 5000)(.50) + (5000 - 4000(.20)$
$= -\$2050$

E(Salvage Value) $= 4000(.30) + 5000(.50) + 6500(.20)$
$= \$5000$

NPW $= -40,000 - 2050(P/A, 6\%, 10) + 5000(P/F, 6\%, 10) = -\$52,296.00$

10-5

The two finalists in a tennis tournament are playing for the championship. The winner will receive $60,000 and the runner-up $35,000. Determine the expected winnings for each participant if the players are considered to be evenly matched. What would the expected winnings be if one player were favored by 4-to-1 odds?

Solution

Evenly matched, both players' expected winnings will be the same.

Winnings $= .5(60,000) + .5(35,000) = \$47,500$

Assume that Player A is favored by 4-to-1 odds.

The probability that A will win is then 4/5 or 0.8.

Player A's expected winnings $= 0.8(60,000) + 0.2(35,000) = \$55,000$

Player B's expected winnings $= 0.2(60,000) + 0.8(35,000) = \$40,000$

10-6

A roulette wheel consists of 18 black slots, 18 red slots, and 2 green slots. If a $100 bet is placed on black, what is the expected gain or loss? (A bet on black or red pays even money.)

Solution

The probability of black occurring $= \dfrac{18}{38}$

Expected value of the bet $= 100\dfrac{18}{38} - 100\dfrac{20}{38} = \dfrac{100}{19} \approx \$5.26$ loss

10-7

Palmer Potatoes Chips. Inc. must purchase new potato peeling equipment for its Martin, Tennessee, plant. The plant engineer has determined that three possible setups can be purchased. All machines are expected to be used 6 years, and PPC's MARR is 10%. Which of the three machines described should be chosen?

Naked Peel

First cost	$45,000		
Annual costs		$p = .2$	$3000
		$p = .7$	4500
		$p = .1$	5500
Salvage value		$p = .7$	$7500
		$p = .3$	9500

Skinner

First cost	$52,000		
Annual costs		$p = .4$	$5000
		$p = .4$	6500
		$p = .2$	8500
Salvage value		$p = .4$	$5500
		$p = .3$	7500
		$p = .3$	8500

Peel-O-Matic

First cost	$76,000		
Annual costs		$p = .3$	$5000
		$p = .5$	7500
		$p = .2$	9500
Salvage value		$p = .6$	$8500
		$p = .4$	9000

Solution

NPV= – First cost + Annual savings(P/A, 10%, 6) + Salvage value(P/F, 10%, 6)

Naked Peel

E(Annual costs) = .2(3000) + .7(4500) + .1(5500) = $4300
E(Salvage value) = .7(7500) + .3(9500) = $8100

NPW = –$59,154

Skinner

E(Annual costs) = $6300
E(Salvage value) = $7000

NPW = –$75,485

Peel-O-Matic

E(Annual costs) = $7150
E(Salvage value) = $8700

NPW = –$102,227

Fixed output: therefore, choose the lowest NPW, Naked Peel.

10-8

Krispy Kookies is considering the purchase of new dough-mixing equipment. From the estimated NPW and probabilities of the four possible outcomes given, calculate the expected annual worth of the equipment if the life of the equipment is 6 years and $i = 8\%$.

Outcome	NPW	Probability
1	$34,560	.15
2	38,760	.25
3	42,790	.40
4	52,330	.20

Solution

E(NPW) = .15(34,560) + .25(38,760) + .40(42,790) + .20(52,330) = $42,456

AW = 42,456(A/P, 8%, 6) = $9183.23

10-9

A new heat exchanger must be installed by CSI, Inc. Alternative A has an initial cost of $33,400, and Alternative B has an initial cost of $47,500. Both alternatives are expected to last 10 for years. The annual cost of operating the heat exchanger depends on ambient temperature in the plant and on energy costs. The estimate of the cost and probabilities for each alternative is given. If CSI has a MARR of 8% and uses rate of return analysis for all capital decisions, which exchanger should be purchased?

	Annual Cost	Probability, p
Alternative A	$4500	.10
	7000	.60
	8000	.25
	9250	.05
Alternative B	$4000	.20
	5275	.60
	6450	.15
	8500	.05

Solution

Alternative *A*
E(Annual cost) = .10(4500) + .60(7000) + .25(8000) + .05(9250) = $7112.50

Alternative *B*
E(Annual cost) = .20(4000) + .60(5275) + .15(6450) + .05(8500) = $5357.50

Incremental analysis is required.

B – A

NPW = 0 at IRR

$$0 = (-47,500 - (-33,400)) + (-5375.50 - (-7112.50))(P/A, i\%, 10)$$
$$0 = -14,100 + 1,737(P/A, i\%, 10)$$
(P/A, i%, 10) = 8.12

i = 4%   P/A = 8.111

IRR ≈ 4%

CSI should purchase the less expensive alternative, Alternative *A*.

10-10

Northeast Airlines is considering entering a bid for a new Asian route. The route is expected to command a rather large price. There is uncertainty associated with all elements of the investment. The winner of the route will have use of it for 5 years before the bidding process is repeated. Assuming a MARR of 8%, use the following information, developed by Northeast concerning estimated cash flows and probabilities, to determine the expected net present worth of the route.

Element	*p* = .15	*p* = .45	*p* = .30	*p* = .10
Bid amount	$11,500,000	$22,250,000	$27,500,000	$38,250,000
Net annual income	3,000,000	5,700,000	7,000,000	9,600,000

Solution

NPW 1 = –11,500,000 + 3,000,000(P/A, 8%, 5) = $479,000
NPW 2 = –22,250,000 + 5,700,000(P/A, 8%, 5) =   510,100
NPW 3 = –27,500,000 + 7,000,000(P/A, 8%, 5) =   451,000
NPW 4 = –38,250,000 + 9,600,000(P/A, 8%, 5) =   82,800

E(NPW) = .15(479,000) + .45(510,100) + .30(451,000) + .10(82,800) = $444,975

10-11

The probability that a machine will last a certain number of years is tabulated as follows.

| | Probability of |
Years of Life	Obtaining Life
10	.15
11	.20
12	.25
13	.20
14	.15
15	.05

What is the expected life of the machine?

Solution

Expected value = 10(.15) + 11(.20) + 12(.25) + 13(.20) + 14(.15) + 15(.05)
         = 12.15 years

10-12

In the game of craps, two dice are tossed. One of the many bets available is the "Hard-way 8." A $1 bet will return to the bettor $4 if in the game the two dice come up 4 and 4 prior to one of the other ways of totaling eight. For the $1 bet, what is the expected result?

a. $0.11
b. $0.33
c. $0.66
d. $0.80

Solution

There are five ways of rolling an eight.→

Die 1	Die 2
2	6
3	5
4	4
5	3
6	2

Hard-way 8 probability = 1/5.

$E(\$) = 1/5(\$4) + 4/5(\$0)$
    $= \$0.80$

The answer is d.

10-13

A dam is being considered to reduce river flooding in the Forked River Basin.   Information concerning the possible alternatives is given.

Dam Height, H (ft)	First Cost	Annual Probability of Flood if Height =	Damages if Flooding Occurs
0	$ 0	0.25	$800,000
20	700,000	0.05	500,000
30	800,000	0.01	300,000
40	900,000	0.002	200,000

Which dam height minimizes the expected total annual cost? The state uses an interest rate of 5% for flood protection projects, and all dams must last 50 years.

Solution

$H = 0$ (No dam is built.)

EUAC = 800,000(.25)
  = $200,000

$H = 20$ ft

EUAC = 700,000(A/P, 5%, 50) + 500,000(.05)
  = $63,360

$H = 30$ ft

EUAC = 800,000(A/P, 5%, 50) + 300,000(.01)
  = $46,840

$H = 40$ ft

EUAC = 900,000(A/P, 5%, 50) + 200,000(.002)
  = $49,720

To minimize annual cost, build the 30-foot dam.

Chapter 11

Depreciation

11-1

Some seed-cleaning equipment was purchased in 2009 for $8500 and is depreciated by the double declining balance (DDB) method for an expected life of 12 years. What is the book value of the equipment at the end of 2014? Original salvage value was estimated to be $2500 at the end of 12 years.

Solution

$$\text{Book value} = P(1 - \tfrac{2}{N})^n$$
$$= 8500(1 - \tfrac{2}{12})^6 = \$2846.63$$

This can be checked by doing the year-by-year computations:

Year		Depreciation
2009	(8500–0)	= $1416.67
2010	(8500–1416.67) =	1180.56
2011	(8500–2597.23) =	983.80
2012	(8500–3581.03) =	819.83
2013	(8500–4400.86) =	683.19
2014	(8500–5084.05) =	569.32
	Σ of depreciation	$5653.37

Book value = 8500 – 5653.37 = $2846.63

11-2

Suds-n-Dogs just purchased new automated wiener-handling equipment for $12,000. The salvage value of the equipment is anticipated to be $1200 at the end of its 5-year life. Use MACRS to determine the depreciation schedule.

Solution

Three-year class is determined.

Year		Depreciation
1	12,000(.3333)	$3999.60
2	12,000(.4445)	5334.00
3	12,000(.1481)	1777.20
4	12,000(.0741)	889.20

11-3

An asset will cost $1750 when purchased this year. It is further expected to have a salvage value of $250 at the end of its 5-year depreciable life. Calculate complete depreciation schedules giving the depreciation charge, $D(n)$, and end-of-year book value, $B(n)$, for straight-line (SL), sum-of-the-years'-digits (SOYD), double declining balance (DDB), and modified accelerated cost recovery (MACRS) depreciation methods. Assume a MACRS recovery period of 5 years.

Solution

	SL		SOYD		DDB		MACRS	
n	$D(n)$	$B(n)$	$D(n)$	$B(n)$	$D(n)$	$B(n)$	$D(n)$	$B(n)$
0		1750		1750		1750		1750.00
1	300	1450	500	1250	700	1050	350.00	1400.00
2	300	1150	400	850	420	630	560.00	840.00
3	300	850	300	550	252	378	336.00	504.00
4	300	550	200	350	128	250	201.60	302.40
5	300	250	100	250	0	250	201.60	100.80
6							100.80	0.00

11-4

Your company is considering the purchase of a secondhand scanning microscope at a cost of $10,500, with an estimated salvage value of $500 and a projected useful life of 4 years. Determine the straight-line (SL), sum-of-years'-digits (SOYD), and double declining balance (DDB) depreciation schedules.

Solution

Year	SL	SOYD	DDB
1	2500	4000	5250.00
2	2500	3000	2625.00
3	2500	2000	1312.50
4	2500	1000	656.25

11-5

A piece of machinery costs $5000 and has an anticipated $1000 resale value at the end of its 5-year useful life. Compute the depreciation schedule for the machinery by the sum-of-the-years'-digits method.

Solution

Sum-of-years'-digits = $\frac{n}{2}(n+1) = \frac{5}{2}(6) = 15$

1st-year depreciation = $\frac{5}{15}(5000 - 1000) = \$1333$

2nd-year depreciation = $\frac{4}{15}(5000 - 1000) = 1067$

3rd-year depreciation = $\frac{3}{15}(5000 - 1000) = 800$

4th-year depreciation = $\frac{2}{15}(5000 - 1000) = 533$

5th-year depreciation = $\frac{1}{15}(5000 - 1000) = 267$

11-6

A new machine costs $12,000 and has a $1200 salvage value at the end of its 8-year useful life. Prepare a year-by-year depreciation schedule by the double declining balance (DDB) method.

Solution

DDB depreciation = $\frac{2}{N}(P - \sum D)$

Year:	1	2	3	4	5	6	7	8*	Total
Depreciation:	3000	2250	1688	1266	949	712	534	401	$10,800

*Book value cannot go below declared salvage value. Therefore, the full value of Year 8's depreciation cannot be taken.

11-7

To meet increased sales, a large dairy is planning to purchase 10 new delivery trucks. Each truck will cost $18,000. Compute the depreciation schedule for each truck, using the modified accelerated cost recovery system (MACRS) method; the recovery period is 5 years.

Solution

Year		Depreciation
1	18,000(.20)	$3600.00
2	18,000(.32)	5760.00
3	18,000(.192)	3456.00
4	18,000(.1152)	2073.60
5	18,000(.1152)	2073.60
6	18,000(.0576)	1036.80

11-8

Hoppy Hops, Inc. purchased hop-harvesting machinery for $150,000 four years ago. Owing to a change in the method of harvesting, the machine was recently sold for $37,500. Determine the MACRS deprecation schedule for the machinery for the 4 years of ownership. Assume a 5-year property class. What is the recaptured depreciation or loss on the sale of the machinery?

a. $2,940
b. $11,580
c. $25,920
d. $34,560

Solution

Year	MACRS %(FC)	Depreciation
1	.2(150,000)	$30,000
2	.32(150,000)	48,000
3	.1920(150,000)	28,800
4	(.1152/2)(150,000)	8,640

$\sum_{\text{Depreciations}} = 30,000 + 48,000 + 28,800 + 8640$
$\qquad\qquad = \$115,440$

$BV_4 = 150,000 - 115,440$
$\qquad = \$34,560$

Recaptured depreciation $= 37,500 - 34,560$
$\qquad\qquad\qquad\qquad = \$2940$

The answer is a.

11-9

A used piece of depreciable property was bought for $20,000. If it has a useful life of 10 years and a salvage value of $5000, and you use the 150% declining balance schedule, how much will it be depreciated in the 9th year?

Solution

Depreciation $= \frac{1.5P}{N}\left(1-\frac{1.5}{N}\right)^{n-1} = \frac{1.5(20,000)}{10}\left(1-\frac{1.5}{10}\right)^{9-1} = \$817.50$

Check BV at end of 8th year

$BV = P\left(1-\frac{1.5}{N}\right)^{n} = 20,000\left(1-\frac{1.5}{10}\right)^{8} = \$5449.80$

Because the salvage value is $5000, you can only depreciate $449.80 (5449.80 − 5000) in the 9th year.

11-10

A front-end loader costs $70,000 and has a depreciable salvage value of $10,000 at the end of its 5- year useful life. Use MACRS depreciation to compute the depreciation schedule and book value of the tractor.

Solution

The 5-year recovery period is determined.

Year		Depreciation	Book Value
1	70,000(.20)	$14,000	70,000 − 14,000 = $56,000
2	70,000(.32)	22,400	56,000 − 22,400 = 33,600
3	70,000(.192)	13,440	33,600 − 13,440 = 20,160
4	70,000(.1152)	8,064	20,160 − 8,064 = 12,096
5	70,000(.1152)	8,064	12,096 − 8,064 = 4,032
6	70,000(.0576)	4,032	4,032 − 4,032 = 0

11-11

An asset is purchased for $100,000. The asset is depreciated by using MACRS depreciation and a 5-year recovery period. At the end of the third year of use, the business changes its product mix and disposes of the asset. The depreciation allowed in the third year is nearest to

a. $9,600
b. $16,000
c. $19,200
d. $20,000

Solution

$D_3 = .192/2(100,000)$
   $= \$9600$

Disposal before end of MACRS recovery period gives ½-year depreciation in disposal year.

The answer is a.

11-12

A lumber company purchased a tract of timber for $70,000. The value of the 25,000 trees on the tract was established to be $50,000. The value of the land was established to be $20,000. In the first year of operation, the lumber company cut down 5000 trees. What was the depletion allowance for the year?

Solution

For standing timber, only cost depletion (not percentage depletion) is permissible. Five thousand of the trees were harvested; therefore 5000/25,000 = 0.20 of the tract was depleted. Land is not considered to be depletable; only the timber, which is valued at a total of $50,000, is subject to depletion.

Therefore, the first year's depletion allowance would be = 0.20($50,000) = $10,000.

11-13

A pump cost $1000 and has a salvage value of $100 after a life of 5 years. Using the double declining balance depreciation method, determine:

a. The depreciation in the first year.
b. The book value after 5 years.
c. The book value after 5 years if the salvage was only $50.

Solution

a. Rate = $\frac{200\%}{5}$ = 40% = .4

   $1000(.4) = \$400$

b. $BV = P(1 - \frac{2}{N})^n$

   BV = max of {salvage value or $1000(1 - .4)^5$} = max of {100, 77.76} = $100

c. BV = max of {salvage value or $1000(1 - .4)^5$} = max of {50, 77.76} = $77.76

11-14

Two years ago Nuts-2-U, Inc. purchased nut-cracking equipment at a total cost of $80,000. The equipment was depreciated by using MACRS with a recovery class of 3 years and an anticipated end-of-useful-life value of $8000. The company has decided the equipment is no longer needed and wishes to determine the minimum value it can accept for the equipment (that is, the lowest value that will result in no loss on the sale). The minimum selling price for the equipment is nearest to

a. $17,775
b. $24,000
c. $35,560
d. $40,000

Solution

Disposal before end of MACRS recovery period gives ½-year depreciation in disposal year.

$$\sum\nolimits_{\text{Depreciation percentages}} = .3333 + .4445/2$$
$$= .5556$$

$$BV_2 = 80,000 - .5556(80,000)$$
$$= \$35,556$$

The answer is c.

11-15

Thick Trunk Sawmill purchases a new automated log planer for $95,000. The asset is depreciated by using straight-line depreciation over a useful life of 10 years to a salvage value of $5000. The book value at the end of Year 6 is nearest to
a. $9,000
b. $38,000
c. $41,000
d. $54,000

Solution

$$D_t = (95,000 - 5000)/10$$
$$= \$9000/\text{year}$$
$$\sum\nolimits_{\text{Depreciations}} = 9000 \times 6$$
$$= \$54,000$$

$$BV_6 = 95,000 - 54,000$$
$$= \$41,000$$

The answer is c.

11-16

In the production of beer, a final filtration is accomplished by the use of kieselguhr, or diatomaceous earth, which is composed of the fossil remains of minute aquatic algae a few microns in diameter, and pure silica. A company has purchased a property for $840,000 that contains an estimated 60,000 tons of kieselguhr. Compute the depreciation charges for the first 3 years, given that production (or extraction) of 3000 tons, 5000 tons, and 6000 tons is planned for Years 1, 2, and 3, respectively. Use the cost-depletion methods, assuming no salvage value for the property.

Solution

Total diatomaceous earth in property = 60,000 tons
Cost of property = $480,000

Then, $\dfrac{\text{depletion allowance}}{\text{tons extracted}} = \dfrac{\$840,000}{60,000 \text{ tons}} = \$14/\text{ton}$

Year	Tons Extracted	Depreciation Charge
1	3000	$3000 \times 14 = \$42,000$
2	4000	$4000 \times 14 = 56,000$
3	5000	$5000 \times 14 = 70,000$

11-17

Adventure Airlines recently purchased a new baggage crusher for $50,000. It is expected to last 14 years and has an estimated salvage value of $8000. Use SOYD depreciation to determine the depreciation charge on the crusher for the third year of its life and the book value at the end of 8 years.

Solution

SOYD depreciation for 3rd year:

Sum-of-years'-digits $= \dfrac{n}{2}(n+1) = \dfrac{14}{2}(14+1) = 105$

3rd-year depreciation $= \dfrac{\text{Remaining life at beginning of year}}{\Sigma \text{ years' digits}}(P-S)$

$\qquad = \dfrac{12}{105}(50,000 - 8000) = \$4800$

Book value at end of 8 years

$\Sigma_{8 \text{ years of depreciation}} = \dfrac{14+13+12+11+10+9+8+7}{105}(50,000 - 8000)$

$\qquad = \dfrac{84}{105}(42,000) = \$33,600$

Book value = Cost – Depreciation to date = $50,000 - 33,600 = \$16,400$

Chapter 12

Income Taxes

12-1
A tool costing $300 has no salvage value and will be depreciated over 3 years according to the sum-of-the-years'-digits method. The cash flows before tax (BTCF) due to the tool are shown. The tax rate is 35%.

Year	BTCF	SOYD Depreciation	Taxable Income	Taxes	ATCF
0	−300				
1	+100				
2	+150				
3	+200				

a. Fill in the table.
b. What is the internal rate of return after tax?

Solution

a.

Year	BTCF	SOYD Depreciation	Taxable Income	Taxes	ATCF
0	−300	—	—	—	−300.00
1	+100	150	−50	−17.50	+117.50
2	+150	100	+50	+17.50	+132.50
3	+200	50	+150	+52.50	+147.50

b. NPW $= -300 + 117.50(P/A, i\%, 3) + 15(P/G, i\%, 3) = 0$

By trial and error:

Try $i = 12\%$: NPW $= \$15.55$
Try $i = 15\%$: NPW $= -\$0.68$

   IRR $= i \approx 15\%$ (by interpolation $i = 14.87\%$)

12-2

A company, whose earnings put it in the 35% marginal tax bracket, is considering the purchase of a new piece of equipment for $25,000. The equipment will be depreciated by using the straight-line method over a 4-year depreciable life to a salvage value of $5000. It is estimated that the equipment will increase the company's earnings by $8000 for each of the 4 years it is used. Should the equipment be purchased? Use an interest rate of 10%.

Solution

Year	BTCF	Depreciation	TI	Taxes	ATCF
0	−25,000				−25,000
1	8,000	5000	3000	1050	6,950
2	8,000	5000	3000	1050	6,950
3	8,000	5000	3000	1050	6,950
4	8,000	5000	3000	1050	6,950
	5,000				5,000

SL depreciation = ¼(25,000 − 5000) = $5000

Find net present worth if NPV > 0 purchase equipment.

NPV = −25,000 + 6950(P/A, 10%, 4) + 5000(P/F, 10%, 4) = $446.50

Therefore, purchase the equipment.

12-3

By purchasing a truck for $30,000, a large profitable company in the 34% income tax bracket was able to save $8000 during Year 1, with the savings decreasing by $1000 each year thereafter. The company depreciated the truck by using the sum-of-years'-digits depreciation method over its 4-year depreciable life, while assuming a zero salvage value for depreciation purposes. The company wants to sell the truck at the end of Year 5. What resale value will yield a 12% after-tax rate of return for the company?

Solution

$$SOYD = \frac{4(5)}{2} = 10$$

Year	Depreciation
1	4/10(30,000 − 0) = 12,000
2	3/10(30,000 − 0) = 9,000
3	2/10(30,000 − 0) = 6,000
4	1/10(30,000 − 0) = 3,000

ATCF calculations:

Year	BTCF	Depreciation	TI	Taxes	ATCF
0	−30,000	—	—	—	−30,000
1	8,000	12,000	−4000	−1360	9,360
2	7,000	9,000	−2000	−680	7,680
3	6,000	6,000	0	0	6,000
4	5,000	3,000	2000	+680	4,320
5	4,000	—	4000	+1360	2,640
	Resale	—	Resale	.34R	.66R

Solve for resale value (R):

$30,000 = 9360(P/A, 12\%, 5) - 1680(P/G, 12\%, 5) + .66R(P/F, 12\%, 5)$
$30,000 = 22,995.84 + .374484R$
$\quad R = \$18,703.50$

12-4

A company has purchased a major piece of equipment that has a useful life of 20 years. An analyst trying to decide on a maintenance program has narrowed the choices to two alternatives. Alternative A is to perform $1000 of major maintenance every year. Alternative B is to perform $5000 of major maintenance only every fourth year. In either case, maintenance will be performed during the last year so that the equipment can be sold for $10,000. If the MARR is 18%, which maintenance plan should be chosen? Is it possible that the decision would change if income taxes were considered? Why or why not?

Solution

Equivalent Annual Cost$_A$ = $1000
Equivalent Annual Cost$_B$ = $5000(A/F, 18\%, 4) = \$958.50$

Therefore, choose Alternative B.

The decision would not change it taxes were considered. Since the cash flows for both alternatives would be reduced by the same percentage because of taxes, so EAC$_A$ > EAC$_B$ would still be true. If we assume a 45% tax rate, for example, the computations as follows.

Alternative A	Year	BTCF	TI	Taxes	ATCF
	1–4	−1000	−1000	−450	−550

EAC$_A$ = $550

Alternative B	Year	BTCF	TI	Taxes	ATCF
	1–3	0	0	0	0
	4	−5000	−5000	−2250	−2750

EAC$_B$ = 2750(A/F, 18\%, 4) = $527.20

12-5

A large company must build a bridge to have access to land for expansion of its manufacturing plant. The bridge could be fabricated of normal steel for an initial cost of $30,000 and should last for 15 years. Maintenance will cost $1000 per year. If the steel used were more corrosion resistant, the annual maintenance cost would be only $100 per year, although the life would be the same. In 15 years there would be no salvage value for either bridge. The company pays a combined state and federal income tax rate of 48% and uses straight-line depreciation. If the minimum attractive after-tax rate of return is 12%, what is the maximum amount that should be spent on the corrosion-resistant bridge?

Solution

Steel

Year	BTCF	Depreciation	TI	Taxes	ATCF
0	−30,000				−30,000
1–15	−1,000	2000	−3000	−1440	+440

Corrosion-Resistant Steel

Year	BTCF	Depreciation	TI	Taxes	ATCF
0	−P				−P
1–15	−100	P/15	−100 − P/15	(−48 − .032P)	−52 + .032P

$NPW_A = NPW_B$ for breakeven:

$$440(P/A, 12\%, 15) - 30,000 = (-52 + .032P)(P/A, 12\%, 15) - P$$
$$-27,003 = -354 + .0281P - P$$
$$P = \$34,078$$

12-6

Gillespie Gold Products, Inc. is considering the purchase of new smelting equipment. The new equipment is expected to increase production and decrease costs with a resulting increase in profits. From the following summary of the equipment under consideration, determine the after-tax cash flow. Use a tax rate of 42% and sum-of-the-years'-digits depreciation.

Cost	$50,000
Net savings/year	15,000 the first year, decreasing by $1000 each year thereafter
Salvage value	4000
Depreciable life	4 years
Actual useful life	6 years

Solution

Year	BTCF	Depreciation	TI	Taxes	ATCF
0	−50,000	—	—	—	−50,000
1	15,000	18,400	−3,400	−1428	16,428
2	14,000	13,800	200	84	13,916
3	13,000	9,200	3,800	1596	11,404
4	12,000	4,600	7,400	3108	8,892
5	11,000	—	11,000	4620	6,380
6	14,000	—	10,000	4200	9,800

$4000 capital recovery in Year 6 is not taxable.

12-7

An asset with 5-year MACRS* life will be purchased for $10,000. It will produce net annual benefits of $2000 per year for 6 years, after which time it will have a net salvage value of zero and will be retired. The company's incremental tax is 34%. Calculate the after-tax cash flows.

*The MACRS annual percentages are 20, 32, 19.20, 11.52, 11.52, and 5.76 for Years 1 through 6.

Solution

Year	BTCF	Depreciation	TI	Taxes	ATCF
0	−10,000				−10,000.00
1	2,000	2000	0	0	2,000.00
2	2,000	3200	−1200	−408.00	2,408.00
3	2,000	1920	80	+27.20	1,972.80
4	2,000	1152	848	+288.32	1,711.68
5	2,000	1152	848	+288.32	1,711.68
6	2,000	576	1424	+484.16	1,515.84

12-8

A state tax of 10% is deductible from the income taxed by the federal government. The federal tax is 34%. The combined effective tax rate is

a. 24.0%
b. 35.0%
c. 40.6%
d. 45.0%

Solution

Effective rate $= S + (1 - S)F$
$= 0.1 + (1 - 0.1)0.34$
$= 0.1 + (0.9)0.34$
$= 0.1 + 0.306$
$= 0.406 = 40.6\%$

The answer is c.

12-9

For engineering economic analysis, a corporation uses an incremental state income tax rate of 7.4% and an incremental federal rate of 34%. Calculate the effective tax rate.

Solution

Effective rate $= S + (1 - S)F$
$= 0.074 + (1 - 0.074)(0.34)$
$= 0.074 + (0.926)0.34$
$= 0.074 + 0.3148$
$= 0.3888 = 38.88\%$

12-10

A one-year savings certificate that pays 15% is purchased for $10,000. If the purchaser pays taxes at the 27% incremental income tax rate, the after-tax rate of return on this investment is

a. 4.05%
b. 10.95%
c. 15.00%
d. 22.95%

Solution

After-tax ROR $= (1 - $ Tax rate$)($Before-tax IRR$) = (1 - 0.27)(0.15) = 10.95\%$

The answer is b.

12-11

A corporation's tax rate is 34%. An outlay of $35,000 is being considered for a new asset. Estimated annual receipts are $20,000 and annual disbursements $10,000. The useful life of the asset is 5 years, and it has no salvage value.

a. What is the prospective rate of return before income tax?
b. What is the prospective rate of return after taxes, assuming straight-line depreciation?

Solution

SL depreciation = $\frac{1}{N}(P-S) = \frac{35,000-0}{5} = \$7000/year.$

Year	BTCF	Depreciation	TI	Taxes	ATCF
0	−35,000	—	—	—	−35,000
1	10,000	7000	3000	1020	8,980
2	10,000	7000	3000	1020	8,980
3	10,000	7000	3000	1020	8,980
4	10,000	7000	3000	1020	8,980
5	10,000	7000	3000	1020	8,980

a. $ROR_{BEFORE\ TAX}$

   $PW_B = PW_C$

   $10,000(P/A, i\%, 5) = 35,000$ At 12% $P/A = 3.605$

   $(P/A, i\%, 5) = \frac{35,000}{10,000} = 3.500$ At $i\%$ $P/A = 3.500$

                                    At 15% $P/A = 3.352$

   By interpolation:

                   $ROR = 13.25\%$

b. $ROR_{AFTER\ TAX}$

   $PW_B = PW_C$

   $8980(P/A, i\%, n) = 35,000$ At 8% $P/A = 3.993$

   $(P/A, i\%, 5) = \frac{35,000}{8,980} = 3.898$ At $i\%$ $P/A = 3.898$

                                    At 9% $P/A = 3.890$

   By interpolation:

                   $ROR = 8.92\%$

12-12

A large and profitable company, in the 34% income tax bracket, is considering the purchase of a new piece of machinery that will yield benefits of $10,000 for Year 1, $15,000 for Year 2, $20,000 for Year 3, $20,000 for Year 4, and $20,000 for Year 5. The machinery is to be depreciated by using the modified accelerated cost recovery system (MACRS) with a 3-year recovery period. The MACRS percentages are 33.33, 44.45, 14.81, 8.41, respectively, for Years 1, 2, 3, and 4. The company believes the machinery can be sold at the end of 5 years of use for 25% of the original purchase price. If the company requires a 12% after-tax rate of return, what is the maximum purchase cost it can pay?

Solution

Year	BTCF	Depreciation	TI	Taxes	ATCF
0	$-P$	—	—	—	$-P$
1	10,000	$.3333P$	$10,000 - .3333P$	$3400 + .1133P$	$6,600 + .1133P$
2	15,000	$.4445P$	$15,000 - .4445P$	$5100 + .1511P$	$9,900 + .1511P$
3	20,000	$.1481P$	$20,000 - .1481P$	$6800 + .0504P$	$13,200 + .0504P$
4	20,000	$.0841P$	$20,000 - .0841P$	$6800 + .0286P$	$13,200 + .0286P$
5	20,000	—	20,000	6,800	13,200
	$.25P$	—	$.25P$	$.085P$	$.165P$

$P = 6600(P/A\ 12\%,\ 3) + 3300(P/G,\ 12\%,\ 3) + 13,200(P/A,\ 12\%,\ 2)(P/F,\ 12\%,\ 3)$
$\qquad + .1133P(P/F,\ 12\%,\ 1) + .1511P(P/F,\ 12\%,\ 2) + .0504P(P/F,\ 12\%,\ 3)$
$\qquad + .0285P(P/F,\ 12\%,\ 4) + .165P(P/F,\ 12\%,\ 5)$
$P = \$61,926.52$

12-13

A company bought an asset at the beginning of 2011 for $100,000. The company now has an offer to sell the asset for $60,000 at the end of 2012. For each of the depreciation methods shown, determine the capital loss or recaptured depreciation that would be realized for 2012.

Depreciation Method	Depreciable Life (years)	Salvage Value*	Recaptured Depreciation	Capital Loss
SL	10	$ 1,000		
SOYD	5	25,000		
DDB	4	0		
150%DB	15	0		

*Assumed for depreciation purposes.

Solution

Depreciation Method	Depreciable Life (years)	Salvage Value	Recaptured Depreciation	Capital Loss
SL	10	$ 1,000		$20,200
SOYD	5	25,000	$ 5,000	
DDB	4	0	35,000	
150%DB	15	0		21,000

SL

Depreciation $= \dfrac{1}{10}(100,000 - 1000) = 9900$

Book value $= 100,000 - 2(9900) = 80,200$

Capital loss $= 80,200 - 60,000 = \$20,200$

SOYD

Depreciation (Year 1 + Year 2) $= \frac{5+4}{15}(100,000 - 25,000) = 45,000$

Book value $= 100,000 - 45,000 = 55,000$

Recaptured depreciation $= 60,000 - 55,000 = \$5000$

DDB

Depreciation Year 1 $= \frac{2}{4}(100,000) = 50,000$

Depreciation Year 2 $= \frac{2}{4}(100,000 - 50,000) = 25,000$

Book value $= 100,000 - 75,000 = 25,000$

Recaptured depreciation $= 60,000 - 25,000 = \$35,000$

150%DB

Depreciation Year 1 $= \frac{1.5}{15}(100,000) = 10,000$

Depreciation Year 2 $= \frac{1.5}{15}(100,000 - 10,000) = 9000$

Book value $= 100,000 - 19,000 = 81,000$

Capital loss $= 81,000 - 60,000 = \$35,000$

12-14

A corporation expects to receive $32,000 each year for 15 years if a particular project is undertaken. There will be an initial investment of $150,000. The expenses associated with the project are expected to be $7530 per year. Assume straight-line depreciation, a 15-year useful life, and no salvage value. Use a combined state and federal 48% income tax rate, and determine the project's after-tax rate of return.

Solution

Year	BTCF	Depreciation	TI	Taxes	ATCF
0	−150,000				−150,000
1–30	24,470	10,000	14,470	6946	17,524

Take the ATCF and compute the interest rate, where the $PW_{BENEFITS}$ equals PW_{COSTS}.

$17,524(P/A, i\%, 15) = 150,000$

$(P/A, i\%, 15) = \frac{150,000}{17,524} = 8.559$

From interest tables, $i = 8\%$.

12-15

A manufacturing firm purchases a machine in January for $100,000. The machine has an estimated useful life of 5 years, with an estimated salvage value of $20,000. The use of the machine should generate $40,000 before-tax profit each year over its 5-year useful life. The firm pays combined taxes at the 40% and uses sum-of-the-years'-digits depreciation.

PART 1 Complete the following table.

Year	BTCF	Depreciation	TI	Taxes	ATCF
0					
1					
2					
3					
4					
5					

PART 2 Does the sum-of-years'-digits depreciation represent a cash flow?

PART 3. Calculate the before-tax rate of return and the after-tax rate of return.

Solution

PART 1

Sum-of-years'-digits depreciation:

Year 1 = $\frac{5}{15}(100,000 - 20,000)$ = $26,667

Year 2 = $\frac{4}{15}(80,000)$ = $21,333

Year 3 = $\frac{3}{15}(80,000)$ = $16,000

Year 4 = $\frac{2}{15}(80,000)$ = $10,667

Year 5 = $\frac{1}{15}(80,000)$ = $ 5,333

Year	BTCF	Depreciation	TI	Taxes	ATCF
0	−100,000	—	—	—	−100,000
1	40,000	26,667	13,333	−5,333	34,667
2	40,000	21,333	18,667	−7,467	32,533
3	40,000	16,000	24,000	−9,600	30,400
4	40,000	10,667	29,333	−11,733	28,267
5	40,000	5,333	34,667	−13,867	26,133
5	20,000	—	—	—	20,000

PART 2

The sum-of-years'-digits depreciation is a bookkeeping allocation of capital expense for purposes of computing taxable income. Therefore it does not represent an actual cash flow (exchange of money).

PART 3

Before-tax ROR:

NPW = 0 at IRR

$0 = -100,000 + 40,000(P/A, i\%, 5) + 20,000(P/F, i\%, 5)$

Try 30%:*	NPW = +2826
Try 35%:	NPW = –6740

By interpolation:

IRR = 31.5%

After-tax ROR:

NPW = 0 at IRR

$0 = -100,000 + 34,667(P/A, i\%, n) - 2133(P/G, i\%, n) + 20,000(P/F, i\%, n)$

Try 20%:*	NPW = +1263
Try 25%:	NPW = –9193

By interpolation:

IRR = 20.60%

*Caution should be exercised when one is interpolating to find an interest rate. Linear interpolation is being imposed on a nonlinear function. Therefore, the solution is approximate. A maximum range over which to interpolate and achieve generally good results is usually considered to be 3 percentage points. Oftentimes, as in this problem, the interest tables you have at your disposal will force you to use a larger range.

12-16

PARC, a large profitable firm, has an opportunity to expand one of its production facilities at a cost of $375,000. The equipment is expected to have an economic life of 10 years and to have a resale value of $25,000 after 10 years of use. If the expansion is undertaken, PARC expects that income will increase by $60,000 for Year 1, and then increase by $5000 each year through Year 10. The annual operating cost is expected to be $5000 for the first year and to increase by $250 per year thereafter. If the equipment is purchased, PARC will depreciate it by using the straight-line method to a zero salvage value at the end of Year 8 for tax purposes. Since PARC is a "large and profitable," firm the applicable tax rate is 34%.

If PARC's minimum attractive rate of return (MARR) is 15%, should the firm undertake this expansion?

Solution

Year	Income	Costs	BTCF
1	60,000	5000	55,000
2	65,000	5250	59,750
3	70,000	5500	64,500
4	75,000	5750	69,250
5	80,000	6000	74,000
6	85,000	6250	78,750
7	90,000	6500	83,500
8	95,000	6750	88,250
9	100,000	7000	93,000
10	105,000	7250	97,750

Year	BTCF	Depreciation	TI	Taxes	ATCF
0	−375,000	—	—	—	−375,000.00
1	55,000	46,875	8,125	2,762.50	52,237.50
2	59,750	46,875	12,875	4,377.50	55,372.50
3	64,500	46,875	17,625	5,992.50	58,507.50
4	69,250	46,875	22,375	7,607.50	61,642.50
5	74,000	46,875	27,125	9,222.50	64,777.50
6	78,750	46,875	31,875	10,837.50	67,912.50
7	83,500	46,875	36,625	12,452.50	71,047.50
8	88,250	46,875	41,375	14,067.50	74,182.50
9	93,000	—	93,000	31,620.00	61,380.00
10	97,750	—	97,750	31,620.00	61,380.00
10	25,000	—	25,000	8,500.00	16,500.00

NPW = −375,000 + [52,237.50(*P/A*, 15%, 8) + 3135(*P/G*, 15%, 8)] + 61,380(*P/F*, 15%, 9) + 77,880(*P/F*, 15%, 10)

NPW = −$64,780.13

PARC should not undertake the expansion.

12-17

A project under consideration by PHI, Inc. is summarized. The company uses straight-line depreciation, pays income taxes at the 30% marginal rate, and requires an after-tax MARR of return of 12%.

First cost	$75,000
Annual revenues	26,000
Annual costs	13,500
Salvage value	1 5,000
Useful life	30 years

a. Use net present worth to determine whether the project should be undertaken.
b. If the company used sum-of-the-years'-digits depreciation, is it possible that the decision would change? (No computations needed.)

Solution

a.

Year	BTCF	Depreciation	TI	Taxes	ATCF
0	−75,000	—	—	—	−75,000
1–30	12,500	2000	10,500	3150	9,350
30	15,000	—	—	—	15,000

NPW = −75,000 + 9350(P/A, 12%, 30) + 15,000(P/F, 12%, 30) = $815

Yes, take the project, since NPW > 0.

b. No. Although total depreciation is the same, SOYD is larger in the early years when it is worth more. Therefore the NPW would increase with SOYD making the project even more desirable.

12-18

A heat exchanger purchased by Hot Spot Manufacturing cost $24,000. The exchanger will save $4500 in each of the next 10 years. Hot Spot will use SOYD depreciation over a 6-year depreciable life. The declared salvage value is $3000. It is expected that the exchanger will be sold for the declared value. Hot Spot pays taxes at a combined rate of 42% and has a MARR of 8%. Was the purchased justified?

Solution

Year		
0	First cost	−24,000
1–10	Annual savings: 4500(P/A, 8%, 10)(0.58)	17,513
1–6	Depr.: [6000(P/A, 8%, 6) − 1000(P/G, 8%, 6)](0.42)	7,230
10	Capital recovery: 3000(P/F, 8%, 10)	1,390
	NPW	$ 2,133

Yes, the purchase was justified.

12-19

The Red Ranger Company recorded revenues of $45,000 and recaptured depreciation of $1200 for the year just ended. During the year, the firm incurred cash expenses of $23,500 and depreciation expenses of $11,575. Red Ranger's taxable income is

a. $9,925
b. $11,125
c. $21,500
d. $34,275

Solution

$$TI = \text{Revenues} - \text{Expenses} - \text{Depreciation} + \text{Recaptured depreciation}$$
$$= 45{,}000 - 23{,}500 - 11{,}575 + 1200$$
$$= \$11{,}125$$

The answer is b.

12-20

A project will require the investment of $108,000 in capital equipment (SOYD with a depreciable life of 8 years and zero salvage value) and $25,000 in other nondepreciable materials that will be purchased during the first year. The annual net income realized from the investment is projected to be $28,000. At the end of the 8 years, the project will be discontinued and the equipment sold for $24,000. Assuming a tax rate of 28% and a MARR of 10%, should the project be undertaken?

Solution

Cash expenses are multiplied by (1 − tax rate).
Incomes are multiplied by (1 − tax rate).
Depreciation is multiplied by tax rate.
Recaptured depreciation is multiplied by (1 − tax rate).

Year		
0	First cost	−108,000
1	Other costs: 25,000(P/F, 10%, 1)(0.72)	−16,364
1–8	Depr.: [24,000(P/A, 10%, 8) − 3000(P/G, 10%, 8)](0.28)	22,387
1–8	Income: 28,000(P/A, 10%, 8)	107,554
8	Recaptured depr.: 24,000(P/F, 10%, 8)(0.72)	8,061
	NPW	$13,638

The project should be undertaken.

12-21

The Salsaz-Hot manufacturing company must replace a machine used to crush tomatoes for its salsa. The industrial engineer favors a machine called the Crusher. Information concerning the machine is given.

First cost	$95,000
Annual operating costs	6,000
Annual insurance cost*	1,750
Annual productivity savings	19,000

*Payable at the beginning of each year

Depreciable salvage value	$10,000
Actual salvage value	14,000
Depreciable life	6 years
Actual useful life	10 years
Depreciation method	SL

Property taxes equal to 5% of the first cost are payable at the end of each year.

Relevant financial information for Salsaz-Hot:

Marginal tax rate	34%
MARR	10%

Determine the net present worth.

Solution

Cash expenses are multiplied by (1 − tax rate).
Incomes are multiplied by (1 − tax rate).
Depreciation is multiplied by tax rate.
Capital recovery is not taxable; therefore it is multiplied by 1.
Recaptured depreciation is multiplied by (1 − tax rate).

Year		
0	First cost	−95,000
1–10	Net savings: 13,000(*P/A*, 10%, 10)(0.66)	52,724
1–10	Property taxes: 0.05(95,000)(*P/A*, 10%, 10)(0.66)	−19,265
0–9	Insurance: [1750 + 1750(*P/A*, 10%, 9)]0(.66)	−7,807
1–6	Depr.: 14,167(*P/A*, 10%, 6)(0.34)	20,977
10	Capital recovery: 10,000(*P/F*, 10%, 10)	3,855
10	Recaptured depr.: 4000(*P/F*, 10%, 10)(0.66)	1,018
	NPW	−$43,498

12-22

Momma Mia's Pizza must replace its current pizza baking oven. The two best alternatives are
Crispy Cruster and Easy Baker.

	Crispy Cruster	Easy Baker
Initial cost	$24,000	$33,000
Annual costs	9,000	6,000
Depreciable salvage value	6,000	5,000
Actual salvage value	6,000	8,000
Depreciable life	3 years	4 years
Actual useful life	5 years	5 years
Depreciation method	SL	SOYD

Assume that Momma pays taxes at the 34% rate and has a MARR of 8%. Which oven should be
chosen?

Solution

Crispy Cruster

Year		
0	First cost	−24,000
1–5	Annual costs: 9000(P/A, 8%, 5)(0.66)	−23,718
1–3	Depr.: 6000(P/A, 8%, 3)(0.34)	5,257
5	Capital recovery 6000(P/F, 8%, 5)	4,084
	NPW	−$38,377

Easy Baker

Year		
0	First cost	−33,000
1–5	Annual costs: 6000(P/A, 8%, 5)(0.66)	−15,813
1–4	Depr.: [11,200(P/A, 8%, 4) − 2800(P/G, 8%, 4)](0.34)	8,185
5	Capital recovery: 5000(P/F, 8%, 5)	3,403
5	Recaptured depreciation: 3000(P/F, 8%, 5)(0.66)	1,348
	NPW	−$35,877

Choose the Easy Baker oven.

12-23

Pinion Potato Chip, Inc., must purchase new potato peeling equipment for its plant in Union City, Tennessee. The plant engineer, Abby Wheeler, has determined that the following three setups that are possibilities.

	Naked Peel	Skinner	Peel-O-Matic
First cost	$45,000	$52,000	$76,000
Annual costs	6,000	5,000	5,000
Declared salvage value	12% of FC	5,500	10,000
Useful life	6 years	6 years	6 years
Actual salvage value	6,500	5,500	12,000

Part A   All assets are depreciated by using the SL method. Determine which setup should be chosen if P^2C Inc. has a MARR of 10% and pays taxes at the 34% marginal rate.

Part B   Owing to economic considerations, P^2C Inc. must eliminate the Peel-O-Matic setup; and because of a change in the tax laws, the firm must use MACRS depreciation. If all other information concerning Naked Peel and Skinner remains the same, which of those alternatives should be chosen?

Solution

Part A

Naked Peel

Year		
0	First cost	−45,000
1–6	Annual costs: 6000(P/A, 10%, 6)(0.66)	−17,246
1–6	Depr.: 6600(P/A, 10%, 6)(0.34)	9,773
6	Capital recovery: 5400(P/F, 10%, 6)	3,048
6	Recaptured depr.: 1100(P/F, 10%, 6)(0.66)	410
	NPW	−$49,015

Skinner

Year		
0	First cost	−52,000
1–6	Annual costs: 5000(P/A, 10%, 6)(0.66)	−14,372
1–6	Depr.: 7750(P/A, 10%, 6)(0.34)	11,475
6	Capital recovery: 5500(P/F, 10%, 6)	3,105
	NPW	−$51,792

Peel-O-Matic

Year		
0	First cost	−76,000
1–6	Annual costs: 5000(*P/A*, 10%, 6)(0.66)	−52,724
1–6	Depr.: 11,000(*P/A*, 10%, 6)(0.34)	16,288
6	Capital recovery: 10,000(*P/F*, 10%, 6)	5,645
6	Recaptured depr.: 2000(*P/F*, 10%, 6)(0.66)	745
	NPW	−$67,694

Choose Naked Peel.

Part B

Naked Peel

Year		
0	First cost	−45,000
1–6	Annual costs: 6000(*P/A*, 10%, 6)(0.66)	−17,246
1	Depr.: (.3333)(45,000)(*P/F*, 10%, 1)(0.34)	4,636
2	Depr.: (.4445)(45,000)(*P/F*, 10%, 2)(0.34)	5,620
3	Depr.: (.1481)(45,000)(*P/F*, 10%, 3)(0.34)	1,702
4	Depr.: (.0741)(45,000)(*P/F*, 10%, 4)(0.34)	774
6	Recaptured depr.: 6500(*P/F*, 10%, 6)(0.66)	2,422
	NPW	−$47,092

Skinner

Year		
0	First cost	−52,000
1–6	Annual costs: 5000(*P/A*, 10%, 6)(0.66)	−14,372
1	Depr.: (.3333)(52,000)(*P/F*, 10%, 1)(0.34)	5,357
2	Depr.: (.4445)(52,000)(*P/F*, 10%, 2)(0.34)	6,494
3	Depr.: (.1481)(52,000)(*P/F*, 10%, 3)(0.34)	1,967
4	Depr.: (.0741)(52,000)(*P/F*, 10%, 4)(0.34)	895
6	Recaptured depr.: 5500(*P/F*, 10%, 6)(0.66)	2,049
	NPW	−$49,610

Choose Naked Peel.

Chapter 13

Replacement Analysis

13-1

One of the four ovens at a bakery is being considered for replacement. A new oven costs $80,000; this price includes a complete guarantee of the maintenance costs for the first 2 years, and it covers a good proportion of the maintenance costs for Years 3 and 4. The salvage value and maintenance costs are given, both for the oven to be replaced and the new oven being considered.

	Old Oven		New Oven	
	Salvage Value	Maintenance	Salvage Value	Maintenance
Year	at End of Year	Costs	at End of Year	Costs
0	$20,000	$ —	$80,000	$ —
1	17,000	9500	75,000	0
2	14,000	9600	70,000	0
3	11,000	9700	66,000	1000
4	7,000	9800	62,000	3000

Both the old oven and the contemplated replacement are similar in productivity and energy costs; the MARR equals 10%. Should the oven be replaced this year?

Solution

The old oven ("defender") has the following data.

Year	S Value at EOP	EAC Capital Recovery: $(P-S)(A/P, 10\%, n)$ $+ Si$	Maint. Costs	EAC Maintenance: $9500 +$ $100(A/G, 10\%, n)$	EAC Total
0	$P = 20,000$	—	—	—	—
1	17,000	5000.00	9500	9,500.00	14,500.00
2	14,000	4857.20	9600	9,547.60	14,404.80
3	11,000	4718.90	9700	9,593.70	14,312.60*
4	7,000	4801.50	9800	9,638.10	14,439.60

*Economic life = 3 years, with EAC = $14,312.60.

193

The new oven ("challenger") has the following data.

Year	S Value at EOP	EAC Capital Recovery: $(P-S)(A/P, 10\%, n)$ + Si	Maint. Costs	EAC Maintenance: 9500 + $100(A/G, 10\%, n)$	EAC Total
0	P = 80,000	—	—	—	—
1	75,000	13,000.00	0	0	13,000.00
2	70,000	12,762.00	0	0	12,762.00
3	66,000	12,229.40	1000	302.10[†]	12,531.50*
4	62,000	11,879.00	3000	883.55[‡]	12,762.55

*Economic life = 3 years, with EAC = $12,531.50.
[†]$1000(A/F, 10\%, 3) = \$302.10$.
[‡]$[1000(F/P, 10\%, 1) + 3000](A/F, 10\%, 4) = \$883.55$.

Since EAC defender > EAC challenger (14,312.6 > 12,531.5), replace the oven this year.

13-2

The cash flow diagram indicates the costs associated with a piece of equipment. The investment cost is $5000, and there is no salvage. During the first 3 years, the equipment is under warranty so there are no maintenance costs. Then the estimated maintenance costs over 15 years follow the pattern shown in the cash flow diagram. Determine the equivalent annual cost (EAC) for $n = 12$ if the minimum attractive rate of return (MARR) = 15%. Use gradient and uniform series factors in your solution.

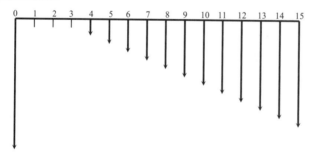

Solution

$$EAC = 5000(P/A, 15\%, 12) + 150(F/A, 15\%, 9)(A/F, 15\%, 12)$$
$$+ 100(P/G, 15\%, 7)(P/F, 15\%, 5)(A/P, 15\%, 12)$$
$$= \$1103$$

13-3
A hospital is considering the purchase of a new $40,000 diagnostic machine that will have no salvage value after installation, as the cost of removal equals any resale value. Maintenance is estimated to be $2000 per year as long as the machine is owned. After 10 years the machine must be scrapped because the radioactive ion source will have caused so much damage to machine components that safe operation is no longer possible. The most economic life of this machine is

a. One year, since it will have no salvage after installation.
b. Ten years, because maintenance doesn't increase.
c. Less than 10 years, but more information is needed to determine the economic life.

Solution

   The correct answer is b.

13-4
A petroleum company, whose minimum attractive rate of return is 10%, needs to paint the vessels and pipes in its refinery periodically to prevent rust. Tuff-Coat, a durable paint, can be purchased for $8.05 a gallon, while Quick-Cover, a less durable paint, costs $3.25 a gallon. The labor cost of applying a gallon of paint is $6.00. Both paints are equally easy to apply and will cover the same area per gallon. Quick-Cover is expected to last 5 years. How long must Tuff-Coat promise to last to justify its use?

Solution

   This replacement problem requires that we solve for a breakeven point. Let N represent the number of years Tuff-Coat must last. The easiest measure of worth to use in this situation is equivalent annual worth (EAW). Although more computationally cumbersome, other measures could be used and, if applied correctly, would result in the same answer.

   Find N such that $EAW_{TC} = EAW_{QC}$
       $14.05(A/P, 10\%, N) = 9.25 (A/P, 10\%, 5)$
              $(A/P, 10\%, N) = 0.17367$

   Searching the $i = 10\%$ table yields $N = 9$ years.

   Tuff-Coat must last at least 9 years. Notice that this solution implicitly assumes that the pipes need to be painted indefinitely (i.e., forever) and that the paint and costs of painting never change (i.e., no inflation or technological improvements affecting the paint or the cost to produce and sell paint, or to apply the paint).

13-5

Ten years ago Hyway Robbery, Inc. installed a conveyor system for $8000. The conveyor system has been fully depreciated to a zero salvage value. The company is considering replacing the conveyor because maintenance costs have been increasing. The estimated end-of-year maintenance costs for the next 5 years are as follow:

Year	Maintenance
1	$1000
2	1250
3	1500
4	1750
5	2000

At any time, the cost of removal just equals the value of the scrap metal recovered from the system. The replacement the company is considering has an equivalent annual cost (EAC) of $1028 at its most economic life. The company has a minimum attractive rate of return (MARR) of 10%.

a. Should the conveyor be replaced now? Show the basis used for your decision.
b. Now assume that the old conveyor could be sold at any time as scrap metal for $500 more than the cost of removal. All other data remain the same. Should the conveyor be replaced?

Solution

a. Since the current value ($0.00) is not changing but maintenance costs are increasing, the most economic life is one year.

Year	Cash Flow
0	0
1	−1000
S	0

Defender uniform equivalent cost: $EAC_D = \$1000$.

Since $EAC_D < EAC_C$, keep the old conveyor for now.

b.

Year	Cash Flow
0	−500
1	−1000
S	+500

$EAC_D = 1000 + 500(A/P, 10\%, 1) - 500(A/F, 10\%, 1) = \$1050$.

Since $EAC_D > EAC_C$, replace the old conveyor.

13-6

Ten years ago, the Cool Chemical Company installed a heat exchanger in its plant for $10,000. The company is considering replacing the heat exchanger because maintenance costs have been increasing. The estimated maintenance costs for the next 5 years are as follows.

Year	Maintenance
1	$1000
2	1200
3	1400
4	1600
5	1800

Regardless of when the heat exchanger is replaced, the cost of removal will be $1500 more than the heat exchanger is worth as scrap metal. The replacement the company is considering has an equivalent annual cost (EAC) of $900 at its most economic life. If the company's minimum attractive rate of return (MARR) is 20%, should the heat exchanger be replaced now?

Solution

Since the current value ($–1500) is not changing but maintenance costs are increasing, the most economic life is one year.

Year	Cash Flow	
0	+1500	(Forgone salvage)
1	–1000	(Maintenance)
S	–1500	(Negative salvage)

Equivalent annual cost of the defender:

$EAC_D = 1000 + 1500(A/F, 20\%, 1) - 1500(A/P, 20\%, 1) = \$700$

Since $EAC_D < EAC_C$, keep the old heat exchanger for now.

13-7

An engineer is trying to determine the economic life of a new metal press. The press costs $10,000 initially. First-year maintenance costs are $1000. Maintenance costs are forecast to increase $1000 per year for each year after the first. Fill in the table and determine the economic life of the press. Consider only maintenance and capital recovery in your analysis. Interest is 5%.

Year	Maintenance Cost	EAC of Capital Recovery	EAC of Maintenance	Total EAC
1	$1000			
2	2000			
↓	↓			
8	8000			

Solution

Year	Maintenance Cost	EAC of Capital Recovery	EAC of Maintenance	Total EAC
1	$1000	$11,500	$1000	$12,500
2	2000	6,151	1465	7,616
3	3000	4,380	1907	6,287
4	4000	3,503	2326	5,829
5	5000	2,983	2723	5,706
6	6000	2,642	3097	5,739
7	7000	2,404	3450	5,854
8	8000	2,229	3781	6,010

Economic life = 5 years (EAC = minimum)

EAC of capital recovery = $10,000 $(A/P, 15\%, n)$
EAC of maintenance = $1000 + 1000 $(A/G, 15\%, n)$

13-8
A manufacturer is contemplating the purchase of an additional forklift truck to improve material handling in the plant. He is considering two popular models, the Convair T6 and the FMC 340. The relevant financial data are given. The manufacturer's MARR is 12%.

Model	First Cost	Life	Salvage Value	Annual Operating Cost
Convair T6	$20,000	6 years	$2000	$8000
FMC 340	29,000	7 years	4000	4000

a.   Which model is more economical?
b.   List two important assumptions that are implicit in your computations in part a.

Solution

a.   Compute the EAW for each model.

Convair: $EAW = -20,000(A/P, 12\%, 6) + 2000(A/F, 12\%, 6) - 8000$
            $= -\$12,617.60$

FMC: $EAW = -29,000(A/P, 12\%, 7) + 4000(A/F, 12\%, 7) - 4000$
            $= -\$9,957.50$

The FMC is more economical.

b.   You have assumed that either truck can be repeated with identical costs indefinitely and that the service to be provided (material handling) is required forever.

13-9

A graduate of an engineering economy course has compiled the following set of estimated costs and salvage values for a proposed machine with a first cost of $15,000; however, he has forgotten how to find the most economic life. Your task is to show him how to do this by calculating the equivalent annual cost (EAC) for $n = 8$, given a MARR of 15%.

Life (n) Years	Estimated End-of-Year Maintenance	Estimated Salvage if Sold in Year n
1	$ 0	$10,000
2	$ 0	9,000
3	300	8,000
4	300	7,000
5	800	6,000
6	1300	5,000
7	1800	4,000
8	2300	3,000
9	2800	2,000
10	3300	1,000

Remember: Calculate only <u>one</u> EAC (for $n = 8$). You are not expected to actually find the most economical life.

Solution

First cost	EAC $= 15,000(A/P, 15\%, 8) = \$3344$
Salvage value	EAC $= -3000(A/F, 15\%, 8) = -\$219$
Maintenance	EAC $= 300(F/A, 15\%, 6)(A/F, 15\%, 8)$
	$+ 500(P/G, 15\%, 5)(P/F, 15\%, 3)(A/P, 15\%, 8) = \$615$
Total	EAC$_8 = \$3740$

(A complete analysis would show that the most economic life is 7 years, with EAC = $3727.)

13-10

One year ago, Machine A was purchased for $15,000, to be used for 5 years. The machine has not performed as expected, and it costs $750 per month for repairs, adjustments, and downtime. Machine B, designed to perform the same functions, can be purchased for $25,000 with monthly costs of $75. The expected life of machine B is 5 years. Operating costs are substantially equal for the two machines, and salvage values for both are negligible. If 6% is used, the incremental annual net equivalent of Machine B is nearest to

a. $2165
b. $2886
c. $4539
d. $5260

Solution

$$\Delta EUAW = -25,000(A/P, 6\%, 5) + 12(750 - 75)$$
$$= \$2165$$

The answer is a.

13-11

An existing machine has operating costs of $300 per year and a salvage value of $100 (for all years). A new replacement machine would cost $1000 to purchase, and its operating cost over the next period of t years (not per year) is $M = 200t + 10t^2$. Assume i = zero percent.

a. What is the most economic life, t^*, for the new machine?
b. Should the old machine be replaced with the new one?

Solution

a. Cost per year = $AC = \dfrac{1000}{t} + \dfrac{M}{t} = \dfrac{1000}{t} + 200 + 10t$

$$\frac{dAC}{t} = \frac{1000}{t^2} + 10 = 0 \implies t^* = +10 \text{ years}$$

b. $AC^* = AC(10) = \dfrac{1000}{10} + 200 + 10(10)$

$$= 400 \geq \text{Annual cost of old machine for any number of years}$$

$\therefore$ No; keep the old machine.

13-12

A truck salesperson is quoted as follows:

"Even though our list price has gone up to $42,000, I'll sell you a new truck for the old price of $40,000, an immediate savings of $2000, and give you a trade-in allowance of $21,000, so your cost is only ($40,000 – 21,000) = $19,000. The book value of your old truck is $12,000, so you're making an additional ($21,000 – 12,000) = $9000 on the deal." The salesperson adds, "Actually I am giving you more trade-in for your old truck than the current market value of $19,500, so you are saving an extra ($21,000 – 19,500) = $1500."

a. In a proper replacement analysis, what is the first cost of the defender?
b. In a proper replacement analysis, what is the first cost of the challenger?

Solution

a. $19,500

The defender's 1st cost is always the current market value, not trade-in or book value.

b. $38,500

With an inflated trade-in value of $1500 (21,000 – 19,500), the new truck can be purchased for $40,000. Therefore, the appropriate value used for replacement analysis is $40,000 – $1500 = $38,500.

13-13

The computer system used for production and administration control at a large cannery is being considered for replacement. Of the available replacement systems, Challenger I has been considered the best. However, it is anticipated that after one year, the Challenger II model will become available, with significant technological modifications. The salvage value projections for the three systems are summarized. Assuming that the performance of all three would otherwise be comparable, should we replace the existing system either this year or next year? Assume that the MARR equals 12%, and the useful life is 5 years in all cases.

	Salvage Value at End of the Year		
Year	Existing Computer	Challenger I	Challenger II
0	$20,000	$25,000	$24,000
1	16,000	22,000	23,000
2	13,000	21,000	23,000
3	11,000	20,000	22,000
4	8,000	16,000	16,000
5	3,000	10,000	10,000

Solution

Existing Computer (defender)

Year	Salvage Value at End of Year	EAC Capital Recovery: $(P - S)(A/P, 12\%, n) + Si$
0	$P = 20,000$	—
1	16,000	6400.00
2	13,000	5701.90
3	11,000	5066.70
4	8,000	4910.40*
5	3,000	5075.80

* Economic life = 4 years; EAC = $4910.40.

Challenger I

Year	Salvage Value at End of Year	EAC Capital Recovery: $(P - S)(A/P, 12\%, n) + Si$
0	$P = 25{,}000$	—
1	22,000	6000.00
2	21,000	4886.80
3	20,000	4481.50*
4	16,000	4882.80
5	10,000	5361.00

*Economic life = 3 years; EAC = \$4481.50.

Challenger II

Year[†]	Salvage Value at End of Year	EAC Capital Recovery: $(P - S)(A/P, 12\%, n) + Si$
0	$P = 24{,}000$	—
1	23,000	3880.00
2	23,000	3351.70*
3	22,000	3472.60
4	16,000	4553.60
5	10,000	5083.60

*Economic life = 2 years; EAC = \$4910.40.
[†]Year numbers do not refer to same time scale used for Challenger 1.

Note: $\text{EAC}_{\text{Challenger II}} < \text{EAC}_{\text{Challenger I}} < \text{EAC}_{\text{Defender}}$; but should we replace the defender now or wait one year for the Challenger II?

Alternative A: Don't wait.

$\text{EAC}_A = \text{EAC}_{\text{Challenger I}} = \$4481.50$

Alternative B: Wait one year for replacement.

$\text{EAC}_B = [6400(P/A, 12\%, 1) + (3351{,}7(P/A, 12\%, 2)(P/F, 12\%, 1)](A/P, 12\%, 3)$
          cost of keeping   cost of Challenger II at its
            one more year   best (2-year economic life)
        = \$4484.49

Since $\text{EAC}_A \approx \text{EAC}_B$, we should preferably wait one year, although strictly speaking we could choose either option.

Chapter 14

Inflation
and
Price Change

14-1

The first sewage treatment plant for Athens, Georgia, cost about $2 million in 1964. The utilized capacity of the plant was 5 million gallons/day (mgd). Using the commonly accepted value of 135 gallons per person per day of sewage flow, find the cost per person for the plant. Adjust the cost to 1984 dollars with inflation at 6%. What is the annual capital expense per person if the useful life is 30 years and the value of money is 10%?

Solution

Population equivalents = 5 mgd/135 = 37,037

$$\text{Cost per capita} = \frac{\$2,000,000}{37,037} = \$54$$

$1984_\$$, $F = 54(F/P, 6\%, 20) = \$173.18$

Annual cost, $A = 173.18(A/P, 10\%, 30) = \$18.37$

14-2

How much life insurance should a person buy if he wants to leave enough money to ensure that his family will receive $25,000 per year in interest, of constant Year-0-value dollars? The interest rate expected from banks is 11%, while the inflation rate is expected to be 4% per year.

Solution

The actual (effective) rate that the family will be getting is

$$i' = \frac{i-f}{1+f} = \frac{0.11-0.04}{1.04} = 0.0673 = 6.73\%$$

To calculate P, $n = \infty$ (capitalized cost)

$$P = \frac{A}{i'} = \frac{25,000}{0.0673} = \$371,471$$

Therefore, he needs to buy about $371,500 of life insurance.

14-3

A European investor lives near one of his country's borders. In Country A (where he lives), banks are offering an 8% interest rate and the inflation rate is 3%. Country B, on the other hand, has an inflation rate of 23%, and banks are offering 26% interest on deposits.

a. What real or effective interest rate does the investor earn when investing in his own country?
b. The investor believes that the currency of Country B will not change in its value relative to the value of the currency of Country A during this year. In which country would he get a larger effective interest rate?
c. Suppose that he invests in a bank in Country B and that his prediction turns out to be wrong: the currency of Country B was devaluated 20% with respect to the exchange value of Country A's currency. What effective interest rate would he obtain in this case?

Solution

a. $i' = ?$ if $i = 80\%$, and $f = 3\%$

$$i = i' + f + i'f$$
$$0.08 = i' + 0.03 + i'(0.03)$$
$$i' = 0.0485$$
$$= 4.85\%$$

b. If investment in Country A: $i'_A = 0.0485$
   If investment in Country B: $i_B = 26\%, f_A = 3\%$

   (The investor <u>lives</u> in Country A; inflation of Country B has no direct affect on him.)

   $$i'_B = \frac{i_B - f_A}{1 + f_A} = \frac{0.26 - 0.03}{1 + 0.03} = 0.2233 = 22.33\%$$

   He can get a larger effective interest rate in Country B.

c. Let $X =$ amount originally invested in B (measured in currency A).

   The amount collected at end of one year (measured in currency A) is

   $$\underbrace{(1.0 - 0.2)}_{\substack{\text{Due to the} \\ \text{devaluation}}} \times \underbrace{(1.26)}_{\substack{\text{Due to initial} \\ \text{deposit } (+)\text{interest}}} = 1.008X$$

   The interest is then $i = \dfrac{1.008X - X}{X} = 0.008$.

   During the year inflation in Country A (where the investor lives) was 3%; therefore,

   $$i = 0.008$$
   $$f = 0.03$$
   $$i' = ?$$

   $$i' = \frac{0.008 - 0.03}{1 + 0.03} = -0.02136$$

   He actually would have lost money (negative effective interest rate of −2.136%).

14-4

Property, in the form of unimproved land, is purchased at a cost of $8000 and is held for 6 years, at which time it is sold for $32,600. An average of $220 each year is paid in property tax and may be accounted for at an interest of 12%. The income tax rate on the long-term capital gain is 15% of the gain. Inflation during the period is 7% per year. What is the annual rate of return for this investment?

Solution

Long-term gains = 32,600 – 8000 = 24,600
Tax on long-term gain = 0.15 × 24,600 = 3690
Property tax = 220(F/A, 12%, 6) = $1785.30

Adjusted FW = 32,600 – 3,690 – 1785.30 = $27,624.70
    also FW = 8000$(1 + i_{eq})^6$

$$\therefore \left(1+i_{eq}\right)=\left(\tfrac{27,124.70}{8000}\right)^{\frac{1}{6}}=1.2257$$

$$\left(1+i_{eq}\right)=\left(1+i\right)\left(1+i_f\right)$$

$$1+i=\frac{1.2257}{1.07}=1.1455 \text{ or } 14.6\% \text{ rate of retrun}$$

14-5

The auto of your dreams costs $20,000 today. You have found a way to earn 15% tax free on an "auto purchase account.". If you expect the cost of your dream auto to increase by 10% per year, how much would you need to deposit in the "auto purchase account" to provide for the purchase of the auto 5 years from now?

Solution

Cost of auto 5 years hence: F = P$(1 + \text{inflation rate})^n$ = 20,000 $(1 + 0.10)^5$ = $32,210

Amount to deposit now to have $32,210 five years hence

P = F(P/F, i%, n) = 32,210(P/F, 15%, 5) = $16,014.81

14-6

On January 1, 1975 the National Price Index was 208.5, and on January 1, 1985, it was 516.71. What was the inflation rate, compounded annually, over that 10-year period? Assuming that the same rate continued to hold for the next 10 years, what would the National Price Index have been on January 1, 1995?

Solution

Set NPW = 0

$$0 = -208.5 + 516.71(P/F, i_f, 10)$$
$$(P/F, i_f, 10) = \frac{208.5}{516.71}$$
$$= 0.4035$$

From interest tables, the *P/F* factor at   9% = 0.4224

10% = 0.3855   ∴ 9% < i_f < 10%

By interpolation, i_f = 9.51%.

National Price Index$_{1995}$ = 516.71$(1 + 0.0951)^{10}$ = 1281.69

14-7

A electronics store offers two options to buy a new laptop computer that has a price of $440.00. A customer can either pay cash and immediately receive a discount of $49, or she can pay for the computer on an installment plan. The installment plan has a nominal rate of 12% compounded bi-yearly and requires an initial down payment of $44, followed by four equal payments (principal and interest) every 6 months for 2 years.

If for the typical customer the cost of money is 5%, what is the maximum effective annual inflation rate for the next 2 years that would make paying cash preferable to paying installments? All figures given are quoted in Time-0 dollars.

Solution

If the installment plan were selected, the monthly payments in nominal dollars would be

$$(-440 + 44)(A/P, 6\%, 4) = -\$114.28$$

The breakeven inflation rate is that such that

$NPV_{BUY} = NPV_{INSTALL}$ or $NPV_{BUY - INSTALL} = 0$

$NPV_{B-I} = [(-440 + 49) + 44] + 114.28(P/A, i_{1/2}, 4) = 0$

Since $(P/A, i_{1/2}, 4) = 3.0364$, the nominal effective semiannual cost of money would have to be $i_{1/2} = 0.115$. The nominal effective annual rate would be $i = (1.115)^2 - 1 = 0.2432$.

The effective annual inflation rate can now be computed from the formula
$$(1.2432) = (1.05)(1 + f)$$
$$f = 0.1840$$

14-8
An automobile that cost $19,500 in 2004 had an equivalent model 4 years later that cost $22,250. If the increase is attributed to inflation, what was the average annual rate of inflation?

Solution

$$F = P(1 + i_f)^n$$
$$22,250 = 19,500(1 + i_f)^4$$
$$\frac{22,250}{19,500} = (1 + i_f)^4$$
$$1 + i_f = (1.141)^{1/4}$$
$$1 + i_f = 1.0335$$
$$i_f = 3.35\%$$

14-9
A machine has a first cost of $100,000 (in today's dollars) and a salvage value of $20,000 (in then-current dollars) at the end of its 10-year life. Each year the machine is used will eliminate the job of one full-time worker. A worker costs $30,000 (today's dollars) in salary and benefits. Labor costs are expected to escalate at 10% per year. Operating and maintenance costs will be $10,000 per year (today's dollars) and will escalate at 7% per year.

Construct a table showing before-tax cash flows in current dollars and in today's dollars. The inflation rate is 7%.

Solution

| End of | Current Dollars | | | | Today's |
Year	Savings	O & M	Capital	Total	Dollars
0			−100,000	−100,000	−100,000
1	33,000	−10,700		22,300	20,841
2	36,300	−11,449		24,851	21,706
3	39,930	−12,250		27,680	22,595
4	43,923	−13,108		30,815	23,509
5	48,315	−14,026		34,290	24,448
6	53,147	−15,007		38,140	25,414
7	58,462	−16,058		42,404	26,407
8	64,308	−17,182		47,126	27,428
9	70,738	−18,385		52,354	28,477
10	77,812	−19,672	20,000	78,141	39,723

14-10
A project that was analyzed under the assumption of 6% inflation was found to have a monetary internal rate of return (IRR) of 22%. What is the real IRR for the project?

Solution

Real IRR = (1.22)/(1.06) – 1 = 0.1509, or 15.09%

14-11
A company requires a real MARR of 12%. What monetary MARR should be used if inflation is expected to be 7%?

Solution

Monetary MARR = (1.12)(1.07) – 1 = 0.1984, or 19.84%

14-12
The real interest rate is 4%. The inflation rate is 8%. What is the apparent interest rate?

Solution

$i = i' + f + i'$

= 0.04 + 0.08 + 0.04(0.08) = 12.32%

14-13
A lot purchased for $4500 is held for 5 years and sold for $13,500. The average annual property tax is $45 and may be accounted for at an interest rate of 12%. The income tax rate on the long-term capital gain is 15% of the gain. What is the rate of return on the investment if the allowance for inflation is treated at an average annual rate of 7%?

Solution

Long-term gain = 13,500 – 4,500 = 9,000
Tax on long-term gain = (0.15)(9000) = 1350
Property tax = 45(*F/A*, 12%, 5) = 285.89

Adjusted FW = 13,500 – 1350 – 285.89 = 11,864.12
  also FW = $4500(1 + i_{eq})^5$

$$\therefore \left(1 + i_{eq}\right) = \left(\tfrac{11,648.12}{4500}\right)^{\frac{1}{5}} = 1.214$$

$$\left(1 + i_{eq}\right) = \left(1 + i\right)\left(1 + i_f\right)$$

$$1 + i = \frac{1.214}{1.075} = 1.129 \text{ or } 12.9\% \text{ rate of retrun}$$

14-14

A solar energy book gives values for a solar heating system as follows: initial cost, $6500; initial fuel savings, $500/year; expected life, 15 years; value of money, 10%; inflation, 12%; and incremental income tax rate, 25%. If we define the payback condition as the time required for the present worth of the accumulated benefit to equal the accumulated present worth of the system cost, what is the time required to reach the payback condition? Since the income tax benefit is related to the annual interest expense, treat it as a reduction of the annual cost.

Solution

Annualizing P: $A = 6500(A/P, 10\%, 15)$
$$= \$854.75$$

$1 + i_C = (1.10)(1 + 0.25 \times 0.10) = 1.1275$

PW of costs $= 854.75(P/A, 12.75\%, 15) = 5595.82$

$$1 + i_{eq} = \frac{1 + i_f}{1 + i} = \frac{1.12}{1.10} = 1.018$$

The solution strategy is to find the time for the PW of benefits to equal the PW of cost. When the combined effects of the two rates on a distributed amount A are opposed, then the net effect retains the direction of the longer rate. The inflation rate is greater than the time value of money, which is abnormal. To solve this problem, find the PW of benefit, and to do that we must get FW of the equivalent rate, i_{eq}.

Try 10 years: FW $= 500(F/A, 1.8\%, 10) = 500\ (10.850) = \$5425.06$
Try 11 years: FW $= 500(F/A, 1.8\%, 11) = 500\ (12.045) = \$6022.72$

10 years < Payback < 11 years   By interpolation, Payback = 10.3 years

14-15

Compute the internal rate of return based on constant (Year-0) dollars for the following after-tax cash flow given in current or actual dollars. Inflation is assumed to be 7% per year. (Round to the nearest dollar.)

Year	After-Tax Cash Flow in Actual Dollars
1998 (Year 0)	−$10,000
1999	3,745
2000	4,007
2001	4,288
2002	4,588

Solution

	After-Tax Cash Flow
Year	in Constant Dollars
1998 (0)	–$10,000
1999 (1)	$3745(1.07)^{-1} = 3500$
2000 (2)	$4007(1.02)^{-2} = 3500$
2001 (3)	$4288(1.07)^{-3} = 3500$
2002 (4)	$4588(1.07)^{-4} = 3500$

NPW = 0 at IRR:

$$0 = -10,000 + 3500(P/A, i\%, 4)$$
$$(P/A, i\%, 4) = 10,000/3500$$
$$= 2.857$$

Searching the interest tables, where $n = 4$, you find $i = $ IRR = 15%.

14-16

The capital cost of a wastewater treatment plant for a small town of 6000 people was estimated to be about $85/person in 1969. If a modest estimate of the rate of inflation is 5.5% for the period to 1984, what was the per capita capital cost of the treatment plant in 1984?

Solution

$$F = P(1+ i_f)^n$$
$$= 85(1 + 0.055)^{15}$$
$$= 85(2.232)$$
$$= \$189.76$$

14-17

Minor Oil Co. owns several gas wells and is negotiating a 10-year contract to sell the gas from these wells to Major Oil Co. The firms are negotiating on the price of the gas per thousand cubic feet (KCF) for the first year, and on the escalation clause, the percentage rate of increase in the price every year thereafter. Minor expects the wells to produce 33,000 KCF the first year, declining at the rate of 18% every year thereafter. Minor has agreed to spend $500,000 now to lay pipelines from each well to Major's nearby refinery. What should the minimum price be the first year, and what should the escalation rate be if Minor wants the revenue each year to remain constant (uniform) over the life of the contract?   Assume an end-of-year convention and a minimum attractive rate of return (MARR) of 15%.

Solution

Required annual income to earn the 15% MARR on $500,000:

EAB = 500,000(A/P, 15%, 10) = $99,650.

First-year price = $99,650/33,000 = $3.02/KCF

Annual production declines (1 – 0.18) of initial rate each year.

Let f = required annual escalation rate

Then (1 – 0.18)(1 + f) = 1 to keep the revenue constant
$$f = 1/(1 – 0.18) – 1$$
$$= 0.2195/\text{year}$$

14-18

Jack purchases a lot for $40,000 cash and plans to sell it after 5 years. What should he sell it for if he wants a 20% before-tax rate of return, after taking the 5% annual inflation rate into account?

Solution

F = 40,000(F/P, 20%, 5)(F/P, 5%, 5)
   = $126,988

14-19

Undeveloped property near the planned site of an interstate highway is estimated to be worth $48,000 in 6 years when the construction of the highway will be completed. Consider a 15% capital gains tax on the gain, an annual property tax of 0.85% of the purchase price, an annual inflation rate of 7%, and an expected return of 15% on the investment. What is the indicated maximum purchase price now?

Solution

Let X = purchase cost

$1 + i_{eq}$ = (1.15)(1.07) = 1.231

Annual property tax = 0.0085X
FW of property tax = 0.0085X(F/A, 23.1%, 6) = 0.0909X

Adjusted return = 48,000 – 0.15(48,000 – X) – 0.0909X

Also = X(1.231)^6 = 3.48X

Therefore,   40,800 + 0.15X – 0.0909X = 3.48X
$$X = \$11,927 \text{ purchase price}$$

14-20
A solar heating system costs $6500 initially and qualifies for a federal tax credit (40% of cost, not to exceed $4000). The cost of money is 10%, and inflation is expected to be 7% during the life of the system. The expected life of the system is 15 years with zero salvage value. The homeowner is in the 40% income tax bracket. The initial (first-year) fuel saving, estimated at $500, is expected to increase in response to inflation. The annual maintenance cost of the system is established at 5% of the annualized cost of the system. What is the time required for the payback condition to be reached for this investment?

Solution

Adjust initial cost by tax credit: $P = 0.60(6500) = 3900$

Annualized cost: $A = 3900(A/P, 10\%, 15) = 512.85$

$1 + i_c = 1.10[1 + 40(0.10)]/1.05 = 1.0895$
$1 + i_m = 1.05$ represents maintenance charge as a rate

PW of costs $= 512.85(P/A, 8.95\%, 15) = 512.85(8.086) = 4146.67$

$1 + i_{eq} = (1 + i)/(1 + i_f) = 1.10/1.07 = 1.028$

Try 9 years: PW $= 500 \ (P/A, 2.8\%, n) = 500(7.868) = \$3934.18$
Try 10 years: PW $= 500 \ (P/A, 2.8\%, n) = 500(8.618) = \$4308.97$

9 years < Payback < 10 years   By interpolation, Payback = 9.6 years

14-21
The net cost of a home solar heating system, expected to last for 20 years, is $8000. If the value of money is 10%, inflation is expected to be 8%, and the initial annual fuel saving is $750, what is the time for the payback condition to be reached for the system? Assume that the homeowner is in the 30% income tax bracket.

Solution

Annualize P: $A = 8000 \ (A/P, 10\%, 20) = 940$

$1 + i_c = (1.10)[1 + 0.10(0.30)] = 1.133$

PW of cost $= 940(P/A, 13.3\%, 20) = 940(6.900) = 6486$

$1 + i_{eq} = (1 + i)/(1 + i_f) = 1.10/1.08 = 1.0185$

Try 9 years: PW $= 940(P/A, 1.85\%, n) = \$6171$
Try 10 years: PW $= 940(P/A, 1.85\%, n) = \$6790$

9 years < Payback < 10 years   By interpolation, Payback = 9.5 years.

14-22

An undeveloped parcel of land in Gibson County, Tennessee, was purchased in 1980 for $4850. The property tax, which was $8 for the first year, increased by $2 per year each year thereafter. The capital gain tax is 13.6% of long-term capital gain. Inflation for the period is an 8% annual rate. A 16% rate of return on the investment is desired. What was the required sale price in 1985?

Solution

$1 + i_{eq} = 1 + (1.16)(1.08) = 1.2528$

Adjusted purchase price = 4850(1.2528) = 14,967.54

FW of property tax = [8 + 2(*A/G*, 25.28%, 5)] [*F/A*, 25.28%, 5]
 = [8 + 2(3.12)](8.252)
 = 91.74

Let X = selling price

Long-term capital gains tax = $0.136(X - 4850) = 0.136X - 659.60$

Adjusted return = $X - [0.136X - 659.60 + 91.74] = 0.864X + 567.86$

$0.864X + 567.86 = 14,967.54$
$0.864X = 14,399.68$
$X = \$16,666.31$ selling price

14-23

The apparent interest rate is 9.18% and the real interest rate is 6%. The inflation rate is

a. 3.00%
b. 3.18%
c. 5.30%
d. 6.00%

Solution

$i = i' + f + i'f$
$0.0918 = 0.06 + f + 0.06f$
$0.0318 = 1.06f$
$f = 0.03$

The answer is a.

14-24

An investor is considering the purchase of a bond. The bond has a face value of $1000 and an interest rate of 6%; it pays interest once a year and matures in 8 years. This investor's real MARR is 25%. If the investor expects an inflation rate of 4% per year for the next 8 years, how much should he be willing to pay for the bond?

a. $250.50
b. $367.50
c. $384.74
d. $1 000.00

Solution

To earn a real 25% return with inflation of 4%, the nominal MARR must be equal to $(1.25)(1.04) - 1 = 30\%$,

$$NPV = 0 \text{ at IRR}$$
$$0 = -FC + 60(P/A, 30\%, 8) + 1000(P/F, 30\%, 8)$$
$$FC = \$250.50$$

The answer is a.

14-25

A $9000 investment in undeveloped land was held for 4 years and sold for $21,250. During this time property tax was paid that amounted, on the average, to 0.4% of the purchase price. Inflation in this time period averaged 7% and the income tax was 15.2% of the long-term capital gain. What rate of return was obtained on the investment?

Solution

Long-term capital gains tax = $0.152(21,250 - 9000) = \$1862$

Property tax = $0.004 \times 9000 = \$36$/year

FW of property tax = $36(F/A, i_{eq}, 4)$

$$1 + i_{eq} = \left(\frac{21,250 - 1,862}{9000}\right)^{\frac{1}{4}} = 1.2115 \quad (1^{st} \text{ estimate})$$

FW of property tax = $36(F/A, 21.15\%, 4) = 36(5.47) = \$197$

$$1 + i_{eq} = \left(\frac{21,250 - 1,862 - 197}{9000}\right)^{\frac{1}{4}} = 1.2084 \quad (2^{nd} \text{ estimate})$$

Rate of return = $\left(\frac{1.2084}{1.07}\right) - 1 = 12.9\%$

14-26

A company has designed a VLSI circuit and a production system to manufacture it. It is believed that it can sell 100,000 circuits per year if the price in then-current dollars is cut 20% per year (for example, if the unit price in the first year is $100, then the price in Years 2 through 5 would be $80, $64, $51.20, and $40.96). The required revenue for the 5 years is $2500 per year in today's dollars. The real and monetary costs of capital are 8.8% and 16.416%, respectively. What should the then-current dollar selling price be in each of the Years 1 through 5?

Solution

Let R be the required revenue in Year 1; then the required revenue in Years 2 through 5 is $0.8R$, $0.64R$, $0.512R$, and $0.0496R$. Since these are in then-current dollars,

$$(2{,}500{,}000)(P/A, 8.8\%, 5) = R(1.16416)^{-1} + 0.8R(1.16416)^{-2} + 0.064R(1.16416)^{-3}$$
$$+ 0.512R(1.16416)^{-4} + 0.4096R(1.16416)^{-5}$$
$$9{,}774{,}800 = 2.32523R$$

$R = 4{,}203{,}804$, or a unit price of $42.04 in Year 1
                                              $33.63 in Year 2
                                              $26.90 in Year 3
                                              $21.52 in Year 4
                                              $17.22 in Year 5

14-27

An electronic device cost $1250 in 2001. If inflation has averaged 2% each year, the price of the device in 2008 was closest to

a. $1400
b. $1408
c. $1425
d. $1436

Solution

$$F = (1 + f)^n$$
$$F = (1 + 0.02)^7$$
$$= \$1435.86$$

The answer is d.

14-28

A bond that pays no interest is called a zero-coupon bond. A $10,000 zero-coupon bond that matures in 10 years can be purchased today. If the expected annual rate of inflation is 3% and the buyer's unadjusted MARR is 8%, what is the maximum that should be paid for the bond?

Solution

$$i = i' + f + i'f$$
$$= 0.08 + 0.03 + 0.08(0.03)$$
$$= 0.1124$$

$$P = 10,000(1 + 0.1124)^{-10}$$
$$= \$3446.59$$

14-29
Sylvia B. bought an 8% tax-free municipal bond. The cost of the bond was \$10,000, and it will pay \$800 each year for 20 years. The bond will mature at that time, returning the original \$10,000. If inflation is expected to average 3% during the period, what is the inflation-adjusted rate of return?

a.   2.40%
b.   4.85%
c.   8.00%
d.   11.24%

Solution

$$i = 8\% \quad f = 3\%$$
$$i = i' + f + i'f$$
$$0.08 = i' + 0.03 + i'(0.03)$$
$$i' = 0.0485 = 4.85\%$$

The answer is b.

14-30
A vacant lot is purchased for \$20,000. After 5 years the lot is to be offered for sale. If the buyer requires a before-tax return on investments of 15% and inflation has averaged 4% per year over the 5-year period, the required selling price is nearest to

a.   \$30,650
b.   \$31,500
c.   \$48,950
d.   \$62,750

Solution

$$F = 20,000(F/P, 4\%, 5)(F/P, 15\%, 5)$$
$$= \$48,947.74$$

The answer is c.

Chapter 15

Selection of a Minimum Attractive Rate of Return

15-1
The capital structure of a firm is as follows.

Source of Capital	Percent of Capitalization	Interest Rate
Loans	35	7%
Bonds	40	8%
Common stock	25	10%

The combined state and federal income tax rate for the firm is 42%. Find the after-tax and before-tax costs of capital to the firm.

Solution

Before-tax cost of capital
$$(0.35 \times 7\%) + (0.40 \times 8\%) + (0.25 \times 10\%) = 8.15\%$$

After-tax cost of capital
$$(0.35 \times 7\%)(1 - 0.42) + (0.40 \times 8\%)(1 - 0.42) + (0.25 \times 10\%) = 5.78\%$$

15-2
A small surveying company identifies its available independent alternatives as follows.

	Alternative	Initial Cost	Rate of Return
A:	Repair existing equipment	$1000	30%
B:	Buy EDM instrument	2500	9%
C:	Buy a new printer	3000	11%
D:	Buy equipment for an additional crew	3000	15%
E:	Buy programmable calculator	500	25%

The owner of the company has $5000 of savings currently invested in securities yielding 8% that could be used for the company.

a. Assuming that the funds are limited to the owner's savings, what is the apparent cutoff rate of return?

b. If the owner can borrow money at 10%, how big a loan should she undertake?

Solution

a.

Alt.	Investment	Cumulative Investment	IRR	
A	$1000	$ 1,000	30%	
E	500	1,500	25%	
D	3000	4,500	15%	← Cutoff rate of return
C	3000	7,500	11%	= 11–15%
B	2500	10,000	9%	

b.   Do all projects with a rate of return exceeding 10%. Thus Alternatives *A*, *E*, *D*, and *C*, with a total initial cost of $7500, would be selected. Since only $5000 is available, $2500 would need to be borrowed.

15-3
Abby Industries, Inc. has the following capital structure.

Type	Amount	Average Minimum Return
Mortgages	$ 25,000,000	7%
Bonds	180,000,000	9%
Common stock	100,000,000	10%
Preferred stock	50,000,000	8%
Retained earnings	120,000,000	10%

Determine the weighted average cost of capital (WACC) for Abby.

Solution

$$\text{WACC} = \frac{25M(.07) + 180M(.09) + 100M(.10) + 50M(.08) + 120M(.10)}{(25M + 180M + 100M + 50M + 120M)} = 9.25\%$$

15-4
Barber Brewing is in the process of determining the capital budget for the coming year. The following projects are under consideration.

	A	B	C	D
First cost	$10,000	$13,000	$20,000	$33,000
Annual income	10,000	9,078	16,000	16,455
Annual cost	7,362	5,200	11,252	7,300

All projects have a 5-year useful life. If Barber's budget is set at $50,000, which alternative(s) should be selected?

Solution

NPW = 0 at IRR.

$0 = -FC +$ Net Income $(P/A, i\%, 5)$ Therefore $(P/A, i\%, 5) = FC/$Net Income

			Rank
IRR_A	$P/A = 10,000/2638 = 3.791$	IRR = 10%	3
IRR_B	$P/A = 13,000/3878 = 3.352$	IRR = 15%	1
IRR_C	$P/A = 20,000/4748 = 4.212$	IRR = 6%	4
IRR_D	$P/A = 33,000/9155 = 3.605$	IRR = 12%	2

Choose projects B and D. Total = $13,000 + 33,000 = \$46,000$.

15-5

A small construction company identifies the following alternatives, which are independent except where noted.

	Alternative	Initial Cost	Incremental Rate of Return	On Investment Over
1.	Repair bulldozer	$5,000	30.0%	0
2.	Replace backhoe			
	with Model A	20,000	15.0%	0
	with Model B	25,000	10.5%	$2A$
3.	Buy new dump truck			
	Model X	20,000	20.0%	0
	Model Y	30,000	14.0%	$3X$
4.	Buy computer			
	Model K	5,000	12.0%	0
	Model L	10,000	9.5%	$4K$

a. Assuming that the company has $55,000 available for investment and is not able to borrow money, what alternatives should be chosen, and what is opportunity coast of capital?

b. If, however, the company can borrow money at 10%, how much should be borrowed, and which alternatives should be selected?

Solution

Rank the alternatives by ΔROR:

Project	Incremental Investment	Cumulative Investment	ΔIRR
1	$ 5,000	$ 5,000	30.0%
3X	20,000	25,000	20.0%
2A	20,000	45,000	15.0%
3Y – 3X	10,000	55,000	14.0%
4K	5,000	60,000	12.0%
2B – 2A	5,000	65,000	10.5%
4L – 4K	5,000	70,000	9.5%

a. With $55,000 available, choose projects:

1	Repair bulldozer
2A	Backhoe Model A
3Y	Dump truck Model Y
	No computer

Opportunity cost of capital = 14%.

b. Borrow $10,000. Choose projects:

1	Repair bulldozer
2B	Backhoe Model B
3Y	Dump truck Model Y
4K	Computer Model K

15-6
The following independent and indivisible investment opportunities are available.

Investment	Initial Cost	Rate of Return
A	$200	20%
B	100	22%
C	50	19%
D	100	18%
E	50	15%
F	Unlimited	7%

a. Which investment(s) should be selected if the minimum attractive rate of return (MARR) is greater than or equal to 18%, assuming an unlimited budget?

b. Which investment(s) should be selected if the available budget is $400 and the MARR is greater than or equal to 14%?

Solution

a. $A, B, C, D \rightarrow$ Choose all IRRs $\geq$ 18%, since budget is unlimited.

b. $A, B, D \rightarrow$ Choose D instead of C because D yields a greater overall return and fully
     invests the $400 budget.

Investment	Initial Cost	Return	Return in $
A	$200	20%	$40.00
B	100	22%	22.00
C	50	19%	9.50
D	100	18%	18.00

Total $ return on $A + B + C = 40 + 22 + 9.50 + 50(0.14)* = \$78.50$
Total $ return on $A + B + D = 40 + 22 + 18 = \$80.00$

*Assumes the remaining $50 can be invested at the MARR. This is not always true.
 Thus the $ return could be even lower.

15-7
A city engineer calculated the present worth of benefits and costs of a number of possible projects,
based on 10% interest and a 10-year analysis period.

Costs and Benefits ($1000s)

Project:	A	B	C	D	E	F	G
Present Worth of Costs	75	70	50	35	60	25	70
Present Worth of Benefits	105	95	63	55	76	32	100

If 10% is a satisfactory minimum attractive rate of return (MARR), and $180,000 is available for
expenditure, which project(s) should be selected?

Solution

Project:	A	B	C	D	E	F	G
Present Worth of Costs	75	70	50	35	60	25	70
Present Worth of Benefits	105	95	63	55	76	32	100
NPW	30	25	13	20	16	7	30
NPW/C	.400	.357	.260	.571	.267	.280	.428
Rank	3	4	7	1	6	5	2

$D + G + A = 35K + 70K + 75K = \$180K$

Choose Projects D, G, and A.

15-8

The CFO of Republic Express (RepEx) has asked each regional manager to submit requests for capital outlays for the next fiscal year. The company's CEO has decided to fund the top request from each region and to fund two additional requests with the provision that no region may have more than two projects funded. Using the information provided, determine which projects should be funded.

Region	Project	Cost	Annual Benefit	Life (years)
Southeastern (SE)	A	$ 90,000	$16,400	15
	B	40,000	15,000	5
	C	60,000	20,400	5
	D	120,000	27,600	20
Midwest (MW)	A	50,000	10,000	20
	B	120,000	36,700	15
	C	75,000	21,600	5
	D	50,000	16,200	5
Northeastern (NE)	A	50,000	16,700	20
	B	80,000	23,500	5
	C	75,000	26,100	10
Western (W)	A	60,000	16,900	15
	B	50,000	15,300	10

Solution

Region	Project	Cost	IRR
Southeastern (SE)	A	$ 90,000	16.3%
	B	40,000	25.4
	C	60,000	20.8
	D	120,000	22.6
Midwest (MW)	A	50,000	19.4
	B	120,000	30.0
	C	75,000	13.5
	D	50,000	18.6
Northeastern (NE)	A	50,000	33.3
	B	80,000	14.4
	C	75,000	32.8
Western (W)	A	60,000	27.4
	B	50,000	28.0

Choose (SE)*B*, (MW)*B*, (NE)*A*, (W)*B*, (NE)*C*, and (W)*A*.

Capital budget = 40,000 + 120,000 + 50,000 + 50,000 + 75,000 + 60,000
= $395,000

Chapter 16

Economic Analysis
in the
Public Sector

16-1
A city engineer is considering installing an irrigation system at the city park's soccer fields. He is trying to decide which one of two alternatives to select. The two alternatives have the following cash flows:

Year	A	B
0	–$15,000	–$25,000
1–10	+5,310	+7,900

If interest is 12%, which alternative should the engineer select? Assume no salvage value. Use incremental benefit/cost analysis.

Solution

	$\underline{A}$	$\underline{B}$
PW$_{COST}$	–15,000	–25,000
PW$_{BENEFITS}$	5310(P/A, 12%, 10) = 30,000	7900(P/A, 12%, 10) = 44,635
B/C ratio	30,000/15,000 = 2	44,635/25,000 = 1.79

$\underline{B-A}$

ΔCost = –10,000

PW$_{COST}$ = –10,000

ΔAnnual benefits = +2590

$$PW_{BENEFITS} = 2590(P/A, 12\%, 10)$$

$$= 14,634$$

$\Delta B/C = 14,634/10,000 = 1.46$

1.46 > 1; therefore choose B, the higher-cost alternative.

16-2

At 10% interest, what is the benefit/cost ratio for the following government project?

Initial cost	$2,000,000
Additional costs at end of Years 1 & 2	30,000
Benefits at end of Years 1 & 2	0
Annual benefits at end of Years 3–10	90,000

Solution

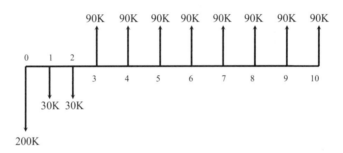

PW_{COST} $= 200K + 30K(P/A, 10\%, 2) = 252,080$

$PW_{BENEFITS}$ $= 90K(P/A, 10\%, 8)(P/F, 10\%, 2) = 396,800$

B/C $= 396,800/252,080$
$= 1.574$

16-3

The city of Tumbleweed has just purchased new traffic enforcement equipment for $18,000. The equipment is anticipated to generate revenues of $25,000 per year and expenses of $15,000 per year in each of the 5 years it will be in use. The salvage value is expected to equal any removal costs. Ignoring income taxes, compute the benefit/cost ratio if $i = 10\%$.

Solution

$PW_{BENEFITS}$ $= 25,000(P/A, 10\%, 5) = \$94,775$

PW_{COSTS} $= 15,000(P/A, 10\%, 5) + 18,000 = \$74,865$

B/C $= 94,775/74,865$
$= 1.2659$

16-4

A tax-exempt municipality is considering the construction of an impoundment for city water supplies. Two different sites have been selected as technically, politically, socially, and financially feasible. The city council has asked you to do a benefit/cost analysis of the alternatives and recommend one of the sites. The city uses a 6% interest rate in all analyses of this type.

Year	Rattlesnake Canyon	Blue Basin
0	–$15,000,000	–$27,000,000
1–75	+2,000,000	+3,000,000

Which site should you recommend?

Solution

	Rattlesnake	Blue Basin
$\dfrac{PW_{BEBEFITS}}{PW_{COSTS}}$ =	$\dfrac{(2)\times10^6\,(P/A,6\%,75)}{(15)\times10^6}$	$\dfrac{(3)\times10^6\,(P/A,6\%,75)}{(27)\times10^6}$
B/C ratio =	2.19 >1 (OK)	1.83 > 1 (OK)

Incremental analysis:

Year	BB – RC
0	–12,000,000
1–75	+1,000,000

$$\text{B/C ratio} \quad = \quad \frac{(1)\times10^6\,(P/A,6\%,75)}{(12)\times10^6} \quad = 1.37 > 1$$

$\therefore$ Choose the higher-cost alternative, Blue Basin.

16-5

The city council of Arson, Michigan, is debating whether to buy a new fire truck to increase protection for the city. The financial analyst has prepared the following data.

	Truck A	Truck B
First cost	$50,000	$60,000
Annual maintenance	5,000	4,000
Salvage value	6,000	6,000
Annual reduction in fire damage	20,000	21,000
Useful life	7 years	7 years

a. Use the modified B/C ratio method to determine whether the city should buy a new truck, and if so, which one to buy, assuming that it will be paid for with money borrowed at an interest rate 7%.

b. How would the decision be affected if inflation were considered? Assume that maintenance cost, salvage value, and fire damage are responsive to inflation.

Solution

a.   In the modified B/C ratio, all annual cash flows are placed in the numerator, while first cost and salvage are placed in the denominator. Either present worth or uniform equivalent methods may be used to relate cash flows.

$$\left(\frac{B}{C}\right)_A = \frac{20,000-5000}{50,000(A/P,7\%,7)-5000(A/F,7\%,7)} = 1.72\,(>1) \qquad \therefore A \text{ is acceptable}$$

$$\left(\frac{B}{C}\right)_B = \frac{21,000-4000}{60,000(A/P,7\%,7)-6000(A/F,7\%,7)} = 1.63\,(>1) \qquad \therefore B \text{ is acceptable}$$

$$\left(\frac{B}{C}\right)_{B-A} = \frac{(21,000-20,000)-(4000-5000)}{10,000(A/P,7\%,7)} = 1.08\,(>1) \qquad \therefore B \text{ is better than } A$$

Truck *B* should be purchased.

b.   Since both future costs (maintenance) and benefits (reduced damage and salvage) are responsive to inflation, the decision is not affected by inflation.

16-6
Four mutually exclusive alternatives, each with a useful life of 20 years and no salvage value, have been presented to the city council of Anytown, U.S.A. Which alternative should be selected?

	A	*B*	*C*	*D*
PW of costs	$4000	$ 9,000	$6000	$2000
PW of benefits	6480	11,250	5700	4700

Solution

	A	*B*	*C*	*D*
B/C ratio =	1.62	2.35	0.95	2.35

$$C < 1 \therefore \text{ eliminate}$$

(rearrange by PW of costs)	*D*	*A*	*B*
PW of cost	$2000	$4000	$ 9,000
PW of benefits	4700	6480	11,250

	A − D
ΔB	$1780
ΔC	2000

$\Delta B/\Delta C = 0.89 < 1.0 \therefore$ Choose *D*, the least expensive alternative.

	B − D
ΔB	$6550
ΔC	7000

$\Delta B/\Delta C = 0.94 < 1.0 \therefore$ Choose *D*, the least expensive alternative.

16-7

Gordon City is considering the construction of a new garbage dump on the outskirts of town. Land acquisition will cost $85,000. Earthwork and other construction required to prepare the site will cost $250,000. Environmental inspection prior to use will cost $15,000. The upkeep and operating costs for the dump are expected to total $50,000 per year during its anticipated 8-year life. The new dump will result in a reduction of $6 in the average annual garbage disposal fee for each of the 27,000 customers it will serve. (Assume that the number of customers will remain relatively constant during the life of the dump.) Changes in the environmental conditions adjacent to the dump will result in an annual cost to the surrounding area estimated at $32,000. At the end of the useful life the dump must be "capped" at a cost of $75,000. Determine the benefit/cost ratio if Gordon City uses 4% as its cost of money.

Solution

$AW_C = 350,000(A/P, 4\%, 8) + 50,000 + 75,000(A/F, 4\%\ 8)$
     $= \$130,000$
$AW_B = (6 \times 27,000) - 32,000$ 32,000 is considered a disbenefit (reduction in benefits)
     $= \$110,112.50$

B/C ratio $= 130,000/110,112.50$
     $= 1.18$

16-8

The local city recorder is deciding between two different phone-answering systems for her office. The information concerning the two machines is as follows.

Machine	Cost	Annual Savings	Useful Life	Salvage
X	$1000	$300	5 years	$0
Y	1200	325	5 years	0

With an assumed interest rate of 12%, which system would you recommend?

Solution

Machine *X*: $PW_C = \$1000$
                $PW_B = \$300(P/A, 12\%, 5) = \$1081.50$

     B/C ratio $= 1.0815/1000 = 1.0815$

Machine *Y*: $PW_C = \$1200$
                $PW_B = \$325(P/A, 12\%, 5) = \$1171.63$

     B/C ratio $= 1171.63/1200 = .9763$ $\therefore$ Select machine *X*.

16-9

A city engineer is deciding which of two bids for a new computer to accept. Using benefit/cost analysis, which alternative should be selected if the interest rate is 10% per year?

Computer	Cost	Annual Benefits	Salvage	Useful Life
A	$48,000	$13,000	$0	6 years
B	40,000	12,000	0	6 years

Solution

Alternative *A*
$PW_B = 13,000(P/A, 10\%, 6) = \$56,615$
$PW_C = 48,000$

$B/C = 56,615/48,000 = 1.179$ (OK)

Alternative *B*
$PW_B = 12,000(P/A, 10\%, 6) = \$52,260$
$PW_C = 40,000$

$B/C = 52,260/40,000 = 1.3065$ (OK)

Incremental analysis

$$\frac{\Delta B}{\Delta C} = \frac{56,516-52,260}{48,000-40,000} = \frac{4355}{8000} = 0.544$$

$\frac{\Delta B}{\Delta C} < 1.0$ ∴ Select the less costly alternative, *B*.

16-10

The Tennessee Department of Highways (TDOH) is considering building its first "tolled bypass" around the town of Greenfield, Tennessee. The initial cost of the bypass is estimated to be $5.7 million. The installation of the tollbooths along the bypass is estimated to cost $1.3 million. The annual maintenance cost of the bypass is expected to be $105,000 while the annual costs associated with the tollbooths are expected to be $65,000 each year. The construction of the bypass is expected to yield Greenfield estimated tax revenues of $225,000 per year. In addition, TDOH has projected user savings of $100,000 each year. Each user of the bypass is will pay a toll of $0.90. TDOH estimates that there will be a total of 500,000 users of the bypass each year. Other relevant data are are follows.

Resurfacing cost (every 7 years)	4% of bypass initial cost
Shoulder grading/rework	90% of resurfacing cost

If the state uses an interest rate of 7%, should the "tolled bypass" be constructed? Assume perpetual life.

Solution

Use benefit/cost analysis. (Use AW analysis.)

Benefits

Annual tax revenues	$225,000.00
Bypass user annual savings	$100,000.00
Tollbooth revenue $0.90(500,000)	$450,000.00
	AW_B = $ 775,000.00

Costs

Tollbooth first cost $1,300,000($A/P$, 7%, ∞)	$ 91,000.00
Bypass first cost $5,700,000($A/P$, 7%, ∞)	$399,000.00
Tollbooth maintenance	$ 65,000.00
Bypass maintenance	$105,000.00
Resurfacing 0.04($5,700,000($A/P$, 7%, 7))	$ 26,536.80
Shoulder grading/rework 0.90{0.04[$5,700,000($A/P$, 7%, 7)]}	$ 23,721.12
	AW_C = $710,257.92

B/C = 775,000/710,275.92 = 1.0912

∴ The bypass should be constructed.

16-11

The town of Oakville is evaluating a proposal to erect and operate a structure for parking in the downtown area. Numerous design proposals were considered. Data for the two best proposals are as follows.

	Design *A*	Design *B*
Cost of site and construction	$2,220,000	$1,850,000
Annual revenue from parking fees	765,000	575,000
Annual maintenance cost	410,000	295,000
Service life	20 years	20 years

At the end of each 5-year period, the parking facility will require a maintenance overhaul. The cost for Design *A* is estimated to be $650,000; for Design *B*, the cost estimate is $375,000. At the end of the service life, the facility will be torn down and the land sold. Demolition costs and proceeds from the sale of the land are as follows.

Demolition costs	$530,000	$550,000
Proceeds from sale of land	530,000	530,000

The city's interest rate is 10%. Determine the B/C ratio of each design proposal.

Solution

Design A

$PW_B = 765,000(P/A, 10\%, 20) = \$6,513,210$

$PW_C = 2,220,000 + 410,000(P/A, 10\%, 20) + 650,000(P/F, 10\%, 5,10, \text{ and } 15) = \$6,500,510$

$$\frac{B}{C} = \frac{\$6,513,210}{\$6,500,510} = 1.001$$

(*Note*: Demolition and proceeds from sale net to $0.)

Design B

$PW_B = 575,000 + 530,000(P/F, 10\%, 20) = \$4,974,308$

$PW_C = 1,850,000 + 295,000(P/A, 10\%, 20) + 375,000(P/F, 10\%, 5, 10, \text{ and } 15)$
$\qquad + 550,000(P/F, 10\%, 20) = \$4,910,535$

$$\frac{B}{C} = \frac{\$4,974,308}{\$4,910,535} = 1.013$$

16-12

A new water treatment plant will cost the city of Frogjump $2,000,000 dollars to build and $100,000 per year to operate for its 20-year life. At the end of 20 years, the salvage value will be 0. Because the new plant will operate more efficiently, the cost of utility bills for each of Frogjump's 6000 customers is expected to be reduced by $50 per year. The amount assigned to the reduction in air quality due to the plant's operation is $5 per resident per year. The population of Frogjump, which is currently 18,000, is expected to remain relatively constant over the life of the plant. If 3% is used for the evaluation of public works projects, should the water treatment plant be built?

Solution

First cost: $2,000,000
Annual operating cost: $100,000/year
Air quality annual cost: $5/year × 18,000 residents = $90,000/year (considered a disbenefit)
Annual benefits: $50/year × 6000 customers = $300,000/year

$AW_B = \$300,000 - 90,000 = 210,000$

$AW_C = \$2,000,000(A/P, 3\%, 20) + 100,000 = \$234,400 \qquad 0.8974$

$\quad B/C = 300,000/342,000 = 0.8772$

$B/C < 1$; therefore, the water treatment plant should not be built.

16-13

A new electric generation plant is expected to cost $43,250,000 to complete. The revenues generated by the new plant are expected to be $3,875,000 per year, while operational expenses are estimated to $2,000,000 per year. If the plant is expected to last 40 years and the electric authority uses 3% as its cost of capital, determine whether the plant should be built.

Solution

$$AW_{BENEFITS} = \$3,875,000$$

$$AW_{COSTS} = 43,500,000(A/P, 3\%, 40) + 2,000,000 = \$3,872,725$$

$$B/C = \frac{AW_{BENEFITS}}{AW_{COSTS}} = \frac{3,875,000}{3,872,725} = 1 \qquad \therefore \text{ Build the plant.}$$

16-14

Mathis City is considering the construction of a municipal park. Land required for the park would be bought in two transactions, the initial purchase and a second purchase for expansion 5 years later. The first land purchase would cost $62,000. The second land purchase would cost $24,000. Construction of the park would take 2 years. In each year of construction, the city is anticipating spending $250,000. When the park is expanded in Year 6 (after the second land purchase at the end of Year 5), the cost is expected to be $80,000.

Various activities at the park (for instance, putt-putt golf) will generate fees paid by users, resulting in annual revenue expected to total $35,000 per year. The monetary value of the citizens' enjoyment of the park is calculated at $26,000 per year. Maintenance and upkeep will be contracted out at a cost of $12,000 per year. The park is expected to be used indefinitely, and Mathis City has a cost of money of 8%. Determine the B/C ratio of the planned park.

Solution

$$AW_B = 35,000 + 26,000$$
$$= \$61,000$$

$$AW_C = 574,550(A/P, 8\%, \infty) + 12,000$$
$$= \$57,964$$

$$PW_C = 62,000 + 24,000(P/F, 8\%, 5) + 250,000(P/F, 8\%, 1) + 250,000(P/F, 8\%, 2)$$
$$+ 80,000(P/F, 8\%, 6)$$
$$= \$574,550$$

$$B/C = 61,000/57,964 = 1.0524$$

16-15

The expansion of the hotel and conference center at Wicker Valley State Park is under study. The initial investment and annual operating benefits and costs are very different because the projects being considered differ greatly in magnitude, as indicated in the tabulation.

	Alternative _A_	Alternative _B_	Alternative _C_
Investment cost	$180,000	$100,000	$280,000
Annual operating costs	16,000	12,000	28,000
Annual benefits	53,000	35,000	77,000

Use a MARR of 10% to determine which alternative should be selected if all three have a 10-year useful life. Use benefit/cost ratio analysis.

Solution

1. B/C ratios of individual alternatives.

$$\left(\frac{B}{C}\right)_A = \frac{AW_B}{AW_C} = \frac{53,000}{180,000(A/P,10\%,10)+16,000} = 1.17\,(>1)$$

$$\left(\frac{B}{C}\right)_B = \frac{AW_B}{AW_C} = \frac{35,000}{100,000(A/P,10\%,10)+12,000} = 1.24\,(>1)$$

$$\left(\frac{B}{C}\right)_C = \frac{AW_B}{AW_C} = \frac{77,000}{280,000(A/P,10\%,10)+28,000} = 1.05(>1)$$

∴ All are economically attractive.

2. Incremental B/C analysis

_A–B_
ΔBenefits = 53,000 – 35,000 = 18,000
ΔCosts   = (180,000 – 1000,000)(A/P, 10%, 10) + (16,000 – 12,000) = 17,016

$$\left(\frac{B}{C}\right)_{A-B} = \frac{18,000}{17,016} = 1.06\,(>1) \qquad ∴ \text{ Choose } A.$$

_C–A_
ΔBenefits = 77,000 – 53,000 = 24,000
ΔCosts   = (280,000 – 180,000)(A/P, 10%, 10) + (28,000 – 16,000) = 28,270

$$\left(\frac{B}{C}\right)_{C-A} = \frac{24,000}{28,270} = 0.85\,(<1) \qquad ∴ \text{ Choose } A.$$

Select Alternative _A_. (If we consider the operating costs as a reduction to the annual benefits, a different numerical value for the B/C ratio might be found. The decision of which alternative is best will, however, be the same.)

16-16

Use benefit/cost ratio analysis to determine which one of the following alternatives should be selected; each has a 6-year useful life. Assume a 10% MARR.

	A	*B*	*C*	*D*
First cost	$880	$560	$700	$900
Annual benefit	240	130	110	250
Annual cost	80	20	0	40
Salvage value	300	200	440	110

Solution

A
$AW_{BENEFITS} = 240 + 300(A/F, 10\%, 6) = 278$
$AW_{COSTS} \quad = 880(A/P, 10\%, 6) + 80 = 282$
$\quad\quad\quad\quad B/C = 0.98$ (< 1, so eliminate Alternative *A*)

B
$AW_{BENEFITS} = 130 + 200(A/F, 10\%, 6) = 155.9$
$AW_{COSTS} \quad = 560(A/P, 10\%, 6) + 20 = 148.57$
$\quad\quad\quad B/C = 1.04$

C
$AW_{BENEFITS} = 110 + 440(A/F, 10\%, 6) = 167$
$AW_{COSTS} \quad = 700(A/P, 10\%, 6) + 0 = 160$
$\quad\quad\quad B/C = 1.04$

D
$AW_{BENEFITS} = 250 + 110(A/F, 10\%, 6) = 264$
$AW_{COSTS} \quad = 900(A/P, 10\%, 6) + 40 = 246$
$\quad\quad\quad B/C = 1.07$

D–C
$AW_{BENEFITS} = (250 - 110) + (110 - 440) \, (A/F, 10\%, 6) = 97$
$AW_{COSTS} \quad = (900 - 700)(A/P, 10\%, 6) + (40 - 0) = 85$
$\quad\quad\quad\quad B/C = 1.14 \quad \therefore \text{ Choose } D.$

D–B
$AW_{BENEFITS} = (250 - 130) + (110 - 200) \, (A/F, 10\%, 6) = 108$
$AW_{COSTS} \quad = (900 - 560)(A/P, 10\%, 6) + (40 - 20) = 98$
$\quad\quad\quad\quad B/C = 1.10 \quad \therefore \text{ Choose } D.$

16-17

Froggy University is considering the purchase of a new garbage incinerator. The "best" alternative costs $55,000 and is expected to save Froggy U. $6000 in garbage fees during the first year, with the savings increasing by $750 each year thereafter. The incinerator will result in a decrease of the air quality around campus, which is estimated to be worth $1000 per year. The incinerator will have no salvage value at the end of its 10-year useful life. If Froggy U. evaluates all capital outlays with a 6% interest and requires B/C analysis, what would you recommend?

Solution

Consider the air quality value to be a disbenefit.

$$\frac{B}{C} = \frac{6000 + 750(A/G,6\%,10) - 1000}{55,000(A/P,6\%,10)} = 1.07 \; (>1) \qquad \therefore \text{ Purchase the incinerator.}$$

6-18

Drygulch is considering damming the nearby Twisted River to create a recreational lake for the community. The earthen dam under consideration has an anticipated cost of $1,000,000. Every 10 years the lake will have to be drained and the dam reworked at an estimated cost of $100,000. The annual expense of operating associated with the lake and the surrounding area is estimated to be $20,000. Drygulch has forecast that the lake will be used by an average of 8000 persons annually. The monetary benefit to each user has been calculated to be $7.75. A fee of $6 will be charged to each of the boats that launch into the lake; an annual total of 1200 boats is estimated. At an interest rate of 4%, determine whether Drygulch should build the dam.

Solution

$$AW_B = (8000 \times 7.75) + (1200 \times 6.00)$$
$$= \$69,200$$

$$AW_C = 1,000,000(A/P, 4\%, \infty) + 100,000(A/F, 4\%, 10) + 20,000$$
$$= \$68,330$$

$$B/C = 69,200/68,330$$
$$= 1.01 \qquad \therefore \text{ Build the dam.}$$

6-19

Two different water delivery methods are available to supply the town of Dry-Hole with much-needed water. Use an interest rate of 6% and the appropriate analysis for public projects to determine which of the following methods should be chosen.

	Deep Well	Canal
First cost	$435,000	$345,000
Annual M & O costs	18,000	25,500
Useful life	20 years	20 years

Solution

$$\left(\frac{B}{C}\right)_{DW-C} = \frac{7500(P/A,6\%,20)}{90,000} = .96 \; (<1) \qquad \therefore \text{ Build the canal}$$

Chapter 17

Accounting
and
Engineering Economy

17-1

The following information has been taken from the financial statements available for the ABC Company.

Accounts payable	$ 4,000
Accounts receivable	12,000
Income taxes	6,000
Owner's equity	75,000
Cost of goods sold	42,000
Selling expense	10,000
Sales revenue	80,000

Determine the net income.

Solution

Net income = Sales revenue − Cost of goods sold − Selling expense − Income taxes
$$= 80,000 - 42,000 - 10,000 - 6000$$
$$= \$22,000$$

17-2

Billy Bob's Towing and Repair Service has provided the following financial information.

Cash	$ 80,000
Accounts receivable	120,000
Accounts payable	200,000
Securities	75,000
Parts inventories	42,000
Prepaid expenses	30,000
Accrued expense	15,000

Determine (a) the current ratio, (b) the quick ratio, and (c) the available working capital.

Solution

a.   Current ratio $= \dfrac{\text{Current Assets}}{\text{Current Liabilities}} = \dfrac{80,000 + 120,000 + 75,000 + 42,000}{200,000 + 15,000} = 1.47$

b.   Quick ratio $= \dfrac{\text{Current Assets - Inventories}}{\text{Current Liabilities}} = \dfrac{80,000 + 120,000 + 75,000}{200,000 + 15,000} = 1.28$

c.   Working capital = Current assets – Current liabilities = $102,000

17-3

The following financial information was taken from the income statement of Firerock Industries.

Revenues	
Sales	$3,200,000
Operating revenue	2,000,000
Non-operating revenue	3,400,000
Expenses	
Total operating expenses	6,700,000
Interest payments	500,000

Taxes paid for the year equaled $110,000. Determine (a) the net income before taxes, (b) the net profit (loss), (c) the interest coverage, and (d) the net profit ratio.

Solution

a.   Net income before taxes = 3.2M + 2.0M + 3.4M – 6.7M – 0.5M = $1,400,000

b.   Net profit = 1.4M – 0.11M = $1,290,000

c.   Interest coverage $= \dfrac{\text{Total Income}}{\text{Interest Payments}} = \dfrac{1.9\text{M}}{0.5\text{M}} = 3.8$

d.   Net profit ratio $= \dfrac{\text{Net Profit}}{\text{Net Sales Revenue}} = \dfrac{1.29\text{M}}{3.2\text{M}} = 0.4031$

17-4
From the information that follows, determine the value of the retained earnings for Lavelle Manufacturing.

Current liabilities	$4,000,000
Current assets	6,500,000
Fixed assets	4,000,000
Common stock	2,500,000
Long-term liabilities	2,000,000
Preferred stock	500,000
Other assets	1,500,000
Capital surplus	1,000,000

Solution

Equity = Common stock + Preferred stock + Capital surplus + Retained earnings

Equity = 2.5M + 0.5M + 1M + Retained earnings
     = 4M + Retained earnings

Assets = Liabilities + Equity

6.5M + 4M + 1.5M = (4M + 2M) + (4M + Retained earnings)

Retained earnings = $2,000,000

17-5
Abby Manufacturing produces numerous children's toys. The Dr. Dolittle Farm is one of the biggest sellers. Indirect cost to be allocated to production of the toy is to be calculated based on direct materials allocation. The total production overhead for the facility that produces the toy is $750,000. The direct material total for the facility is $8,350,000.
     The cost of the direct materials used in production of the Dr. Dolittle is $7.45 per unit. The total labor (both direct and indirect) for the production of the toy is $9.35 per unit. The production schedule for the coming year calls for 300,000 units to be produced.   If Abby desires a 35% profit on the toy, what should the wholesale price be?

Solution

Total labor   = 9.35 × 300,000 = 2,805,000
Total materials   = 7.45 × 300,000 = 2,235,000
Overhead   = (2,235,000/8,350,000) × 750,000 = $200,748.50

Total production cost = 2,805,000 + 2,235,000 + 200,748.50 = $5,240,748.50
Cost per unit   = 5,240,748.50/300,000 = $17.47

Wholesale price = 17.47 × 1.35 = $23.58

17-6

Brown Box, Inc. manufactures shipping boxes for a wide variety of industries. Their model XLLong has the following direct manufacturing costs per unit.

Direct materials costs	$0.25
Direct labor costs	2.75

Overhead for the entire manufacturing plant is $4,000,000 per year. Direct labor costs are used to allocate the overhead. The total direct labor costs are estimated to be $5,500,000. The expected demand for this particular model is 200,000 boxes for the year. Determine the cost per unit.

Solution

Cost per unit = Direct materials cost + Direct labor costs + Overhead costs

Overhead cost allocation:

Direct labor cost = 200,000 × $2.75 = 550,000

Allocation of overhead = 4,000,000 × $\frac{550,000}{5,500,000}$ = 400,000/200,000 = $2/box

Cost per unit = 0.25 + 2.75 + 2.00 = $5.00

17-7

The following financial information is known about Rapid Delivery, Inc.

Acid-test ratio	1.3867
Cash on hand	$ 72,000
Accounts receivable	102,000
Market value of securities held	34,000
Inventories	143,000
Other assets	16,000
Fixed assets	215,000
Total liabilities	400,000

Determine (a) the current assets, (b) the current liabilities, (c) the total assets, and (d) the owner's equity.

Solution

a.   Current assets = 72,000 + 102,000 + 34,000 + 143,000 = $351,000

b.   Acid-test ratio $= \dfrac{\text{Current Assets -- Inventories}}{\text{Current Liabilities}}$

   Current liabilities $= \dfrac{\text{Current Assets -- Inventories}}{\text{Acid-test ratio}} = \dfrac{72{,}000 + 102{,}000 + 34{,}000}{1.3867} = \$149{,}996$

c.   Total assets = 351,000 + 215,000 + 16,000 = $582,000

d.   Owner's equity = Total assets – Total liabilities
   $$= 582{,}000 - 400{,}000$$
   $$= \$182{,}000$$

17-8

Determine the current and quick ratios for Harbor Master Boats, Inc. Based on these two ratios, does the company appear to be reasonably sound from a financial viewpoint?

Harbor Master Boats, Inc.
Balance Sheet, January 1, 20XX

Assets		**Liabilities**	
Current assets		Current liabilities	
Cash	900,000	Accounts payable	2,400,000
Accounts receivable	1,100,000	Notes payable	2,000,000
Inventory	2,000,000	Accrued expense	900,000
Total current assets	4,000,000	Total current liabilities	5,300,000
Fixed assets		Long-term debt	3,000,000
Land	300,000	Total liabilities	8,300,000
Plant	2,500,000	**Equity**	
Equipment	6,000,000	Stock	2,000,000
Total fixed assets	8,800,000	Retained earnings	2,500,000
		Total net worth	4,500,000
Total assets	12,800,000	Total liabilities and net worth	12,800,000

Solution

$$\text{Current ratio} = \frac{\text{Current Assets}}{\text{Current Liabilities}} = \frac{4,000,000}{5,300,000} = .755$$

$$\text{Quick ratio} = \frac{\text{Current Assets -- Inventories}}{\text{Current Liabilities}} = \frac{4,000,000 - 2,000,000}{5,300,000} = .377$$

Based on these two ratios, the company is not in very sound financially. The current ratio typically should be greater than 2. The quick ratio indicates the company's inability to pay off current liabilities with "quick" capital.

COMPOUND INTEREST TABLES

Values of Interest Factors When *n* Equals Infinity

Single Payment:

$(F/P, i, \infty) = \infty$

$(P/F, i, \infty) = 0$

Arithmetic Gradient Series:

$(A/G, i, \infty) = 1/i$

$(P/G, i, \infty) = 1/i^2$

Uniform Payment Series:

$(A/F, i, \infty) = 0$

$(A/P, i, \infty) = i$

$(F/A, i, \infty) = \infty$

$(P/A, i, \infty) = 1/i$

| | Single Payment | | Uniform Payment Series | | | | Arithmetic Gradient | | |

Compound Interest Factors

n	Compound Amount Factor Find F Given P F/P	Present Worth Factor Find P Given F P/F	Sinking Fund Factor Find A Given F A/F	Capital Recovery Factor Find A Given P A/P	Compound Amount Factor Find F Given A F/A	Present Worth Factor Find P Given A P/A	Gradient Uniform Series Find A Given G A/G	Gradient Present Worth Find P Given G P/G	n
1	1.003	.9975	1.0000	1.0025	1.000	0.998	0.000	0.000	1
2	1.005	.9950	.4994	.5019	2.003	1.993	0.499	1.995	2
3	1.008	.9925	.3325	.3350	3.008	2.985	1.998	2.980	3
4	1.010	.9901	.2491	.2516	4.015	3.975	1.497	5.950	4
5	1.013	.9876	.1990	.2015	5.025	4.963	1.995	9.901	5
6	1.015	.9851	.1656	.1681	6.038	5.948	2.493	14.826	6
7	1.018	.9827	.1418	.1443	7.053	6.931	2.990	20.722	7
8	1.020	.9802	.1239	.1264	8.070	7.911	3.487	27.584	8
9	1.023	.9778	.1100	.1125	9.091	8.889	3.983	35.406	9
10	1.025	.9753	.0989	.1014	10.113	9.864	4.479	44.184	10
11	1.028	.9729	.0898	.0923	11.139	10.837	4.975	53.913	11
12	1.030	.9705	.0822	.0847	12.167	11.807	5.470	64.589	12
13	1.033	.9681	.0758	.0783	13.197	12.775	5.965	76.205	13
14	1.036	.9656	.0703	.0728	14.230	13.741	6.459	88.759	14
15	1.038	.9632	.0655	.0680	15.266	14.704	6.953	102.244	15
16	1.041	.9608	.0613	.0638	16.304	15.665	7.447	116.657	16
17	1.043	.9584	.0577	.0602	17.344	16.624	7.944	131.992	17
18	1.046	.9561	.0544	.0569	18.388	17.580	8.433	148.245	18
19	1.049	.9537	.0515	.0540	19.434	18.533	8.925	165.411	19
20	1.051	.9513	.0488	.0513	20.482	19.485	9.417	183.485	20
21	1.054	.9489	.0464	.0489	21.534	20.434	9.908	202.463	21
22	1.056	.9465	.0443	.0468	22.587	21.380	10.400	222.341	22
23	1.059	.9442	.0423	.0448	23.644	22.324	10.890	243.113	23
24	1.062	.9418	.0405	.0430	24.703	23.266	11.380	264.775	24
25	1.064	.9395	.0388	.0413	25.765	24.206	11.870	287.323	25
26	1.067	.9371	.0373	.0398	26.829	25.143	12.360	310.752	26
27	1.070	.9348	.0358	.0383	27.896	26.078	12.849	335.057	27
28	1.072	.9325	.0345	.0370	28.966	27.010	13.337	360.233	28
29	1.075	.9301	.0333	.0358	30.038	27.940	13.825	386.278	29
30	1.078	.9278	.0321	.0346	31.114	28.868	14.313	413.185	30
36	1.094	.9140	.0266	.0291	37.621	34.387	17.231	592.499	36
40	1.105	.9049	.0238	.0263	42.014	38.020	19.167	728.740	40
48	1.127	.8871	.0196	.0221	50.932	45.179	23.021	1 040.055	48
50	1.133	.8826	.0188	.0213	53.189	46.947	23.980	1 125.777	50
52	1.139	.8782	.0180	.0205	55.458	48.705	24.938	1 214.588	52
60	1.162	.8609	.0155	.0180	64.647	55.653	28.751	1 600.085	60
70	1.191	.8396	.0131	.0156	76.395	64.144	33.481	2 147.611	70
72	1.197	.8355	.0127	.0152	78.780	65.817	34.422	2 265.557	72
80	1.221	.8189	.0113	.0138	88.440	72.427	38.169	2 764.457	80
84	1.233	.8108	.0107	.0132	93.343	75.682	40.033	3 029.759	84
90	1.252	.7987	.00992	.0124	100.789	80.504	42.816	3 446.870	90
96	1.271	.7869	.00923	.0117	108.349	85.255	45.584	3 886.283	96
100	1.284	.7790	.00881	.0113	113.451	88.383	47.422	4 191.242	100
104	1.297	.7713	.00843	.0109	118.605	91.480	49.252	4 505.557	104
120	1.349	.7411	.00716	.00966	139.743	103.563	56.508	5 852.112	120
240	1.821	.5492	.00305	.00555	328.306	180.312	107.586	19 398.985	240
360	2.457	.4070	.00172	.00422	582.745	237.191	152.890	36 263.930	360
480	3.315	.3016	.00108	.00358	926.074	279.343	192.670	53 820.752	480

1/2% Compound Interest Factors **1/2%**

	Single Payment		Uniform Payment Series				Arithmetic Gradient		
	Compound Amount Factor Find F Given P	Present Worth Factor Find P Given F	Sinking Fund Factor Find A Given F	Capital Recovery Factor Find A Given P	Compound Amount Factor Find F Given A	Present Worth Factor Find P Given A	Gradient Uniform Series Find A Given G	Gradient Present Worth Find P Given G	
n	F/P	P/F	A/F	A/P	F/A	P/A	A/G	P/G	n
1	1.005	.9950	1.0000	1.0050	1.000	0.995	0	0	1
2	1.010	.9901	.4988	.5038	2.005	1.985	0.499	0.991	2
3	1.015	.9851	.3317	.3367	3.015	2.970	0.996	2.959	3
4	1.020	.9802	.2481	.2531	4.030	3.951	1.494	5.903	4
5	1.025	.9754	.1980	.2030	5.050	4.926	1.990	9.803	5
6	1.030	.9705	.1646	.1696	6.076	5.896	2.486	14.660	6
7	1.036	.9657	.1407	.1457	7.106	6.862	2.980	20.448	7
8	1.041	.9609	.1228	.1278	8.141	7.823	3.474	27.178	8
9	1.046	.9561	.1089	.1139	9.182	8.779	3.967	34.825	9
10	1.051	.9513	.0978	.1028	10.228	9.730	4.459	43.389	10
11	1.056	.9466	.0887	.0937	11.279	10.677	4.950	52.855	11
12	1.062	.9419	.0811	.0861	12.336	11.619	5.441	63.218	12
13	1.067	.9372	.0746	.0796	13.397	12.556	5.931	74.465	13
14	1.072	.9326	.0691	.0741	14.464	13.489	6.419	86.590	14
15	1.078	.9279	.0644	.0694	15.537	14.417	6.907	99.574	15
16	1.083	.9233	.0602	.0652	16.614	15.340	7.394	113.427	16
17	1.088	.9187	.0565	.0615	17.697	16.259	7.880	128.125	17
18	1.094	.9141	.0532	.0582	18.786	17.173	8.366	143.668	18
19	1.099	.9096	.0503	.0553	19.880	18.082	8.850	160.037	19
20	1.105	.9051	.0477	.0527	20.979	18.987	9.334	177.237	20
21	1.110	.9006	.0453	.0503	22.084	19.888	9.817	195.245	21
22	1.116	.8961	.0431	.0481	23.194	20.784	10.300	214.070	22
23	1.122	.8916	.0411	.0461	24.310	21.676	10.781	233.680	23
24	1.127	.8872	.0393	.0443	25.432	22.563	11.261	254.088	24
25	1.133	.8828	.0377	.0427	26.559	23.446	11.741	275.273	25
26	1.138	.8784	.0361	.0411	27.692	24.324	12.220	297.233	26
27	1.144	.8740	.0347	.0397	28.830	25.198	12.698	319.955	27
28	1.150	.8697	.0334	.0384	29.975	26.068	13.175	343.439	28
29	1.156	.8653	.0321	.0371	31.124	26.933	13.651	367.672	29
30	1.161	.8610	.0310	.0360	32.280	27.794	14.127	392.640	30
36	1.197	.8356	.0254	.0304	39.336	32.871	16.962	557.564	36
40	1.221	.8191	.0226	.0276	44.159	36.172	18.836	681.341	40
48	1.270	.7871	.0185	.0235	54.098	42.580	22.544	959.928	48
50	1.283	.7793	.0177	.0227	56.645	44.143	23.463	1 035.70	50
52	1.296	.7716	.0169	.0219	59.218	45.690	24.378	1 113.82	52
60	1.349	.7414	.0143	.0193	69.770	51.726	28.007	1 448.65	60
70	1.418	.7053	.0120	.0170	83.566	58.939	32.468	1 913.65	70
72	1.432	.6983	.0116	.0166	86.409	60.340	33.351	2 012.35	72
80	1.490	.6710	.0102	.0152	98.068	65.802	36.848	2 424.65	80
84	1.520	.6577	.00961	.0146	104.074	68.453	38.576	2 640.67	84
90	1.567	.6383	.00883	.0138	113.311	72.331	41.145	2 976.08	90
96	1.614	.6195	.00814	.0131	122.829	76.095	43.685	3 324.19	96
100	1.647	.6073	.00773	.0127	129.334	78.543	45.361	3 562.80	100
104	1.680	.5953	.00735	.0124	135.970	80.942	47.025	3 806.29	104
120	1.819	.5496	.00610	.0111	163.880	90.074	53.551	4 823.52	120
240	3.310	.3021	.00216	.00716	462.041	139.581	96.113	13 415.56	240
360	6.023	.1660	.00100	.00600	1 004.5	166.792	128.324	21 403.32	360
480	10.957	.0913	.00050	.00550	1 991.5	181.748	151.795	27 588.37	480

3/4% Compound Interest Factors 3/4%

	Single Payment		Uniform Payment Series				Arithmetic Gradient		
	Compound Amount Factor Find F Given P	Present Worth Factor Find P Given F	Sinking Fund Factor Find A Given F	Capital Recovery Factor Find A Given P	Compound Amount Factor Find F Given A	Present Worth Factor Find P Given A	Gradient Uniform Series Find A Given G	Gradient Present Worth Find P Given G	
n	F/P	P/F	A/F	A/P	F/A	P/A	A/G	P/G	n
1	1.008	.9926	1.0000	1.0075	1.000	0.993	0	0	1
2	1.015	.9852	.4981	.5056	2.008	1.978	0.499	0.987	2
3	1.023	.9778	.3308	.3383	3.023	2.956	0.996	2.943	3
4	1.030	.9706	.2472	.2547	4.045	3.926	1.492	5.857	4
5	1.038	.9633	.1970	.2045	5.076	4.889	1.986	9.712	5
6	1.046	.9562	.1636	.1711	6.114	5.846	2.479	14.494	6
7	1.054	.9490	.1397	.1472	7.160	6.795	2.971	20.187	7
8	1.062	.9420	.1218	.1293	8.213	7.737	3.462	26.785	8
9	1.070	.9350	.1078	.1153	9.275	8.672	3.951	34.265	9
10	1.078	.9280	.0967	.1042	10.344	9.600	4.440	42.619	10
11	1.086	.9211	.0876	.0951	11.422	10.521	4.927	51.831	11
12	1.094	.9142	.0800	.0875	12.508	11.435	5.412	61.889	12
13	1.102	.9074	.0735	.0810	13.602	12.342	5.897	72.779	13
14	1.110	.9007	.0680	.0755	14.704	13.243	6.380	84.491	14
15	1.119	.8940	.0632	.0707	15.814	14.137	6.862	97.005	15
16	1.127	.8873	.0591	.0666	16.932	15.024	7.343	110.318	16
17	1.135	.8807	.0554	.0629	18.059	15.905	7.822	124.410	17
18	1.144	.8742	.0521	.0596	19.195	16.779	8.300	139.273	18
19	1.153	.8676	.0492	.0567	20.339	17.647	8.777	154.891	19
20	1.161	.8612	.0465	.0540	21.491	18.508	9.253	171.254	20
21	1.170	.8548	.0441	.0516	22.653	19.363	9.727	188.352	21
22	1.179	.8484	.0420	.0495	23.823	20.211	10.201	206.170	22
23	1.188	.8421	.0400	.0475	25.001	21.053	10.673	224.695	23
24	1.196	.8358	.0382	.0457	26.189	21.889	11.143	243.924	24
25	1.205	.8296	.0365	.0440	27.385	22.719	11.613	263.834	25
26	1.214	.8234	.0350	.0425	28.591	23.542	12.081	284.421	26
27	1.224	.8173	.0336	.0411	29.805	24.360	12.548	305.672	27
28	1.233	.8112	.0322	.0397	31.029	25.171	13.014	327.576	28
29	1.242	.8052	.0310	.0385	32.261	25.976	13.479	350.122	29
30	1.251	.7992	.0298	.0373	33.503	26.775	13.942	373.302	30
36	1.309	.7641	.0243	.0318	41.153	31.447	16.696	525.038	36
40	1.348	.7416	.0215	.0290	46.447	34.447	18.507	637.519	40
48	1.431	.6986	.0174	.0249	57.521	40.185	22.070	886.899	48
50	1.453	.6882	.0166	.0241	60.395	41.567	22.949	953.911	50
52	1.475	.6780	.0158	.0233	63.312	42.928	23.822	1 022.64	52
60	1.566	.6387	.0133	.0208	75.425	48.174	27.268	1 313.59	60
70	1.687	.5927	.0109	.0184	91.621	54.305	31.465	1 708.68	70
72	1.713	.5839	.0105	.0180	95.008	55.477	32.289	1 791.33	72
80	1.818	.5500	.00917	.0167	109.074	59.995	35.540	2 132.23	80
84	1.873	.5338	.00859	.0161	116.428	62.154	37.137	2 308.22	84
90	1.959	.5104	.00782	.0153	127.881	65.275	39.496	2 578.09	90
96	2.049	.4881	.00715	.0147	139.858	68.259	41.812	2 854.04	96
100	2.111	.4737	.00675	.0143	148.147	70.175	43.332	3 040.85	100
104	2.175	.4597	.00638	.0139	156.687	72.035	44.834	3 229.60	104
120	2.451	.4079	.00517	.0127	193.517	78.942	50.653	3 998.68	120
240	6.009	.1664	.00150	.00900	667.901	111.145	85.422	9 494.26	240
360	14.731	.0679	.00055	.00805	1 830.8	124.282	107.115	13 312.50	360
480	36.111	.0277	.00021	.00771	4 681.5	129.641	119.662	15 513.16	480

1% Compound Interest Factors **1%**

	Single Payment		Uniform Payment Series				Arithmetic Gradient		
	Compound Amount Factor Find F Given P	Present Worth Factor Find P Given F	Sinking Fund Factor Find A Given F	Capital Recovery Factor Find A Given P	Compound Amount Factor Find F Given A	Present Worth Factor Find P Given A	Gradient Uniform Series Find A Given G	Gradient Present Worth Find P Given G	
n	F/P	P/F	A/F	A/P	F/A	P/A	A/G	P/G	n
1	1.010	.9901	1.0000	1.0100	1.000	0.990	0	0	1
2	1.020	.9803	.4975	.5075	2.010	1.970	0.498	0.980	2
3	1.030	.9706	.3300	.3400	3.030	2.941	0.993	2.921	3
4	1.041	.9610	.2463	.2563	4.060	3.902	1.488	5.804	4
5	1.051	.9515	.1960	.2060	5.101	4.853	1.980	9.610	5
6	1.062	.9420	.1625	.1725	6.152	5.795	2.471	14.320	6
7	1.072	.9327	.1386	.1486	7.214	6.728	2.960	19.917	7
8	1.083	.9235	.1207	.1307	8.286	7.652	3.448	26.381	8
9	1.094	.9143	.1067	.1167	9.369	8.566	3.934	33.695	9
10	1.105	.9053	.0956	.1056	10.462	9.471	4.418	41.843	10
11	1.116	.8963	.0865	.0965	11.567	10.368	4.900	50.806	11
12	1.127	.8874	.0788	.0888	12.682	11.255	5.381	60.568	12
13	1.138	.8787	.0724	.0824	13.809	12.134	5.861	71.112	13
14	1.149	.8700	.0669	.0769	14.947	13.004	6.338	82.422	14
15	1.161	.8613	.0621	.0721	16.097	13.865	6.814	94.481	15
16	1.173	.8528	.0579	.0679	17.258	14.718	7.289	107.273	16
17	1.184	.8444	.0543	.0643	18.430	15.562	7.761	120.783	17
18	1.196	.8360	.0510	.0610	19.615	16.398	8.232	134.995	18
19	1.208	.8277	.0481	.0581	20.811	17.226	8.702	149.895	19
20	1.220	.8195	.0454	.0554	22.019	18.046	9.169	165.465	20
21	1.232	.8114	.0430	.0530	23.239	18.857	9.635	181.694	21
22	1.245	.8034	.0409	.0509	24.472	19.660	10.100	198.565	22
23	1.257	.7954	.0389	.0489	25.716	20.456	10.563	216.065	23
24	1.270	.7876	.0371	.0471	26.973	21.243	11.024	234.179	24
25	1.282	.7798	.0354	.0454	28.243	22.023	11.483	252.892	25
26	1.295	.7720	.0339	.0439	29.526	22.795	11.941	272.195	26
27	1.308	.7644	.0324	.0424	30.821	23.560	12.397	292.069	27
28	1.321	.7568	.0311	.0411	32.129	24.316	12.852	312.504	28
29	1.335	.7493	.0299	.0399	33.450	25.066	13.304	333.486	29
30	1.348	.7419	.0287	.0387	34.785	25.808	13.756	355.001	30
36	1.431	.6989	.0232	.0332	43.077	30.107	16.428	494.620	36
40	1.489	.6717	.0205	.0305	48.886	32.835	18.178	596.854	40
48	1.612	.6203	.0163	.0263	61.223	37.974	21.598	820.144	48
50	1.645	.6080	.0155	.0255	64.463	39.196	22.436	879.417	50
52	1.678	.5961	.0148	.0248	67.769	40.394	23.269	939.916	52
60	1.817	.5504	.0122	.0222	81.670	44.955	26.533	1 192.80	60
70	2.007	.4983	.00993	.0199	100.676	50.168	30.470	1 528.64	70
72	2.047	.4885	.00955	.0196	104.710	51.150	31.239	1 597.86	72
80	2.217	.4511	.00822	.0182	121.671	54.888	34.249	1 879.87	80
84	2.307	.4335	.00765	.0177	130.672	56.648	35.717	2 023.31	84
90	2.449	.4084	.00690	.0169	144.863	59.161	37.872	2 240.56	90
96	2.599	.3847	.00625	.0163	159.927	61.528	39.973	2 459.42	96
100	2.705	.3697	.00587	.0159	170.481	63.029	41.343	2 605.77	100
104	2.815	.3553	.00551	.0155	181.464	64.471	42.688	2 752.17	104
120	3.300	.3030	.00435	.0143	230.039	69.701	47.835	3 334.11	120
240	10.893	.0918	.00101	.0110	989.254	90.819	75.739	6 878.59	240
360	35.950	.0278	.00029	.0103	3 495.0	97.218	89.699	8 720.43	360
480	118.648	.00843	.00008	.0101	11 764.8	99.157	95.920	9 511.15	480

1¹/4%				Compound Interest Factors					1¹/4%
	Single Payment		Uniform Payment Series				Arithmetic Gradient		
	Compound Amount Factor Find F Given P F/P	Present Worth Factor Find P Given F P/F	Sinking Fund Factor Find A Given F A/F	Capital Recovery Factor Find A Given P A/P	Compound Amount Factor Find F Given A F/A	Present Worth Factor Find P Given A P/A	Gradient Uniform Series Find A Given G A/G	Gradient Present Worth Find P Given G P/G	
n									n
1	1.013	.9877	1.0000	1.0125	1.000	0.988	0	0	1
2	1.025	.9755	.4969	.5094	2.013	1.963	0.497	0.976	2
3	1.038	.9634	.3292	.3417	3.038	2.927	0.992	2.904	3
4	1.051	.9515	.2454	.2579	4.076	3.878	1.485	5.759	4
5	1.064	.9398	.1951	.2076	5.127	4.818	1.976	9.518	5
6	1.077	.9282	.1615	.1740	6.191	5.746	2.464	14.160	6
7	1.091	.9167	.1376	.1501	7.268	6.663	2.951	19.660	7
8	1.104	.9054	.1196	.1321	8.359	7.568	3.435	25.998	8
9	1.118	.8942	.1057	.1182	9.463	8.462	3.918	33.152	9
10	1.132	.8832	.0945	.1070	10.582	9.346	4.398	41.101	10
11	1.146	.8723	.0854	.0979	11.714	10.218	4.876	49.825	11
12	1.161	.8615	.0778	.0903	12.860	11.079	5.352	59.302	12
13	1.175	.8509	.0713	.0838	14.021	11.930	5.827	69.513	13
14	1.190	.8404	.0658	.0783	15.196	12.771	6.299	80.438	14
15	1.205	.8300	.0610	.0735	16.386	13.601	6.769	92.058	15
16	1.220	.8197	.0568	.0693	17.591	14.420	7.237	104.355	16
17	1.235	.8096	.0532	.0657	18.811	15.230	7.702	117.309	17
18	1.251	.7996	.0499	.0624	20.046	16.030	8.166	130.903	18
19	1.266	.7898	.0470	.0595	21.297	16.849	8.628	145.119	19
20	1.282	.7800	.0443	.0568	22.563	17.599	9.088	159.940	20
21	1.298	.7704	.0419	.0544	23.845	18.370	9.545	175.348	21
22	1.314	.7609	.0398	.0523	25.143	19.131	10.001	191.327	22
23	1.331	.7515	.0378	.0503	26.458	19.882	10.455	207.859	23
24	1.347	.7422	.0360	.0485	27.788	20.624	10.906	224.930	24
25	1.364	.7330	.0343	.0468	29.136	21.357	11.355	242.523	25
26	1.381	.7240	.0328	.0453	30.500	22.081	11.803	260.623	26
27	1.399	.7150	.0314	.0439	31.881	22.796	12.248	279.215	27
28	1.416	.7062	.0300	.0425	32.280	23.503	12.691	298.284	28
29	1.434	.6975	.0288	.0413	34.696	24.200	13.133	317.814	29
30	1.452	.6889	.0277	.0402	36.129	24.889	13.572	337.792	30
36	1.564	.6394	.0222	.0347	45.116	28.847	16.164	466.297	36
40	1.644	.6084	.0194	.0319	51.490	31.327	17.852	559.247	40
48	1.845	.5509	.0153	.0278	65.229	35.932	21.130	759.248	48
50	1.861	.5373	.0145	.0270	68.882	37.013	21.930	811.692	50
52	1.908	.5242	.0138	.0263	72.628	38.068	22.722	864.960	52
60	2.107	.4746	.0113	.0238	88.575	42.035	25.809	1 084.86	60
70	2.386	.4191	.00902	.0215	110.873	46.470	29.442	1 370.47	70
72	2.446	.4088	.00864	.0211	115.675	47.293	30.205	1 428.48	72
80	2.701	.3702	.00735	.0198	136.120	50.387	32.983	1 661.89	80
84	2.839	.3522	.00680	.0193	147.130	51.822	34.326	1 778.86	84
90	3.059	.3269	.00607	.0186	164.706	53.846	36.286	1 953.85	90
96	3.296	.3034	.00545	.0179	183.643	55.725	38.180	2 127.55	96
100	3.463	.2887	.00507	.0176	197.074	56.901	39.406	2 242.26	100
104	3.640	.2747	.00474	.0172	211.190	58.021	40.604	2 355.90	104
120	4.440	.2252	.00363	.0161	275.220	61.983	45.119	2 796.59	120
240	19.716	.0507	.00067	.0132	1 497.3	75.942	67.177	5 101.55	240
360	87.543	.0114	.00014	.0126	6 923.4	79.086	75.840	5 997.91	360
480	388.713	.00257	.00003	.0125	31 017.1	79.794	78.762	6 284.74	480

1½%				Compound Interest Factors					1½%
	Single Payment		Uniform Payment Series				Arithmetic Gradient		
	Compound Amount Factor Find F Given P F/P	Present Worth Factor Find P Given F P/F	Sinking Fund Factor Find A Given F A/F	Capital Recovery Factor Find A Given P A/P	Compound Amount Factor Find F Given A F/A	Present Worth Factor Find P Given A P/A	Gradient Uniform Series Find A Given G A/G	Gradient Present Worth Find P Given G P/G	
n									n
1	1.015	.9852	1.0000	1.0150	1.000	0.985	0	0	1
2	1.030	.9707	.4963	.5113	2.015	1.956	0.496	0.970	2
3	1.046	.9563	.3284	.3434	3.045	2.912	0.990	2.883	3
4	1.061	.9422	.2444	.2594	4.091	3.854	1.481	5.709	4
5	1.077	.9283	.1941	.2091	5.152	4.783	1.970	9.422	5
6	1.093	.9145	.1605	.1755	6.230	5.697	2.456	13.994	6
7	1.110	.9010	.1366	.1516	7.323	6.598	2.940	19.400	7
8	1.126	.8877	.1186	.1336	8.433	7.486	3.422	25.614	8
9	1.143	.8746	.1046	.1196	9.559	8.360	3.901	32.610	9
10	1.161	.8617	.0934	.1084	10.703	9.222	4.377	40.365	10
11	1.178	.8489	.0843	.0993	11.863	10.071	4.851	48.855	11
12	1.196	.8364	.0767	.0917	13.041	10.907	5.322	58.054	12
13	1.214	.8240	.0702	.0852	14.237	11.731	5.791	67.943	13
14	1.232	.8118	.0647	.0797	15.450	12.543	6.258	78.496	14
15	1.250	.7999	.0599	.0749	16.682	13.343	6.722	89.694	15
16	1.269	.7880	.0558	.0708	17.932	14.131	7.184	101.514	16
17	1.288	.7764	.0521	.0671	19.201	14.908	7.643	113.937	17
18	1.307	.7649	.0488	.0638	20.489	15.673	8.100	126.940	18
19	1.327	.7536	.0459	.0609	21.797	16.426	8.554	140.505	19
20	1.347	.7425	.0432	.0582	23.124	17.169	9.005	154.611	20
21	1.367	.7315	.0409	.0559	24.470	17.900	9.455	169.241	21
22	1.388	.7207	.0387	.0537	25.837	18.621	9.902	184.375	22
23	1.408	.7100	.0366	.0517	27.225	19.331	10.346	199.996	23
24	1.430	.6995	.0349	.0499	28.633	20.030	10.788	216.085	24
25	1.451	.6892	.0333	.0483	30.063	20.720	11.227	232.626	25
26	1.473	.6790	.0317	.0467	31.514	21.399	11.664	249.601	26
27	1.495	.6690	.0303	.0453	32.987	22.068	12.099	266.995	27
28	1.517	.6591	.0290	.0440	34.481	22.727	12.531	284.790	28
29	1.540	.6494	.0278	.0428	35.999	23.376	12.961	302.972	29
30	1.563	.6398	.0266	.0416	37.539	24.016	13.388	321.525	30
36	1.709	.5851	.0212	.0362	47.276	27.661	15.901	439.823	36
40	1.814	.5513	.0184	.0334	54.268	29.916	17.528	524.349	40
48	2.043	.4894	.0144	.0294	69.565	34.042	20.666	703.537	48
50	2.105	.4750	.0136	.0286	73.682	35.000	21.428	749.955	50
52	2.169	.4611	.0128	.0278	77.925	35.929	22.179	796.868	52
60	2.443	.4093	.0104	.0254	96.214	39.380	25.093	988.157	60
70	2.835	.3527	.00817	.0232	122.363	43.155	28.529	1 231.15	70
72	2.921	.3423	.00781	.0228	128.076	43.845	29.189	1 279.78	72
80	3.291	.3039	.00655	.0215	152.710	46.407	31.742	1 473.06	80
84	3.493	.2863	.00602	.0210	166.172	47.579	32.967	1 568.50	84
90	3.819	.2619	.00532	.0203	187.929	49.210	34.740	1 709.53	90
96	4.176	.2395	.00472	.0197	211.719	50.702	36.438	1 847.46	96
100	4.432	.2256	.00437	.0194	228.802	51.625	37.529	1 937.43	100
104	4.704	.2126	.00405	.0190	246.932	52.494	38.589	2 025.69	104
120	5.969	.1675	.00302	.0180	331.286	55.498	42.518	2 359.69	120
240	35.632	.0281	.00043	.0154	2 308.8	64.796	59.737	3 870.68	240
360	212.700	.00470	.00007	.0151	14 113.3	66.353	64.966	4 310.71	360
480	1 269.7	.00079	.00001	.0150	84 577.8	66.614	66.288	4 415.74	480

| | Single Payment | | Uniform Payment Series | | | | Arithmetic Gradient | | |

1³/₄% Compound Interest Factors 1³/₄%

n	Compound Amount Factor Find F Given P F/P	Present Worth Factor Find P Given F P/F	Sinking Fund Factor Find A Given F A/F	Capital Recovery Factor Find A Given P A/P	Compound Amount Factor Find F Given A F/A	Present Worth Factor Find P Given A P/A	Gradient Uniform Series Find A Given G A/G	Gradient Present Worth Find P Given G P/G	n
1	1.018	.9828	1.0000	1.0175	1.000	0.983	0	0	1
2	1.035	.9659	.4957	.5132	2.018	1.949	0.496	0.966	2
3	1.053	.9493	.3276	.3451	3.053	2.898	0.989	2.865	3
4	1.072	.9330	.2435	.2610	4.106	3.831	1.478	5.664	4
5	1.091	.9169	.1931	.2106	5.178	4.748	1.965	9.332	5
6	1.110	.9011	.1595	.1770	6.269	5.649	2.450	13.837	6
7	1.129	.8856	.1355	.1530	7.378	6.535	2.931	19.152	7
8	1.149	.8704	.1175	.1350	8.508	7.405	3.409	25.245	8
9	1.169	.8554	.1036	.1211	9.656	8.261	3.885	32.088	9
10	1.189	.8407	.0924	.1099	10.825	9.101	4.357	39.655	10
11	1.210	.8263	.0832	.1007	12.015	9.928	4.827	47.918	11
12	1.231	.8121	.0756	.0931	13.225	10.740	5.294	56.851	12
13	1.253	.7981	.0692	.0867	14.457	11.538	5.758	66.428	13
14	1.275	.7844	.0637	.0812	15.710	12.322	6.219	76.625	14
15	1.297	.7709	.0589	.0764	16.985	13.093	6.677	87.417	15
16	1.320	.7576	.0547	.0722	18.282	13.851	7.132	98.782	16
17	1.343	.7446	.0510	.0685	19.602	14.595	7.584	110.695	17
18	1.367	.7318	.0477	.0652	20.945	15.327	8.034	123.136	18
19	1.390	.7192	.0448	.0623	22.311	16.046	8.481	136.081	19
20	1.415	.7068	.0422	.0597	23.702	16.753	8.924	149.511	20
21	1.440	.6947	.0398	.0573	25.116	17.448	9.365	163.405	21
22	1.465	.6827	.0377	.0552	26.556	18.130	9.804	177.742	22
23	1.490	.6710	.0357	.0532	28.021	18.801	10.239	192.503	23
24	1.516	.6594	.0339	.0514	29.511	19.461	10.671	207.671	24
25	1.543	.6481	.0322	.0497	31.028	20.109	11.101	223.225	25
26	1.570	.6369	.0307	.0482	32.571	20.746	11.528	239.149	26
27	1.597	.6260	.0293	.0468	34.141	21.372	11.952	255.425	27
28	1.625	.6152	.0280	.0455	35.738	21.987	12.373	272.036	28
29	1.654	.6046	.0268	.0443	37.363	22.592	12.791	288.967	29
30	1.683	.5942	.0256	.0431	39.017	23.186	13.206	306.200	30
36	1.867	.5355	.0202	.0377	49.566	26.543	15.640	415.130	36
40	2.002	.4996	.0175	.0350	57.234	28.594	17.207	492.017	40
48	2.300	.4349	.0135	.0310	74.263	32.294	20.209	652.612	48
50	2.381	.4200	.0127	.0302	78.903	33.141	20.932	693.708	50
52	2.465	.4057	.0119	.0294	83.706	33.960	21.644	735.039	52
60	2.832	.3531	.00955	.0271	104.676	36.964	24.389	901.503	60
70	3.368	.2969	.00739	.0249	135.331	40.178	27.586	1 108.34	70
72	3.487	.2868	.00704	.0245	142.127	40.757	28.195	1 149.12	72
80	4.006	.2496	.00582	.0233	171.795	42.880	30.533	1 309.25	80
84	4.294	.2329	.00531	.0228	188.246	43.836	31.644	1 387.16	84
90	4.765	.2098	.00465	.0221	215.166	45.152	33.241	1 500.88	90
96	5.288	.1891	.00408	.0216	245.039	46.337	34.756	1 610.48	96
100	5.668	.1764	.00375	.0212	266.753	47.062	35.721	1 681.09	100
104	6.075	.1646	.00345	.0209	290.028	47.737	36.652	1 749.68	104
120	8.019	.1247	.00249	.0200	401.099	50.017	40.047	2 003.03	120
240	64.308	.0156	.00028	.0178	3 617.6	56.254	53.352	3 001.27	240
360	515.702	.00194	.00003	.0175	29 411.5	57.032	56.443	3 219.08	360
480	4 135.5	.00024		.0175	236 259.0	57.129	57.027	3 257.88	480

2%				Compound Interest Factors					2%
	Single Payment		Uniform Payment Series				Arithmetic Gradient		
	Compound Amount Factor Find F Given P F/P	Present Worth Factor Find P Given F P/F	Sinking Fund Factor Find A Given F A/F	Capital Recovery Factor Find A Given P A/P	Compound Amount Factor Find F Given A F/A	Present Worth Factor Find P Given A P/A	Gradient Uniform Series Find A Given G A/G	Gradient Present Worth Find P Given G P/G	
n									n
1	1.020	.9804	1.0000	1.0200	1.000	0.980	0	0	1
2	1.040	.9612	.4951	.5151	2.020	1.942	0.495	0.961	2
3	1.061	.9423	.3268	.3468	3.060	2.884	0.987	2.846	3
4	1.082	.9238	.2426	.2626	4.122	3.808	1.475	5.617	4
5	1.104	.9057	.1922	.2122	5.204	4.713	1.960	9.240	5
6	1.126	.8880	.1585	.1785	6.308	5.601	2.442	13.679	6
7	1.149	.8706	.1345	.1545	7.434	6.472	2.921	18.903	7
8	1.172	.8535	.1165	.1365	8.583	7.325	3.396	24.877	8
9	1.195	.8368	.1025	.1225	9.755	8.162	3.868	31.571	9
10	1.219	.8203	.0913	.1113	10.950	8.983	4.337	38.954	10
11	1.243	.8043	.0822	.1022	12.169	9.787	4.802	46.996	11
12	1.268	.7885	.0746	.0946	13.412	10.575	5.264	55.669	12
13	1.294	.7730	.0681	.0881	14.680	11.348	5.723	64.946	13
14	1.319	.7579	.0626	.0826	15.974	12.106	6.178	74.798	14
15	1.346	.7430	.0578	.0778	17.293	12.849	6.631	85.200	15
16	1.373	.7284	.0537	.0737	18.639	13.578	7.080	96.127	16
17	1.400	.7142	.0500	.0700	20.012	14.292	7.526	107.553	17
18	1.428	.7002	.0467	.0667	21.412	14.992	7.968	119.456	18
19	1.457	.6864	.0438	.0638	22.840	15.678	8.407	131.812	19
20	1.486	.6730	.0412	.0612	24.297	16.351	8.843	144.598	20
21	1.516	.6598	.0388	.0588	25.783	17.011	9.276	157.793	21
22	1.546	.6468	.0366	.0566	27.299	17.658	9.705	171.377	22
23	1.577	.6342	.0347	.0547	28.845	18.292	10.132	185.328	23
24	1.608	.6217	.0329	.0529	30.422	18.914	10.555	199.628	24
25	1.641	.6095	.0312	.0512	32.030	19.523	10.974	214.256	25
26	1.673	.5976	.0297	.0497	33.671	20.121	11.391	229.196	26
27	1.707	.5859	.0283	.0483	35.344	20.707	11.804	244.428	27
28	1.741	.5744	.0270	.0470	37.051	21.281	12.214	259.936	28
29	1.776	.5631	.0258	.0458	38.792	21.844	12.621	275.703	29
30	1.811	.5521	.0247	.0447	40.568	22.396	13.025	291.713	30
36	2.040	.4902	.0192	.0392	51.994	25.489	15.381	392.036	36
40	2.208	.4529	.0166	.0366	60.402	27.355	16.888	461.989	40
48	2.587	.3865	.0126	.0326	79.353	30.673	19.755	605.961	48
50	2.692	.3715	.0118	.0318	84.579	31.424	20.442	642.355	50
52	2.800	.3571	.0111	.0311	90.016	32.145	21.116	678.779	52
60	3.281	.3048	.00877	.0288	114.051	34.761	23.696	823.692	60
70	4.000	.2500	.00667	.0267	149.977	37.499	26.663	999.829	70
72	4.161	.2403	.00633	.0263	158.056	37.984	27.223	1 034.050	72
80	4.875	.2051	.00516	.0252	193.771	39.744	29.357	1 166.781	80
84	5.277	.1895	.00468	.0247	213.865	40.525	30.361	1 230.413	84
90	5.943	.1683	.00405	.0240	247.155	41.587	31.793	1 322.164	90
96	6.693	.1494	.00351	.0235	284.645	42.529	33.137	1 409.291	96
100	7.245	.1380	.00320	.0232	312.230	43.098	33.986	1 464.747	100
104	7.842	.1275	.00292	.0229	342.090	43.624	34.799	1 518.082	104
120	10.765	.0929	.00205	.0220	488.255	45.355	37.711	1 710.411	120
240	115.887	.00863	.00017	.0202	5 744.4	49.569	47.911	2 374.878	240
360	1 247.5	.00080	.00002	.0200	62 326.8	49.960	49.711	2 483.567	360
480	13 429.8	.00007		.0200	671 442.0	49.996	49.964	2 498.027	480

2¹/₂%				Compound Interest Factors					2¹/₂%
	Single Payment		Uniform Payment Series				Arithmetic Gradient		
	Compound Amount Factor Find F Given P F/P	Present Worth Factor Find P Given F P/F	Sinking Fund Factor Find A Given F A/F	Capital Recovery Factor Find A Given P A/P	Compound Amount Factor Find F Given A F/A	Present Worth Factor Find P Given A P/A	Gradient Uniform Series Find A Given G A/G	Gradient Present Worth Find P Given G P/G	
n									n
1	1.025	.9756	1.0000	1.0250	1.000	0.976	0	0	1
2	1.051	.9518	.4938	.5188	2.025	1.927	0.494	0.952	2
3	1.077	.9286	.3251	.3501	3.076	2.856	0.984	2.809	3
4	1.104	.9060	.2408	.2658	4.153	3.762	1.469	5.527	4
5	1.131	.8839	.1902	.2152	5.256	4.646	1.951	9.062	5
6	1.160	.8623	.1566	.1816	6.388	5.508	2.428	13.374	6
7	1.189	.8413	.1325	.1575	7.547	6.349	2.901	18.421	7
8	1.218	.8207	.1145	.1395	8.736	7.170	3.370	24.166	8
9	1.249	.8007	.1005	.1255	9.955	7.971	3.835	30.572	9
10	1.280	.7812	.0893	.1143	11.203	8.752	4.296	37.603	10
11	1.312	.7621	.0801	.1051	12.483	9.514	4.753	45.224	11
12	1.345	.7436	.0725	.0975	13.796	10.258	5.206	53.403	12
13	1.379	.7254	.0660	.0910	15.140	10.983	5.655	62.108	13
14	1.413	.7077	.0605	.0855	16.519	11.691	6.100	71.309	14
15	1.448	.6905	.0558	.0808	17.932	12.381	6.540	80.975	15
16	1.485	.6736	.0516	.0766	19.380	13.055	6.977	91.080	16
17	1.522	.6572	.0479	.0729	20.865	13.712	7.409	101.595	17
18	1.560	.6412	.0447	.0697	22.386	14.353	7.838	112.495	18
19	1.599	.6255	.0418	.0668	23.946	14.979	8.262	123.754	19
20	1.639	.6103	.0391	.0641	25.545	15.589	8.682	135.349	20
21	1.680	.5954	.0368	.0618	27.183	16.185	9.099	147.257	21
22	1.722	.5809	.0346	.0596	28.863	16.765	9.511	159.455	22
23	1.765	.5667	.0327	.0577	30.584	17.332	9.919	171.922	23
24	1.809	.5529	.0309	.0559	32.349	17.885	10.324	184.638	24
25	1.854	.5394	.0293	.0543	34.158	18.424	10.724	197.584	25
26	1.900	.5262	.0278	.0528	36.012	18.951	11.120	210.740	26
27	1.948	.5134	.0264	.0514	37.912	19.464	11.513	224.088	27
28	1.996	.5009	.0251	.0501	39.860	19.965	11.901	237.612	28
29	2.046	.4887	.0239	.0489	41.856	20.454	12.286	251.294	29
30	2.098	.4767	.0228	.0478	43.903	20.930	12.667	265.120	30
31	2.150	.4651	.0217	.0467	46.000	21.395	13.044	279.073	31
32	2.204	.4538	.0208	.0458	48.150	24.849	13.417	293.140	32
33	2.259	.4427	.0199	.0449	50.354	22.292	13.786	307.306	33
34	2.315	.4319	.0190	.0440	52.613	22.724	14.151	321.559	34
35	2.373	.4214	.0182	.0432	54.928	23.145	14.512	335.886	35
40	2.685	.3724	.0148	.0398	67.402	25.103	16.262	408.221	40
45	3.038	.3292	.0123	.0373	81.516	26.833	17.918	480.806	45
50	3.437	.2909	.0103	.0353	97.484	28.362	19.484	552.607	50
55	3.889	.2572	.00865	.0337	115.551	29.714	20.961	622.827	55
60	4.400	.2273	.00735	.0324	135.991	30.909	22.352	690.865	60
65	4.978	.2009	.00628	.0313	159.118	31.965	23.660	756.280	65
70	5.632	.1776	.00540	.0304	185.284	32.898	24.888	818.763	70
75	6.372	.1569	.00465	.0297	214.888	33.723	26.039	878.114	75
80	7.210	.1387	.00403	.0290	248.382	34.452	27.117	934.217	80
85	8.157	.1226	.00349	.0285	286.278	35.096	28.123	987.026	85
90	9.229	.1084	.00304	.0280	329.154	35.666	29.063	1 036.54	90
95	10.442	.0958	.00265	.0276	377.663	36.169	29.938	1 082.83	95
100	11.814	.0846	.00231	.0273	432.548	36.614	30.752	1 125.97	100

3%				Compound Interest Factors					3%

	Single Payment		Uniform Payment Series				Arithmetic Gradient		
	Compound Amount Factor Find F Given P F/P	Present Worth Factor Find P Given F P/F	Sinking Fund Factor Find A Given F A/F	Capital Recovery Factor Find A Given P A/P	Compound Amount Factor Find F Given A F/A	Present Worth Factor Find P Given A P/A	Gradient Uniform Series Find A Given G A/G	Gradient Present Worth Find P Given G P/G	
n									n
1	1.030	.9709	1.0000	1.0300	1.000	0.971	0	0	1
2	1.061	.9426	.4926	.5226	2.030	1.913	0.493	0.943	2
3	1.093	.9151	.3235	.3535	3.091	2.829	0.980	2.773	3
4	1.126	.8885	.2390	.2690	4.184	3.717	1.463	5.438	4
5	1.159	.8626	.1884	.2184	5.309	4.580	1.941	8.889	5
6	1.194	.8375	.1546	.1846	6.468	5.417	2.414	13.076	6
7	1.230	.8131	.1305	.1605	7.662	6.230	2.882	17.955	7
8	1.267	.7894	.1125	.1425	8.892	7.020	3.345	23.481	8
9	1.305	.7664	.0984	.1284	10.159	7.786	3.803	29.612	9
10	1.344	.7441	.0872	.1172	11.464	8.530	4.256	36.309	10
11	1.384	.7224	.0781	.1081	12.808	9.253	4.705	43.533	11
12	1.426	.7014	.0705	.1005	14.192	9.954	5.148	51.248	12
13	1.469	.6810	.0640	.0940	15.618	10.635	5.587	59.419	13
14	1.513	.6611	.0585	.0885	17.086	11.296	6.021	68.014	14
15	1.558	.6419	.0538	.0838	18.599	11.938	6.450	77.000	15
16	1.605	.6232	.0496	.0796	20.157	12.561	6.874	86.348	16
17	1.653	.6050	.0460	.0760	21.762	13.166	7.294	96.028	17
18	1.702	.5874	.0427	.0727	23.414	13.754	7.708	106.014	18
19	1.754	.5703	.0398	.0698	25.117	14.324	8.118	116.279	19
20	1.806	.5537	.0372	.0672	26.870	14.877	8.523	126.799	20
21	1.860	.5375	.0349	.0649	28.676	15.415	8.923	137.549	21
22	1.916	.5219	.0327	.0627	30.537	15.937	9.319	148.509	22
23	1.974	.5067	.0308	.0608	32.453	16.444	9.709	159.656	23
24	2.033	.4919	.0290	.0590	34.426	16.936	10.095	170.971	24
25	2.094	.4776	.0274	.0574	36.459	17.413	10.477	182.433	25
26	2.157	.4637	.0259	.0559	38.553	17.877	10.853	194.026	26
27	2.221	.4502	.0246	.0546	40.710	18.327	11.226	205.731	27
28	2.288	.4371	.0233	.0533	42.931	18.764	11.593	217.532	28
29	2.357	.4243	.0221	.0521	45.219	19.188	11.956	229.413	29
30	2.427	.4120	.0210	.0510	47.575	19.600	12.314	241.361	30
31	2.500	.4000	.0200	.0500	50.003	20.000	12.668	253.361	31
32	2.575	.3883	.0190	.0490	52.503	20.389	13.017	265.399	32
33	2.652	.3770	.0182	.0482	55.078	20.766	13.362	277.464	33
34	2.732	.3660	.0173	.0473	57.730	21.132	13.702	289.544	34
35	2.814	.3554	.0165	.0465	60.462	21.487	14.037	301.627	35
40	3.262	.3066	.0133	.0433	75.401	23.115	15.650	361.750	40
45	3.782	.2644	.0108	.0408	92.720	24.519	17.156	420.632	45
50	4.384	.2281	.00887	.0389	112.797	25.730	18.558	477.480	50
55	5.082	.1968	.00735	.0373	136.072	26.774	19.860	531.741	55
60	5.892	.1697	.00613	.0361	163.053	27.676	21.067	583.052	60
65	6.830	.1464	.00515	.0351	194.333	28.453	22.184	631.201	65
70	7.918	.1263	.00434	.0343	230.594	29.123	23.215	676.087	70
75	9.179	.1089	.00367	.0337	272.631	29.702	24.163	717.698	75
80	10.641	.0940	.00311	.0331	321.363	30.201	25.035	756.086	80
85	12.336	.0811	.00265	.0326	377.857	30.631	25.835	791.353	85
90	14.300	.0699	.00226	.0323	443.349	31.002	26.567	823.630	90
95	16.578	.0603	.00193	.0319	519.272	31.323	27.235	853.074	95
100	19.219	.0520	.00165	.0316	607.287	31.599	27.844	879.854	100

3$\frac{1}{2}$% | | | | Compound Interest Factors | | | | | 3$\frac{1}{2}$%

	Single Payment		Uniform Payment Series				Arithmetic Gradient		
	Compound Amount Factor Find F Given P F/P	Present Worth Factor Find P Given F P/F	Sinking Fund Factor Find A Given F A/F	Capital Recovery Factor Find A Given P A/P	Compound Amount Factor Find F Given A F/A	Present Worth Factor Find P Given A P/A	Gradient Uniform Series Find A Given G A/G	Gradient Present Worth Find P Given G P/G	
n									n
1	1.035	.9662	1.0000	1.0350	1.000	0.966	0	0	1
2	1.071	.9335	.4914	.5264	2.035	1.900	0.491	0.933	2
3	1.109	.9019	.3219	.3569	3.106	2.802	0.977	2.737	3
4	1.148	.8714	.2373	.2723	4.215	3.673	1.457	5.352	4
5	1.188	.8420	.1865	.2215	5.362	4.515	1.931	8.719	5
6	1.229	.8135	.1527	.1877	6.550	5.329	2.400	12.787	6
7	1.272	.7860	.1285	.1635	7.779	6.115	2.862	17.503	7
8	1.317	.7594	.1105	.1455	9.052	6.874	3.320	22.819	8
9	1.363	.7337	.0964	.1314	10.368	7.608	3.771	28.688	9
10	1.411	.7089	.0852	.1202	11.731	8.317	4.217	35.069	10
11	1.460	.6849	.0761	.1111	13.142	9.002	4.657	41.918	11
12	1.511	.6618	.0685	.1035	14.602	9.663	5.091	49.198	12
13	1.564	.6394	.0621	.0971	16.113	10.303	5.520	56.871	13
14	1.619	.6178	.0566	.0916	17.677	10.921	5.943	64.902	14
15	1.675	.5969	.0518	.0868	19.296	11.517	6.361	73.258	15
16	1.734	.5767	.0477	.0827	20.971	12.094	6.773	81.909	16
17	1.795	.5572	.0440	.0790	22.705	12.651	7.179	90.824	17
18	1.857	.5384	.0408	.0758	24.500	13.190	7.580	99.976	18
19	1.922	.5202	.0379	.0729	26.357	13.710	7.975	109.339	19
20	1.990	.5026	.0354	.0704	28.280	14.212	8.365	118.888	20
21	2.059	.4856	.0330	.0680	30.269	14.698	8.749	128.599	21
22	2.132	.4692	.0309	.0659	32.329	15.167	9.128	138.451	22
23	2.206	.4533	.0290	.0640	34.460	15.620	9.502	148.423	23
24	2.283	.4380	.0273	.0623	36.666	16.058	9.870	158.496	24
25	2.363	.4231	.0257	.0607	38.950	16.482	10.233	168.652	25
26	2.446	.4088	.0242	.0592	41.313	16.890	10.590	178.873	26
27	2.532	.3950	.0229	.0579	43.759	17.285	10.942	189.143	27
28	2.620	.3817	.0216	.0566	46.291	17.667	11.289	199.448	28
29	2.712	.3687	.0204	.0554	48.911	18.036	11.631	209.773	29
30	2.807	.3563	.0194	.0544	51.623	18.392	11.967	220.105	30
31	2.905	.3442	.0184	.0534	54.429	18.736	12.299	230.432	31
32	3.007	.3326	.0174	.0524	57.334	19.069	12.625	240.742	32
33	3.112	.3213	.0166	.0516	60.341	19.390	12.946	251.025	33
34	3.221	.3105	.0158	.0508	63.453	19.701	13.262	261.271	34
35	3.334	.3000	.0150	.0500	66.674	20.001	13.573	271.470	35
40	3.959	.2526	.0118	.0468	84.550	21.355	15.055	321.490	40
45	4.702	.2127	.00945	.0445	105.781	22.495	16.417	369.307	45
50	5.585	.1791	.00763	.0426	130.998	23.456	17.666	414.369	50
55	6.633	.1508	.00621	.0412	160.946	24.264	18.808	456.352	55
60	7.878	.1269	.00509	.0401	196.516	24.945	19.848	495.104	60
65	9.357	.1069	.00419	.0392	238.762	25.518	20.793	530.598	65
70	11.113	.0900	.00346	.0385	288.937	26.000	21.650	562.895	70
75	13.199	.0758	.00287	.0379	348.529	26.407	22.423	592.121	75
80	15.676	.0638	.00238	.0374	419.305	26.749	23.120	618.438	80
85	18.618	.0537	.00199	.0370	503.365	27.037	23.747	642.036	85
90	22.112	.0452	.00166	.0367	603.202	27.279	24.308	663.118	90
95	26.262	.0381	.00139	.0364	721.778	27.483	24.811	681.890	95
100	31.191	.0321	.00116	.0362	862.608	27.655	25.259	698.554	100

4%					Compound Interest Factors					4%
	Single Payment		Uniform Payment Series				Arithmetic Gradient			
	Compound Amount Factor Find F Given P F/P	Present Worth Factor Find P Given F P/F	Sinking Fund Factor Find A Given F A/F	Capital Recovery Factor Find A Given P A/P	Compound Amount Factor Find F Given A F/A	Present Worth Factor Find P Given A P/A	Gradient Uniform Series Find A Given G A/G	Gradient Present Worth Find P Given G P/G		
n										n
1	1.040	.9615	1.0000	1.0400	1.000	0.962	0	0		1
2	1.082	.9246	.4902	.5302	2.040	1.886	0.490	0.925		2
3	1.125	.8890	.3203	.3603	3.122	2.775	0.974	2.702		3
4	1.170	.8548	.2355	.2755	4.246	3.630	1.451	5.267		4
5	1.217	.8219	.1846	.2246	5.416	4.452	1.922	8.555		5
6	1.265	.7903	.1508	.1908	6.633	5.242	2.386	12.506		6
7	1.316	.7599	.1266	.1666	7.898	6.002	2.843	17.066		7
8	1.369	.7307	.1085	.1485	9.214	6.733	3.294	22.180		8
9	1.423	.7026	.0945	.1345	10.583	7.435	3.739	27.801		9
10	1.480	.6756	.0833	.1233	12.006	8.111	4.177	33.881		10
11	1.539	.6496	.0741	.1141	13.486	8.760	4.609	40.377		11
12	1.601	.6246	.0666	.1066	15.026	9.385	5.034	47.248		12
13	1.665	.6006	.0601	.1001	16.627	9.986	5.453	54.454		13
14	1.732	.5775	.0547	.0947	18.292	10.563	5.866	61.962		14
15	1.801	.5553	.0499	.0899	20.024	11.118	6.272	69.735		15
16	1.873	.5339	.0458	.0858	21.825	11.652	6.672	77.744		16
17	1.948	.5134	.0422	.0822	23.697	12.166	7.066	85.958		17
18	2.026	.4936	.0390	.0790	25.645	12.659	7.453	94.350		18
19	2.107	.4746	.0361	.0761	27.671	13.134	7.834	102.893		19
20	2.191	.4564	.0336	.0736	29.778	13.590	8.209	111.564		20
21	2.279	.4388	.0313	.0713	31.969	14.029	8.578	120.341		21
22	2.370	.4220	.0292	.0692	34.248	14.451	8.941	129.202		22
23	2.465	.4057	.0273	.0673	36.618	14.857	9.297	138.128		23
24	2.563	.3901	.0256	.0656	39.083	15.247	9.648	147.101		24
25	2.666	.3751	.0240	.0640	41.646	15.622	9.993	156.104		25
26	2.772	.3607	.0226	.0626	44.312	15.983	10.331	165.121		26
27	2.883	.3468	.0212	.0612	47.084	16.330	10.664	174.138		27
28	2.999	.3335	.0200	.0600	49.968	16.663	10.991	183.142		28
29	3.119	.3207	.0189	.0589	52.966	16.984	11.312	192.120		29
30	3.243	.3083	.0178	.0578	56.085	17.292	11.627	201.062		30
31	3.373	.2965	.0169	.0569	59.328	17.588	11.937	209.955		31
32	3.508	.2851	.0159	.0559	62.701	17.874	12.241	218.792		32
33	3.648	.2741	.0151	.0551	66.209	18.148	12.540	227.563		33
34	3.794	.2636	.0143	.0543	69.858	18.411	12.832	236.260		34
35	3.946	.2534	.0136	.0536	73.652	18.665	13.120	244.876		35
40	4.801	.2083	.0105	.0505	95.025	19.793	14.476	286.530		40
45	5.841	.1712	.00826	.0483	121.029	20.720	15.705	325.402		45
50	7.107	.1407	.00655	.0466	152.667	21.482	16.812	361.163		50
55	8.646	.1157	.00523	.0452	191.159	22.109	17.807	393.689		55
60	10.520	.0951	.00420	.0442	237.990	22.623	18.697	422.996		60
65	12.799	.0781	.00339	.0434	294.968	23.047	19.491	449.201		65
70	15.572	.0642	.00275	.0427	364.290	23.395	20.196	472.479		70
75	18.945	.0528	.00223	.0422	448.630	23.680	20.821	493.041		75
80	23.050	.0434	.00181	.0418	551.244	23.915	21.372	511.116		80
85	28.044	.0357	.00148	.0415	676.089	24.109	21.857	526.938		85
90	34.119	.0293	.00121	.0412	827.981	24.267	22.283	540.737		90
95	41.511	.0241	.00099	.0410	1 012.8	24.398	22.655	552.730		95
100	50.505	.0198	.00081	.0408	1 237.6	24.505	22.980	563.125		100

4¹/₂%			Compound Interest Factors					4¹/₂%

	Single Payment		Uniform Payment Series				Arithmetic Gradient	
	Compound Amount Factor Find F Given P F/P	Present Worth Factor Find P Given F P/F	Sinking Fund Factor Find A Given F A/F	Capital Recovery Factor Find A Given P A/P	Compound Amount Factor Find F Given A F/A	Present Worth Factor Find P Given A P/A	Gradient Uniform Series Find A Given G A/G	Gradient Present Worth Find P Given G P/G	
n									n
1	1.045	.9569	1.0000	1.0450	1.000	0.957	0	0	1
2	1.092	.9157	.4890	.5340	2.045	1.873	0.489	0.916	2
3	1.141	.8763	.3188	.3638	3.137	2.749	0.971	2.668	3
4	1.193	.8386	.2337	.2787	4.278	3.588	1.445	5.184	4
5	1.246	.8025	.1828	.2278	5.471	4.390	1.912	8.394	5
6	1.302	.7679	.1489	.1939	6.717	5.158	2.372	12.233	6
7	1.361	.7348	.1247	.1697	8.019	5.893	2.824	16.642	7
8	1.422	.7032	.1066	.1516	9.380	6.596	3.269	21.564	8
9	1.486	.6729	.0926	.1376	10.802	7.269	3.707	26.948	9
10	1.553	.6439	.0814	.1264	12.288	7.913	4.138	32.743	10
11	1.623	.6162	.0722	.1172	13.841	8.529	4.562	38.905	11
12	1.696	.5897	.0647	.1097	15.464	9.119	4.978	45.391	12
13	1.772	.5643	.0583	.1033	17.160	9.683	5.387	52.163	13
14	1.852	.5400	.0528	.0978	18.932	10.223	5.789	59.182	14
15	1.935	.5167	.0481	.0931	20.784	10.740	6.184	66.416	15
16	2.022	.4945	.0440	.0890	22.719	11.234	6.572	73.833	16
17	2.113	.4732	.0404	.0854	24.742	11.707	6.953	81.404	17
18	2.208	.4528	.0372	.0822	26.855	12.160	7.327	89.102	18
19	2.308	.4333	.0344	.0794	29.064	12.593	7.695	96.901	19
20	2.412	.4146	.0319	.0769	31.371	13.008	8.055	104.779	20
21	2.520	.3968	.0296	.0746	33.783	13.405	8.409	112.715	21
22	2.634	.3797	.0275	.0725	36.303	13.784	8.755	120.689	22
23	2.752	.3634	.0257	.0707	38.937	14.148	9.096	128.682	23
24	2.876	.3477	.0240	.0690	41.689	14.495	9.429	136.680	24
25	3.005	.3327	.0224	.0674	44.565	14.828	9.756	144.665	25
26	3.141	.3184	.0210	.0660	47.571	15.147	10.077	152.625	26
27	3.282	.3047	.0197	.0647	50.711	15.451	10.391	160.547	27
28	3.430	.2916	.0185	.0635	53.993	15.743	10.698	168.420	28
29	3.584	.2790	.0174	.0624	57.423	16.022	10.999	176.232	29
30	3.745	.2670	.0164	.0614	61.007	16.289	11.295	183.975	30
31	3.914	.2555	.0154	.0604	64.752	16.544	11.583	191.640	31
32	4.090	.2445	.0146	.0596	68.666	16.789	11.866	199.220	32
33	4.274	.2340	.0137	.0587	72.756	17.023	12.143	206.707	33
34	4.466	.2239	.0130	.0580	77.030	17.247	12.414	214.095	34
35	4.667	.2143	.0123	.0573	81.497	17.461	12.679	221.380	35
40	5.816	.1719	.00934	.0543	107.030	18.402	13.917	256.098	40
45	7.248	.1380	.00720	.0522	138.850	19.156	15.020	287.732	45
50	9.033	.1107	.00560	.0506	178.503	19.762	15.998	316.145	50
55	11.256	.0888	.00439	.0494	227.918	20.248	16.860	341.375	55
60	14.027	.0713	.00345	.0485	289.497	20.638	17.617	363.571	60
65	17.481	.0572	.00273	.0477	366.237	20.951	18.278	382.946	65
70	21.784	.0459	.00217	.0472	461.869	21.202	18.854	399.750	70
75	27.147	.0368	.00172	.0467	581.043	21.404	19.354	414.242	75
80	33.830	.0296	.00137	.0464	729.556	21.565	19.785	426.680	80
85	42.158	.0237	.00109	.0461	914.630	21.695	20.157	437.309	85
90	52.537	.0190	.00087	.0459	1 145.3	21.799	20.476	446.359	90
95	65.471	.0153	.00070	.0457	1 432.7	21.883	20.749	454.039	95
100	81.588	.0123	.00056	.0456	1 790.9	21.950	20.981	460.537	100

5%					Compound Interest Factors					5%
	Single Payment		Uniform Payment Series				Arithmetic Gradient			
	Compound Amount Factor Find F Given P F/P	Present Worth Factor Find P Given F P/F	Sinking Fund Factor Find A Given F A/F	Capital Recovery Factor Find A Given P A/P	Compound Amount Factor Find F Given A F/A	Present Worth Factor Find P Given A P/A	Gradient Uniform Series Find A Given G A/G	Gradient Present Worth Find P Given G P/G	
n									n
1	1.050	.9524	1.0000	1.0500	1.000	0.952	0	0	1
2	1.102	.9070	.4878	.5378	2.050	1.859	0.488	0.907	2
3	1.158	.8638	.3172	.3672	3.152	2.723	0.967	2.635	3
4	1.216	.8227	.2320	.2820	4.310	3.546	1.439	5.103	4
5	1.276	.7835	.1810	.2310	5.526	4.329	1.902	8.237	5
6	1.340	.7462	.1470	.1970	6.802	5.076	2.358	11.968	6
7	1.407	.7107	.1228	.1728	8.142	5.786	2.805	16.232	7
8	1.477	.6768	.1047	.1547	9.549	6.463	3.244	20.970	8
9	1.551	.6446	.0907	.1407	11.027	7.108	3.676	26.127	9
10	1.629	.6139	.0795	.1295	12.578	7.722	4.099	31.652	10
11	1.710	.5847	.0704	.1204	14.207	8.306	4.514	37.499	11
12	1.796	.5568	.0628	.1128	15.917	8.863	4.922	43.624	12
13	1.886	.5303	.0565	.1065	17.713	9.394	5.321	49.988	13
14	1.980	.5051	.0510	.1010	19.599	9.899	5.713	56.553	14
15	2.079	.4810	.0463	.0963	21.579	10.380	6.097	63.288	15
16	2.183	.4581	.0423	.0923	23.657	10.838	6.474	70.159	16
17	2.292	.4363	.0387	.0887	25.840	11.274	6.842	77.140	17
18	2.407	.4155	.0355	.0855	28.132	11.690	7.203	84.204	18
19	2.527	.3957	.0327	.0827	30.539	12.085	7.557	91.327	19
20	2.653	.3769	.0302	.0802	33.066	12.462	7.903	98.488	20
21	2.786	.3589	.0280	.0780	35.719	12.821	8.242	105.667	21
22	2.925	.3419	.0260	.0760	38.505	13.163	8.573	112.846	22
23	3.072	.3256	.0241	.0741	41.430	13.489	8.897	120.008	23
24	3.225	.3101	.0225	.0725	44.502	13.799	9.214	127.140	24
25	3.386	.2953	.0210	.0710	47.727	14.094	9.524	134.227	25
26	3.556	.2812	.0196	.0696	51.113	14.375	9.827	141.258	26
27	3.733	.2678	.0183	.0683	54.669	14.643	10.122	148.222	27
28	3.920	.2551	.0171	.0671	58.402	14.898	10.411	155.110	28
29	4.116	.2429	.0160	.0660	62.323	15.141	10.694	161.912	29
30	4.322	.2314	.0151	.0651	66.439	15.372	10.969	168.622	30
31	4.538	.2204	.0141	.0641	70.761	15.593	11.238	175.233	31
32	4.765	.2099	.0133	.0633	75.299	15.803	11.501	181.739	32
33	5.003	.1999	.0125	.0625	80.063	16.003	11.757	188.135	33
34	5.253	.1904	.0118	.0618	85.067	16.193	12.006	194.416	34
35	5.516	.1813	.0111	.0611	90.320	16.374	12.250	200.580	35
40	7.040	.1420	.00828	.0583	120.799	17.159	13.377	229.545	40
45	8.985	.1113	.00626	.0563	159.699	17.774	14.364	255.314	45
50	11.467	.0872	.00478	.0548	209.347	18.256	15.223	277.914	50
55	14.636	.0683	.00367	.0537	272.711	18.633	15.966	297.510	55
60	18.679	.0535	.00283	.0528	353.582	18.929	16.606	314.343	60
65	23.840	.0419	.00219	.0522	456.795	19.161	17.154	328.691	65
70	30.426	.0329	.00170	.0517	588.525	19.343	17.621	340.841	70
75	38.832	.0258	.00132	.0513	756.649	19.485	18.018	351.072	75
80	49.561	.0202	.00103	.0510	971.222	19.596	18.353	359.646	80
85	63.254	.0158	.00080	.0508	1 245.1	19.684	18.635	366.800	85
90	80.730	.0124	.00063	.0506	1 594.6	19.752	18.871	372.749	90
95	103.034	.00971	.00049	.0505	2 040.7	19.806	19.069	377.677	95
100	131.500	.00760	.00038	.0504	2 610.0	19.848	19.234	381.749	100

6% Compound Interest Factors 6%

	Single Payment		Uniform Payment Series				Arithmetic Gradient		
	Compound Amount Factor Find F Given P	Present Worth Factor Find P Given F	Sinking Fund Factor Find A Given F	Capital Recovery Factor Find A Given P	Compound Amount Factor Find F Given A	Present Worth Factor Find P Given A	Gradient Uniform Series Find A Given G	Gradient Present Worth Find P Given G	
n	F/P	P/F	A/F	A/P	F/A	P/A	A/G	P/G	n
1	1.060	.9434	1.0000	1.0600	1.000	0.943	0	0	1
2	1.124	.8900	.4854	.5454	2.060	1.833	0.485	0.890	2
3	1.191	.8396	.3141	.3741	3.184	2.673	0.961	2.569	3
4	1.262	.7921	.2286	.2886	4.375	3.465	1.427	4.945	4
5	1.338	.7473	.1774	.2374	5.637	4.212	1.884	7.934	5
6	1.419	.7050	.1434	.2034	6.975	4.917	2.330	11.459	6
7	1.504	.6651	.1191	.1791	8.394	5.582	2.768	15.450	7
8	1.594	.6274	.1010	.1610	9.897	6.210	3.195	19.841	8
9	1.689	.5919	.0870	.1470	11.491	6.802	3.613	24.577	9
10	1.791	.5584	.0759	.1359	13.181	7.360	4.022	29.602	10
11	1.898	.5268	.0668	.1268	14.972	7.887	4.421	34.870	11
12	2.012	.4970	.0593	.1193	16.870	8.384	4.811	40.337	12
13	2.133	.4688	.0530	.1130	18.882	8.853	5.192	45.963	13
14	2.261	.4423	.0476	.1076	21.015	9.295	5.564	51.713	14
15	2.397	.4173	.0430	.1030	23.276	9.712	5.926	57.554	15
16	2.540	.3936	.0390	.0990	25.672	10.106	6.279	63.459	16
17	2.693	.3714	.0354	.0954	28.213	10.477	6.624	69.401	17
18	2.854	.3503	.0324	.0924	30.906	10.828	6.960	75.357	18
19	3.026	.3305	.0296	.0896	33.760	11.158	7.287	81.306	19
20	3.207	.3118	.0272	.0872	36.786	11.470	7.605	87.230	20
21	3.400	.2942	.0250	.0850	39.993	11.764	7.915	93.113	21
22	3.604	.2775	.0230	.0830	43.392	12.042	8.217	98.941	22
23	3.820	.2618	.0213	.0813	46.996	12.303	8.510	104.700	23
24	4.049	.2470	.0197	.0797	50.815	12.550	8.795	110.381	24
25	4.292	.2330	.0182	.0782	54.864	12.783	9.072	115.973	25
26	4.549	.2198	.0169	.0769	59.156	13.003	9.341	121.468	26
27	4.822	.2074	.0157	.0757	63.706	13.211	9.603	126.860	27
28	5.112	.1956	.0146	.0746	68.528	13.406	9.857	132.142	28
29	5.418	.1846	.0136	.0736	73.640	13.591	10.103	137.309	29
30	5.743	.1741	.0126	.0726	79.058	13.765	10.342	142.359	30
31	6.088	.1643	.0118	.0718	84.801	13.929	10.574	147.286	31
32	6.453	.1550	.0110	.0710	90.890	14.084	10.799	152.090	32
33	6.841	.1462	.0103	.0703	97.343	14.230	11.017	156.768	33
34	7.251	.1379	.00960	.0696	104.184	14.368	11.228	161.319	34
35	7.686	.1301	.00897	.0690	111.435	14.498	11.432	165.743	35
40	10.286	.0972	.00646	.0665	154.762	15.046	12.359	185.957	40
45	13.765	.0727	.00470	.0647	212.743	15.456	13.141	203.109	45
50	18.420	.0543	.00344	.0634	290.335	15.762	13.796	217.457	50
55	24.650	.0406	.00254	.0625	394.171	15.991	14.341	229.322	55
60	32.988	.0303	.00188	.0619	533.126	16.161	14.791	239.043	60
65	44.145	.0227	.00139	.0614	719.080	16.289	15.160	246.945	65
70	59.076	.0169	.00103	.0610	967.928	16.385	15.461	253.327	70
75	79.057	.0126	.00077	.0608	1 300.9	16.456	15.706	258.453	75
80	105.796	.00945	.00057	.0606	1 746.6	16.509	15.903	262.549	80
85	141.578	.00706	.00043	.0604	2 343.0	16.549	16.062	265.810	85
90	189.464	.00528	.00032	.0603	3 141.1	16.579	16.189	268.395	90
95	253.545	.00394	.00024	.0602	4 209.1	16.601	16.290	270.437	95
100	339.300	.00295	.00018	.0602	5 638.3	16.618	16.371	272.047	100

7%					Compound Interest Factors				7%
	Single Payment		Uniform Payment Series				Arithmetic Gradient		
	Compound Amount Factor Find F Given P F/P	Present Worth Factor Find P Given F P/F	Sinking Fund Factor Find A Given F A/F	Capital Recovery Factor Find A Given P A/P	Compound Amount Factor Find F Given A F/A	Present Worth Factor Find P Given A P/A	Gradient Uniform Series Find A Given G A/G	Gradient Present Worth Find P Given G P/G	
n									n
1	1.070	.9346	1.0000	1.0700	1.000	0.935	0	0	1
2	1.145	.8734	.4831	.5531	2.070	1.808	0.483	0.873	2
3	1.225	.8163	.3111	.3811	3.215	2.624	0.955	2.506	3
4	1.311	.7629	.2252	.2952	4.440	3.387	1.416	4.795	4
5	1.403	.7130	.1739	.2439	5.751	4.100	1.865	7.647	5
6	1.501	.6663	.1398	.2098	7.153	4.767	2.303	10.978	6
7	1.606	.6227	.1156	.1856	8.654	5.389	2.730	14.715	7
8	1.718	.5820	.0975	.1675	10.260	5.971	3.147	18.789	8
9	1.838	.5439	.0835	.1535	11.978	6.515	3.552	23.140	9
10	1.967	.5083	.0724	.1424	13.816	7.024	3.946	27.716	10
11	2.105	.4751	.0634	.1334	15.784	7.499	4.330	32.467	11
12	2.252	.4440	.0559	.1259	17.888	7.943	4.703	37.351	12
13	2.410	.4150	.0497	.1197	20.141	8.358	5.065	42.330	13
14	2.579	.3878	.0443	.1143	22.551	8.745	5.417	47.372	14
15	2.759	.3624	.0398	.1098	25.129	9.108	5.758	52.446	15
16	2.952	.3387	.0359	.1059	27.888	9.447	6.090	57.527	16
17	3.159	.3166	.0324	.1024	30.840	9.763	6.411	62.592	17
18	3.380	.2959	.0294	.0994	33.999	10.059	6.722	67.622	18
19	3.617	.2765	.0268	.0968	37.379	10.336	7.024	72.599	19
20	3.870	.2584	.0244	.0944	40.996	10.594	7.316	77.509	20
21	4.141	.2415	.0223	.0923	44.865	10.836	7.599	82.339	21
22	4.430	.2257	.0204	.0904	49.006	11.061	7.872	87.079	22
23	4.741	.2109	.0187	.0887	53.436	11.272	8.137	91.720	23
24	5.072	.1971	.0172	.0872	58.177	11.469	8.392	96.255	24
25	5.427	.1842	.0158	.0858	63.249	11.654	8.639	100.677	25
26	5.807	.1722	.0146	.0846	68.677	11.826	8.877	104.981	26
27	6.214	.1609	.0134	.0834	74.484	11.987	9.107	109.166	27
28	6.649	.1504	.0124	.0824	80.698	12.137	9.329	113.227	28
29	7.114	.1406	.0114	.0814	87.347	12.278	9.543	117.162	29
30	7.612	.1314	.0106	.0806	94.461	12.409	9.749	120.972	30
31	8.145	.1228	.00980	.0798	102.073	12.532	9.947	124.655	31
32	8.715	.1147	.00907	.0791	110.218	12.647	10.138	128.212	32
33	9.325	.1072	.00841	.0784	118.934	12.754	10.322	131.644	33
34	9.978	.1002	.00780	.0778	128.259	12.854	10.499	134.951	34
35	10.677	.0937	.00723	.0772	138.237	12.948	10.669	138.135	35
40	14.974	.0668	.00501	.0750	199.636	13.332	11.423	152.293	40
45	21.002	.0476	.00350	.0735	285.750	13.606	12.036	163.756	45
50	29.457	.0339	.00246	.0725	406.530	13.801	12.529	172.905	50
55	41.315	.0242	.00174	.0717	575.930	13.940	12.921	180.124	55
60	57.947	.0173	.00123	.0712	813.523	14.039	13.232	185.768	60
65	81.273	.0123	.00087	.0709	1 146.8	14.110	13.476	190.145	65
70	113.990	.00877	.00062	.0706	1 614.1	14.160	13.666	193.519	70
75	159.877	.00625	.00044	.0704	2 269.7	14.196	13.814	196.104	75
80	224.235	.00446	.00031	.0703	3 189.1	14.222	13.927	198.075	80
85	314.502	.00318	.00022	.0702	4 478.6	14.240	14.015	199.572	85
90	441.105	.00227	.00016	.0702	6 287.2	14.253	14.081	200.704	90
95	618.673	.00162	.00011	.0701	8 823.9	14.263	14.132	201.558	95
100	867.720	.00115	.00008	.0701	12 381.7	14.269	14.170	202.200	100

8%				Compound Interest Factors					8%
	Single Payment		Uniform Payment Series				Arithmetic Gradient		
	Compound Amount Factor Find F Given P F/P	Present Worth Factor Find P Given F P/F	Sinking Fund Factor Find A Given F A/F	Capital Recovery Factor Find A Given P A/P	Compound Amount Factor Find F Given A F/A	Present Worth Factor Find P Given A P/A	Gradient Uniform Series Find A Given G A/G	Gradient Present Worth Find P Given G P/G	
n	F/P	P/F	A/F	A/P	F/A	P/A	A/G	P/G	n
1	1.080	.9259	1.0000	1.0800	1.000	0.926	0	0	1
2	1.166	.8573	.4808	.5608	2.080	1.783	0.481	0.857	2
3	1.260	.7938	.3080	.3880	3.246	2.577	0.949	2.445	3
4	1.360	.7350	.2219	.3019	4.506	3.312	1.404	4.650	4
5	1.469	.6806	.1705	.2505	5.867	3.993	1.846	7.372	5
6	1.587	.6302	.1363	.2163	7.336	4.623	2.276	10.523	6
7	1.714	.5835	.1121	.1921	8.923	5.206	2.694	14.024	7
8	1.851	.5403	.0940	.1740	10.637	5.747	3.099	17.806	8
9	1.999	.5002	.0801	.1601	12.488	6.247	3.491	21.808	9
10	2.159	.4632	.0690	.1490	14.487	6.710	3.871	25.977	10
11	2.332	.4289	.0601	.1401	16.645	7.139	4.240	30.266	11
12	2.518	.3971	.0527	.1327	18.977	7.536	4.596	34.634	12
13	2.720	.3677	.0465	.1265	21.495	7.904	4.940	39.046	13
14	2.937	.3405	.0413	.1213	24.215	8.244	5.273	43.472	14
15	3.172	.3152	.0368	.1168	27.152	8.559	5.594	47.886	15
16	3.426	.2919	.0330	.1130	30.324	8.851	5.905	52.264	16
17	3.700	.2703	.0296	.1096	33.750	9.122	6.204	56.588	17
18	3.996	.2502	.0267	.1067	37.450	9.372	6.492	60.843	18
19	4.316	.2317	.0241	.1041	41.446	9.604	6.770	65.013	19
20	4.661	.2145	.0219	.1019	45.762	9.818	7.037	69.090	20
21	5.034	.1987	.0198	.0998	50.423	10.017	7.294	73.063	21
22	5.437	.1839	.0180	.0980	55.457	10.201	7.541	76.926	22
23	5.871	.1703	.0164	.0964	60.893	10.371	7.779	80.673	23
24	6.341	.1577	.0150	.0950	66.765	10.529	8.007	84.300	24
25	6.848	.1460	.0137	.0937	73.106	10.675	8.225	87.804	25
26	7.396	.1352	.0125	.0925	79.954	10.810	8.435	91.184	26
27	7.988	.1252	.0114	.0914	87.351	10.935	8.636	94.439	27
28	8.627	.1159	.0105	.0905	95.339	11.051	8.829	97.569	28
29	9.317	.1073	.00962	.0896	103.966	11.158	9.013	100.574	29
30	10.063	.0994	.00883	.0888	113.283	11.258	9.190	103.456	30
31	10.868	.0920	.00811	.0881	123.346	11.350	9.358	106.216	31
32	11.737	.0852	.00745	.0875	134.214	11.435	9.520	108.858	32
33	12.676	.0789	.00685	.0869	145.951	11.514	9.674	111.382	33
34	13.690	.0730	.00630	.0863	158.627	11.587	9.821	113.792	34
35	14.785	.0676	.00580	.0858	172.317	11.655	9.961	116.092	35
40	21.725	.0460	.00386	.0839	259.057	11.925	10.570	126.042	40
45	31.920	.0313	.00259	.0826	386.506	12.108	11.045	133.733	45
50	46.902	.0213	.00174	.0817	573.771	12.233	11.411	139.593	50
55	68.914	.0145	.00118	.0812	848.925	12.319	11.690	144.006	55
60	101.257	.00988	.00080	.0808	1 253.2	12.377	11.902	147.300	60
65	148.780	.00672	.00054	.0805	1 847.3	12.416	12.060	149.739	65
70	218.607	.00457	.00037	.0804	2 720.1	12.443	12.178	151.533	70
75	321.205	.00311	.00025	.0802	4 002.6	12.461	12.266	152.845	75
80	471.956	.00212	.00017	.0802	5 887.0	12.474	12.330	153.800	80
85	693.458	.00144	.00012	.0801	8 655.7	12.482	12.377	154.492	85
90	1 018.9	.00098	.00008	.0801	12 724.0	12.488	12.412	154.993	90
95	1 497.1	.00067	.00005	.0801	18 701.6	12.492	12.437	155.352	95
100	2 199.8	.00045	.00004	.0800	27 484.6	12.494	12.455	155.611	100

9%				Compound Interest Factors					9%
	Single Payment		Uniform Payment Series				Arithmetic Gradient		
	Compound Amount Factor Find F Given P	Present Worth Factor Find P Given F	Sinking Fund Factor Find A Given F	Capital Recovery Factor Find A Given P	Compound Amount Factor Find F Given A	Present Worth Factor Find P Given A	Gradient Uniform Series Find A Given G	Gradient Present Worth Find P Given G	
n	F/P	P/F	A/F	A/P	F/A	P/A	A/G	P/G	n
1	1.090	.9174	1.0000	1.0900	1.000	0.917	0	0	1
2	1.188	.8417	.4785	.5685	2.090	1.759	0.478	0.842	2
3	1.295	.7722	.3051	.3951	3.278	2.531	0.943	2.386	3
4	1.412	.7084	.2187	.3087	4.573	3.240	1.393	4.511	4
5	1.539	.6499	.1671	.2571	5.985	3.890	1.828	7.111	5
6	1.677	.5963	.1329	.2229	7.523	4.486	2.250	10.092	6
7	1.828	.5470	.1087	.1987	9.200	5.033	2.657	13.375	7
8	1.993	.5019	.0907	.1807	11.028	5.535	3.051	16.888	8
9	2.172	.4604	.0768	.1668	13.021	5.995	3.431	20.571	9
10	2.367	.4224	.0658	.1558	15.193	6.418	3.798	24.373	10
11	2.580	.3875	.0569	.1469	17.560	6.805	4.151	28.248	11
12	2.813	.3555	.0497	.1397	20.141	7.161	4.491	32.159	12
13	3.066	.3262	.0436	.1336	22.953	7.487	4.818	36.073	13
14	3.342	.2992	.0384	.1284	26.019	7.786	5.133	39.963	14
15	3.642	.2745	.0341	.1241	29.361	8.061	5.435	43.807	15
16	3.970	.2519	.0303	.1203	33.003	8.313	5.724	47.585	16
17	4.328	.2311	.0270	.1170	36.974	8.544	6.002	51.282	17
18	4.717	.2120	.0242	.1142	41.301	8.756	6.269	54.886	18
19	5.142	.1945	.0217	.1117	46.019	8.950	6.524	58.387	19
20	5.604	.1784	.0195	.1095	51.160	9.129	6.767	61.777	20
21	6.109	.1637	.0176	.1076	56.765	9.292	7.001	65.051	21
22	6.659	.1502	.0159	.1059	62.873	9.442	7.223	68.205	22
23	7.258	.1378	.0144	.1044	69.532	9.580	7.436	71.236	23
24	7.911	.1264	.0130	.1030	76.790	9.707	7.638	74.143	24
25	8.623	.1160	.0118	.1018	84.701	9.823	7.832	76.927	25
26	9.399	.1064	.0107	.1007	93.324	9.929	8.016	79.586	26
27	10.245	.0976	.00973	.0997	102.723	10.027	8.191	82.124	27
28	11.167	.0895	.00885	.0989	112.968	10.116	8.357	84.542	28
29	12.172	.0822	.00806	.0981	124.136	10.198	8.515	86.842	29
30	13.268	.0754	.00734	.0973	136.308	10.274	8.666	89.028	30
31	14.462	.0691	.00669	.0967	149.575	10.343	8.808	91.102	31
32	15.763	.0634	.00610	.0961	164.037	10.406	8.944	93.069	32
33	17.182	.0582	.00556	.0956	179.801	10.464	9.072	94.931	33
34	18.728	.0534	.00508	.0951	196.983	10.518	9.193	96.693	34
35	20.414	.0490	.00464	.0946	215.711	10.567	9.308	98.359	35
40	31.409	.0318	.00296	.0930	337.883	10.757	9.796	105.376	40
45	48.327	.0207	.00190	.0919	525.860	10.881	10.160	110.556	45
50	74.358	.0134	.00123	.0912	815.085	10.962	10.430	114.325	50
55	114.409	.00874	.00079	.0908	1 260.1	11.014	10.626	117.036	55
60	176.032	.00568	.00051	.0905	1 944.8	11.048	10.768	118.968	60
65	270.847	.00369	.00033	.0903	2 998.3	11.070	10.870	120.334	65
70	416.731	.00240	.00022	.0902	4 619.2	11.084	10.943	121.294	70
75	641.193	.00156	.00014	.0901	7 113.3	11.094	10.994	121.965	75
80	986.555	.00101	.00009	.0901	10 950.6	11.100	11.030	122.431	80
85	1 517.9	.00066	.00006	.0901	16 854.9	11.104	11.055	122.753	85
90	2 335.5	.00043	.00004	.0900	25 939.3	11.106	11.073	122.976	90
95	3 593.5	.00028	.00003	.0900	39 916.8	11.108	11.085	123.129	95
100	5 529.1	.00018	.00002	.0900	61 422.9	11.109	11.093	123.233	100

10%					Compound Interest Factors					10%
	Single Payment		Uniform Payment Series				Arithmetic Gradient			
	Compound Amount Factor Find F Given P	Present Worth Factor Find P Given F	Sinking Fund Factor Find A Given F	Capital Recovery Factor Find A Given P	Compound Amount Factor Find F Given A	Present Worth Factor Find P Given A	Gradient Uniform Series Find A Given G	Gradient Present Worth Find P Given G		
n	F/P	P/F	A/F	A/P	F/A	P/A	A/G	P/G	n
1	1.100	.9091	1.0000	1.1000	1.000	0.909	0	0	1
2	1.210	.8264	.4762	.5762	2.100	1.736	0.476	0.826	2
3	1.331	.7513	.3021	.4021	3.310	2.487	0.937	2.329	3
4	1.464	.6830	.2155	.3155	4.641	3.170	1.381	4.378	4
5	1.611	.6209	.1638	.2638	6.105	3.791	1.810	6.862	5
6	1.772	.5645	.1296	.2296	7.716	4.355	2.224	9.684	6
7	1.949	.5132	.1054	.2054	9.487	4.868	2.622	12.763	7
8	2.144	.4665	.0874	.1874	11.436	5.335	3.004	16.029	8
9	2.358	.4241	.0736	.1736	13.579	5.759	3.372	19.421	9
10	2.594	.3855	.0627	.1627	15.937	6.145	3.725	22.891	10
11	2.853	.3505	.0540	.1540	18.531	6.495	4.064	26.396	11
12	3.138	.3186	.0468	.1468	21.384	6.814	4.388	29.901	12
13	3.452	.2897	.0408	.1408	24.523	7.103	4.699	33.377	13
14	3.797	.2633	.0357	.1357	27.975	7.367	4.996	36.801	14
15	4.177	.2394	.0315	.1315	31.772	7.606	5.279	40.152	15
16	4.595	.2176	.0278	.1278	35.950	7.824	5.549	43.416	16
17	5.054	.1978	.0247	.1247	40.545	8.022	5.807	46.582	17
18	5.560	.1799	.0219	.1219	45.599	8.201	6.053	49.640	18
19	6.116	.1635	.0195	.1195	51.159	8.365	6.286	52.583	19
20	6.728	.1486	.0175	.1175	57.275	8.514	6.508	55.407	20
21	7.400	.1351	.0156	.1156	64.003	8.649	6.719	58.110	21
22	8.140	.1228	.0140	.1140	71.403	8.772	6.919	60.689	22
23	8.954	.1117	.0126	.1126	79.543	8.883	7.108	63.146	23
24	9.850	.1015	.0113	.1113	88.497	8.985	7.288	65.481	24
25	10.835	.0923	.0102	.1102	98.347	9.077	7.458	67.696	25
26	11.918	.0839	.00916	.1092	109.182	9.161	7.619	69.794	26
27	13.110	.0763	.00826	.1083	121.100	9.237	7.770	71.777	27
28	14.421	.0693	.00745	.1075	134.210	9.307	7.914	73.650	28
29	15.863	.0630	.00673	.1067	148.631	9.370	8.049	75.415	29
30	17.449	.0573	.00608	.1061	164.494	9.427	8.176	77.077	30
31	19.194	.0521	.00550	.1055	181.944	9.479	8.296	78.640	31
32	21.114	.0474	.00497	.1050	201.138	9.526	8.409	80.108	32
33	23.225	.0431	.00450	.1045	222.252	9.569	8.515	81.486	33
34	25.548	.0391	.00407	.1041	245.477	9.609	8.615	82.777	34
35	28.102	.0356	.00369	.1037	271.025	9.644	8.709	83.987	35
40	45.259	.0221	.00226	.1023	442.593	9.779	9.096	88.953	40
45	72.891	.0137	.00139	.1014	718.905	9.863	9.374	92.454	45
50	117.391	.00852	.00086	.1009	1 163.9	9.915	9.570	94.889	50
55	189.059	.00529	.00053	.1005	1 880.6	9.947	9.708	96.562	55
60	304.482	.00328	.00033	.1003	3 034.8	9.967	9.802	97.701	60
65	490.371	.00204	.00020	.1002	4 893.7	9.980	9.867	98.471	65
70	789.748	.00127	.00013	.1001	7 887.5	9.987	9.911	98.987	70
75	1 271.9	.00079	.00008	.1001	12 709.0	9.992	9.941	99.332	75
80	2 048.4	.00049	.00005	.1000	20 474.0	9.995	9.961	99.561	80
85	3 299.0	.00030	.00003	.1000	32 979.7	9.997	9.974	99.712	85
90	5 313.0	.00019	.00002	.1000	53 120.3	9.998	9.983	99.812	90
95	8 556.7	.00012	.00001	.1000	85 556.9	9.999	9.989	99.877	95
100	13 780.6	.00007	.00001	.1000	137 796.3	9.999	9.993	99.920	100

12%				Compound Interest Factors					12%
	Single Payment		Uniform Payment Series				Arithmetic Gradient		
	Compound Amount Factor Find F Given P F/P	Present Worth Factor Find P Given F P/F	Sinking Fund Factor Find A Given F A/F	Capital Recovery Factor Find A Given P A/P	Compound Amount Factor Find F Given A F/A	Present Worth Factor Find P Given A P/A	Gradient Uniform Series Find A Given G A/G	Gradient Present Worth Find P Given G P/G	
n									n
1	1.120	.8929	1.0000	1.1200	1.000	0.893	0	0	1
2	1.254	.7972	.4717	.5917	2.120	1.690	0.472	0.797	2
3	1.405	.7118	.2963	.4163	3.374	2.402	0.925	2.221	3
4	1.574	.6355	.2092	.3292	4.779	3.037	1.359	4.127	4
5	1.762	.5674	.1574	.2774	6.353	3.605	1.775	6.397	5
6	1.974	.5066	.1232	.2432	8.115	4.111	2.172	8.930	6
7	2.211	.4523	.0991	.2191	10.089	4.564	2.551	11.644	7
8	2.476	.4039	.0813	.2013	12.300	4.968	2.913	14.471	8
9	2.773	.3606	.0677	.1877	14.776	5.328	3.257	17.356	9
10	3.106	.3220	.0570	.1770	17.549	5.650	3.585	20.254	10
11	3.479	.2875	.0484	.1684	20.655	5.938	3.895	23.129	11
12	3.896	.2567	.0414	.1614	24.133	6.194	4.190	25.952	12
13	4.363	.2292	.0357	.1557	28.029	6.424	4.468	28.702	13
14	4.887	.2046	.0309	.1509	32.393	6.628	4.732	31.362	14
15	5.474	.1827	.0268	.1468	37.280	6.811	4.980	33.920	15
16	6.130	.1631	.0234	.1434	42.753	6.974	5.215	36.367	16
17	6.866	.1456	.0205	.1405	48.884	7.120	5.435	38.697	17
18	7.690	.1300	.0179	.1379	55.750	7.250	5.643	40.908	18
19	8.613	.1161	.0158	.1358	63.440	7.366	5.838	42.998	19
20	9.646	.1037	.0139	.1339	72.052	7.469	6.020	44.968	20
21	10.804	.0926	.0122	.1322	81.699	7.562	6.191	46.819	21
22	12.100	.0826	.0108	.1308	92.503	7.645	6.351	48.554	22
23	13.552	.0738	.00956	.1296	104.603	7.718	6.501	50.178	23
24	15.179	.0659	.00846	.1285	118.155	7.784	6.641	51.693	24
25	17.000	.0588	.00750	.1275	133.334	7.843	6.771	53.105	25
26	19.040	.0525	.00665	.1267	150.334	7.896	6.892	54.418	26
27	21.325	.0469	.00590	.1259	169.374	7.943	7.005	55.637	27
28	23.884	.0419	.00524	.1252	190.699	7.984	7.110	56.767	28
29	26.750	.0374	.00466	.1247	214.583	8.022	7.207	57.814	29
30	29.960	.0334	.00414	.1241	241.333	8.055	7.297	58.782	30
31	33.555	.0298	.00369	.1237	271.293	8.085	7.381	59.676	31
32	37.582	.0266	.00328	.1233	304.848	8.112	7.459	60.501	32
33	42.092	.0238	.00292	.1229	342.429	8.135	7.530	61.261	33
34	47.143	.0212	.00260	.1226	384.521	8.157	7.596	61.961	34
35	52.800	.0189	.00232	.1223	431.663	8.176	7.658	62.605	35
40	93.051	.0107	.00130	.1213	767.091	8.244	7.899	65.116	40
45	163.988	.00610	.00074	.1207	1 358.2	8.283	8.057	66.734	45
50	289.002	.00346	.00042	.1204	2 400.0	8.304	8.160	67.762	50
55	509.321	.00196	.00024	.1202	4 236.0	8.317	8.225	68.408	55
60	897.597	.00111	.00013	.1201	7 471.6	8.324	8.266	68.810	60
65	1 581.9	.00063	.00008	.1201	13 173.9	8.328	8.292	69.058	65
70	2 787.8	.00036	.00004	.1200	23 223.3	8.330	8.308	69.210	70
75	4 913.1	.00020	.00002	.1200	40 933.8	8.332	8.318	69.303	75
80	8 658.5	.00012	.00001	.1200	72 145.7	8.332	8.324	69.359	80
85	15 259.2	.00007	.00001	.1200	127 151.7	8.333	8.328	69.393	85
90	26 891.9	.00004		.1200	224 091.1	8.333	8.330	69.414	90
95	47 392.8	.00002		.1200	394 931.4	8.333	8.331	69.426	95
100	83 522.3	.00001		.1200	696 010.5	8.333	8.332	69.434	100

15%				Compound Interest Factors						15%
	Single Payment		**Uniform Payment Series**				**Arithmetic Gradient**			
	Compound Amount Factor Find F Given P	Present Worth Factor Find P Given F	Sinking Fund Factor Find A Given F	Capital Recovery Factor Find A Given P	Compound Amount Factor Find F Given A	Present Worth Factor Find P Given A	Gradient Uniform Series Find A Given G	Gradient Present Worth Find P Given G		
n	F/P	P/F	A/F	A/P	F/A	P/A	A/G	P/G	n
1	1.150	.8696	1.0000	1.1500	1.000	0.870	0	0	1
2	1.322	.7561	.4651	.6151	2.150	1.626	0.465	0.756	2
3	1.521	.6575	.2880	.4380	3.472	2.283	0.907	2.071	3
4	1.749	.5718	.2003	.3503	4.993	2.855	1.326	3.786	4
5	2.011	.4972	.1483	.2983	6.742	3.352	1.723	5.775	5
6	2.313	.4323	.1142	.2642	8.754	3.784	2.097	7.937	6
7	2.660	.3759	.0904	.2404	11.067	4.160	2.450	10.192	7
8	3.059	.3269	.0729	.2229	13.727	4.487	2.781	12.481	8
9	3.518	.2843	.0596	.2096	16.786	4.772	3.092	14.755	9
10	4.046	.2472	.0493	.1993	20.304	5.019	3.383	16.979	10
11	4.652	.2149	.0411	.1911	24.349	5.234	3.655	19.129	11
12	5.350	.1869	.0345	.1845	29.002	5.421	3.908	21.185	12
13	6.153	.1625	.0291	.1791	34.352	5.583	4.144	23.135	13
14	7.076	.1413	.0247	.1747	40.505	5.724	4.362	24.972	14
15	8.137	.1229	.0210	.1710	47.580	5.847	4.565	26.693	15
16	9.358	.1069	.0179	.1679	55.717	5.954	4.752	28.296	16
17	10.761	.0929	.0154	.1654	65.075	6.047	4.925	29.783	17
18	12.375	.0808	.0132	.1632	75.836	6.128	5.084	31.156	18
19	14.232	.0703	.0113	.1613	88.212	6.198	5.231	32.421	19
20	16.367	.0611	.00976	.1598	102.444	6.259	5.365	33.582	20
21	18.822	.0531	.00842	.1584	118.810	6.312	5.488	34.645	21
22	21.645	.0462	.00727	.1573	137.632	6.359	5.601	35.615	22
23	24.891	.0402	.00628	.1563	159.276	6.399	5.704	36.499	23
24	28.625	.0349	.00543	.1554	184.168	6.434	5.798	37.302	24
25	32.919	.0304	.00470	.1547	212.793	6.464	5.883	38.031	25
26	37.857	.0264	.00407	.1541	245.712	6.491	5.961	38.692	26
27	43.535	.0230	.00353	.1535	283.569	6.514	6.032	39.289	27
28	50.066	.0200	.00306	.1531	327.104	6.534	6.096	39.828	28
29	57.575	.0174	.00265	.1527	377.170	6.551	6.154	40.315	29
30	66.212	.0151	.00230	.1523	434.745	6.566	6.207	40.753	30
31	76.144	.0131	.00200	.1520	500.957	6.579	6.254	41.147	31
32	87.565	.0114	.00173	.1517	577.100	6.591	6.297	41.501	32
33	100.700	.00993	.00150	.1515	664.666	6.600	6.336	41.818	33
34	115.805	.00864	.00131	.1513	765.365	6.609	6.371	42.103	34
35	133.176	.00751	.00113	.1511	881.170	6.617	6.402	42.359	35
40	267.864	.00373	.00056	.1506	1779.1	6.642	6.517	43.283	40
45	538.769	.00186	.00028	.1503	3585.1	6.654	6.583	43.805	45
50	1083.7	.00092	.00014	.1501	7217.7	6.661	6.620	44.096	50
55	2179.6	.00046	.00007	.1501	14524.1	6.664	6.641	44.256	55
60	4384.0	.00023	.00003	.1500	29220.0	6.665	6.653	44.343	60
65	8817.8	.00011	.00002	.1500	58778.6	6.666	6.659	44.390	65
70	17735.7	.00006	.00001	.1500	118231.5	6.666	6.663	44.416	70
75	35672.9	.00003		.1500	237812.5	6.666	6.665	44.429	75
80	71750.9	.00001		.1500	478332.6	6.667	6.666	44.436	80
85	144316.7	.00001		.1500	962104.4	6.667	6.666	44.440	85

18%					Compound Interest Factors				18%

	Single Payment		Uniform Payment Series				Arithmetic Gradient		
	Compound Amount Factor Find F Given P F/P	Present Worth Factor Find P Given F P/F	Sinking Fund Factor Find A Given F A/F	Capital Recovery Factor Find A Given P A/P	Compound Amount Factor Find F Given A F/A	Present Worth Factor Find P Given A P/A	Gradient Uniform Series Find A Given G A/G	Gradient Present Worth Find P Given G P/G	
n									n
1	1.180	.8475	1.0000	1.1800	1.000	0.847	0	0	1
2	1.392	.7182	.4587	.6387	2.180	1.566	0.459	0.718	2
3	1.643	.6086	.2799	.4599	3.572	2.174	0.890	1.935	3
4	1.939	.5158	.1917	.3717	5.215	2.690	1.295	3.483	4
5	2.288	.4371	.1398	.3198	7.154	3.127	1.673	5.231	5
6	2.700	.3704	.1059	.2859	9.442	3.498	2.025	7.083	6
7	3.185	.3139	.0824	.2624	12.142	3.812	2.353	8.967	7
8	3.759	.2660	.0652	.2452	15.327	4.078	2.656	10.829	8
9	4.435	.2255	.0524	.2324	19.086	4.303	2.936	12.633	9
10	5.234	.1911	.0425	.2225	23.521	4.494	3.194	14.352	10
11	6.176	.1619	.0348	.2148	28.755	4.656	3.430	15.972	11
12	7.288	.1372	.0286	.2086	34.931	4.793	3.647	17.481	12
13	8.599	.1163	.0237	.2037	42.219	4.910	3.845	18.877	13
14	10.147	.0985	.0197	.1997	50.818	5.008	4.025	20.158	14
15	11.974	.0835	.0164	.1964	60.965	5.092	4.189	21.327	15
16	14.129	.0708	.0137	.1937	72.939	5.162	4.337	22.389	16
17	16.672	.0600	.0115	.1915	87.068	5.222	4.471	23.348	17
18	19.673	.0508	.00964	.1896	103.740	5.273	4.592	24.212	18
19	23.214	.0431	.00810	.1881	123.413	5.316	4.700	24.988	19
20	27.393	.0365	.00682	.1868	146.628	5.353	4.798	25.681	20
21	32.324	.0309	.00575	.1857	174.021	5.384	4.885	26.300	21
22	38.142	.0262	.00485	.1848	206.345	5.410	4.963	26.851	22
23	45.008	.0222	.00409	.1841	244.487	5.432	5.033	27.339	23
24	53.109	.0188	.00345	.1835	289.494	5.451	5.095	27.772	24
25	62.669	.0160	.00292	.1829	342.603	5.467	5.150	28.155	25
26	73.949	.0135	.00247	.1825	405.272	5.480	5.199	28.494	26
27	87.260	.0115	.00209	.1821	479.221	5.492	5.243	28.791	27
28	102.966	.00971	.00177	.1818	566.480	5.502	5.281	29.054	28
29	121.500	.00823	.00149	.1815	669.447	5.510	5.315	29.284	29
30	143.370	.00697	.00126	.1813	790.947	5.517	5.345	29.486	30
31	169.177	.00591	.00107	.1811	934.317	5.523	5.371	29.664	31
32	199.629	.00501	.00091	.1809	1 103.5	5.528	5.394	29.819	32
33	235.562	.00425	.00077	.1808	1 303.1	5.532	5.415	29.955	33
34	277.963	.00360	.00065	.1806	1 538.7	5.536	5.433	30.074	34
35	327.997	.00305	.00055	.1806	1 816.6	5.539	5.449	30.177	35
40	750.377	.00133	.00024	.1802	4 163.2	5.548	5.502	30.527	40
45	1 716.7	.00058	.00010	.1801	9 531.6	5.552	5.529	30.701	45
50	3 927.3	.00025	.00005	.1800	21 813.0	5.554	5.543	30.786	50
55	8 984.8	.00011	.00002	.1800	49 910.1	5.555	5.549	30.827	55
60	20 555.1	.00005	.00001	.1800	114 189.4	5.555	5.553	30.846	60
65	47 025.1	.00002		.1800	261 244.7	5.555	5.554	30.856	65
70	107 581.9	.00001		.1800	597 671.7	5.556	5.555	30.860	70

20% Compound Interest Factors **20%**

	Single Payment		Uniform Payment Series				Arithmetic Gradient		
	Compound Amount Factor Find F Given P	Present Worth Factor Find P Given F	Sinking Fund Factor Find A Given F	Capital Recovery Factor Find A Given P	Compound Amount Factor Find F Given A	Present Worth Factor Find P Given A	Gradient Uniform Series Find A Given G	Gradient Present Worth Find P Given G	
n	F/P	P/F	A/F	A/P	F/A	P/A	A/G	P/G	n
1	1.200	.8333	1.0000	1.2000	1.000	0.833	0	0	1
2	1.440	.6944	.4545	.6545	2.200	1.528	0.455	0.694	2
3	1.728	.5787	.2747	.4747	3.640	2.106	0.879	1.852	3
4	2.074	.4823	.1863	.3863	5.368	2.589	1.274	3.299	4
5	2.488	.4019	.1344	.3344	7.442	2.991	1.641	4.906	5
6	2.986	.3349	.1007	.3007	9.930	3.326	1.979	6.581	6
7	3.583	.2791	.0774	.2774	12.916	3.605	2.290	8.255	7
8	4.300	.2326	.0606	.2606	16.499	3.837	2.576	9.883	8
9	5.160	.1938	.0481	.2481	20.799	4.031	2.836	11.434	9
10	6.192	.1615	.0385	.2385	25.959	4.192	3.074	12.887	10
11	7.430	.1346	.0311	.2311	32.150	4.327	3.289	14.233	11
12	8.916	.1122	.0253	.2253	39.581	4.439	3.484	15.467	12
13	10.699	.0935	.0206	.2206	48.497	4.533	3.660	16.588	13
14	12.839	.0779	.0169	.2169	59.196	4.611	3.817	17.601	14
15	15.407	.0649	.0139	.2139	72.035	4.675	3.959	18.509	15
16	18.488	.0541	.0114	.2114	87.442	4.730	4.085	19.321	16
17	22.186	.0451	.00944	.2094	105.931	4.775	4.198	20.042	17
18	26.623	.0376	.00781	.2078	128.117	4.812	4.298	20.680	18
19	31.948	.0313	.00646	.2065	154.740	4.843	4.386	21.244	19
20	38.338	.0261	.00536	.2054	186.688	4.870	4.464	21.739	20
21	46.005	.0217	.00444	.2044	225.026	4.891	4.533	22.174	21
22	55.206	.0181	.00369	.2037	271.031	4.909	4.594	22.555	22
23	66.247	.0151	.00307	.2031	326.237	4.925	4.647	22.887	23
24	79.497	.0126	.00255	.2025	392.484	4.937	4.694	23.176	24
25	95.396	.0105	.00212	.2021	471.981	4.948	4.735	23.428	25
26	114.475	.00874	.00176	.2018	567.377	4.956	4.771	23.646	26
27	137.371	.00728	.00147	.2015	681.853	4.964	4.802	23.835	27
28	164.845	.00607	.00122	.2012	819.223	4.970	4.829	23.999	28
29	197.814	.00506	.00102	.2010	984.068	4.975	4.853	24.141	29
30	237.376	.00421	.00085	.2008	1181.9	4.979	4.873	24.263	30
31	284.852	.00351	.00070	.2007	1419.3	4.982	4.891	24.368	31
32	341.822	.00293	.00059	.2006	1704.1	4.985	4.906	24.459	32
33	410.186	.00244	.00049	.2005	2045.9	4.988	4.919	24.537	33
34	492.224	.00203	.00041	.2004	2456.1	4.990	4.931	24.604	34
35	590.668	.00169	.00034	.2003	2948.3	4.992	4.941	24.661	35
40	1469.8	.00068	.00014	.2001	7343.9	4.997	4.973	24.847	40
45	3657.3	.00027	.00005	.2001	18281.3	4.999	4.988	24.932	45
50	9100.4	.00011	.00002	.2000	45497.2	4.999	4.995	24.970	50
55	22644.8	.00004	.00001	.2000	113219.0	5.000	4.998	24.987	55
60	56347.5	.00002		.2000	281732.6	5.000	4.999	24.994	60

25%   Compound Interest Factors   25%

	Single Payment		Uniform Payment Series				Arithmetic Gradient		
	Compound Amount Factor Find F Given P	Present Worth Factor Find P Given F	Sinking Fund Factor Find A Given F	Capital Recovery Factor Find A Given P	Compound Amount Factor Find F Given A	Present Worth Factor Find P Given A	Gradient Uniform Series Find A Given G	Gradient Present Worth Find P Given G	
n	F/P	P/F	A/F	A/P	F/A	P/A	A/G	P/G	n
1	1.250	.8000	1.0000	1.2500	1.000	0.800	0	0	1
2	1.563	.6400	.4444	.6944	2.250	1.440	0.444	0.640	2
3	1.953	.5120	.2623	.5123	3.813	1.952	0.852	1.664	3
4	2.441	.4096	.1734	.4234	5.766	2.362	1.225	2.893	4
5	3.052	.3277	.1218	.3718	8.207	2.689	1.563	4.204	5
6	3.815	.2621	.0888	.3388	11.259	2.951	1.868	5.514	6
7	4.768	.2097	.0663	.3163	15.073	3.161	2.142	6.773	7
8	5.960	.1678	.0504	.3004	19.842	3.329	2.387	7.947	8
9	7.451	.1342	.0388	.2888	25.802	3.463	2.605	9.021	9
10	9.313	.1074	.0301	.2801	33.253	3.571	2.797	9.987	10
11	11.642	.0859	.0235	.2735	42.566	3.656	2.966	10.846	11
12	14.552	.0687	.0184	.2684	54.208	3.725	3.115	11.602	12
13	18.190	.0550	.0145	.2645	68.760	3.780	3.244	12.262	13
14	22.737	.0440	.0115	.2615	86.949	3.824	3.356	12.833	14
15	28.422	.0352	.00912	.2591	109.687	3.859	3.453	13.326	15
16	35.527	.0281	.00724	.2572	138.109	3.887	3.537	13.748	16
17	44.409	.0225	.00576	.2558	173.636	3.910	3.608	14.108	17
18	55.511	.0180	.00459	.2546	218.045	3.928	3.670	14.415	18
19	69.389	.0144	.00366	.2537	273.556	3.942	3.722	14.674	19
20	86.736	.0115	.00292	.2529	342.945	3.954	3.767	14.893	20
21	108.420	.00922	.00233	.2523	429.681	3.963	3.805	15.078	21
22	135.525	.00738	.00186	.2519	538.101	3.970	3.836	15.233	22
23	169.407	.00590	.00148	.2515	673.626	3.976	3.863	15.362	23
24	211.758	.00472	.00119	.2512	843.033	3.981	3.886	15.471	24
25	264.698	.00378	.00095	.2509	1 054.8	3.985	3.905	15.562	25
26	330.872	.00302	.00076	.2508	1 319.5	3.988	3.921	15.637	26
27	413.590	.00242	.00061	.2506	1 650.4	3.990	3.935	15.700	27
28	516.988	.00193	.00048	.2505	2 064.0	3.992	3.946	15.752	28
29	646.235	.00155	.00039	.2504	2 580.9	3.994	3.955	15.796	29
30	807.794	.00124	.00031	.2503	3 227.2	3.995	3.963	15.832	30
31	1 009.7	.00099	.00025	.2502	4 035.0	3.996	3.969	15.861	31
32	1 262.2	.00079	.00020	.2502	5 044.7	3.997	3.975	15.886	32
33	1 577.7	.00063	.00016	.2502	6 306.9	3.997	3.979	15.906	33
34	1 972.2	.00051	.00013	.2501	7 884.6	3.998	3.983	15.923	34
35	2 465.2	.00041	.00010	.2501	9 856.8	3.998	3.986	15.937	35
40	7 523.2	.00013	.00003	.2500	30 088.7	3.999	3.995	15.977	40
45	22 958.9	.00004	.00001	.2500	91 831.5	4.000	3.998	15.991	45
50	70 064.9	.00001		.2500	280 255.7	4.000	3.999	15.997	50
55	213 821.2			.2500	855 280.7	4.000	4.000	15.999	55

30%				Compound Interest Factors					30%
	Single Payment		Uniform Payment Series				Arithmetic Gradient		
	Compound Amount Factor Find F Given P	Present Worth Factor Find P Given F	Sinking Fund Factor Find A Given F	Capital Recovery Factor Find A Given P	Compound Amount Factor Find F Given A	Present Worth Factor Find P Given A	Gradient Uniform Series Find A Given G	Gradient Present Worth Find P Given G	
n	F/P	P/F	A/F	A/P	F/A	P/A	A/G	P/G	n
1	1.300	.7692	1.0000	1.3000	1.000	0.769	0	0	1
2	1.690	.5917	.4348	.7348	2.300	1.361	0.435	0.592	2
3	2.197	.4552	.2506	.5506	3.990	1.816	0.827	1.502	3
4	2.856	.3501	.1616	.4616	6.187	2.166	1.178	2.552	4
5	3.713	.2693	.1106	.4106	9.043	2.436	1.490	3.630	5
6	4.827	.2072	.0784	.3784	12.756	2.643	1.765	4.666	6
7	6.275	.1594	.0569	.3569	17.583	2.802	2.006	5.622	7
8	8.157	.1226	.0419	.3419	23.858	2.925	2.216	6.480	8
9	10.604	.0943	.0312	.3312	32.015	3.019	2.396	7.234	9
10	13.786	.0725	.0235	.3235	42.619	3.092	2.551	7.887	10
11	17.922	.0558	.0177	.3177	56.405	3.147	2.683	8.445	11
12	23.298	.0429	.0135	.3135	74.327	3.190	2.795	8.917	12
13	30.287	.0330	.0102	.3102	97.625	3.223	2.889	9.314	13
14	39.374	.0254	.00782	.3078	127.912	3.249	2.969	9.644	14
15	51.186	.0195	.00598	.3060	167.286	3.268	3.034	9.917	15
16	66.542	.0150	.00458	.3046	218.472	3.283	3.089	10.143	16
17	86.504	.0116	.00351	.3035	285.014	3.295	3.135	10.328	17
18	112.455	.00889	.00269	.3027	371.518	3.304	3.172	10.479	18
19	146.192	.00684	.00207	.3021	483.973	3.311	3.202	10.602	19
20	190.049	.00526	.00159	.3016	630.165	3.316	3.228	10.702	20
21	247.064	.00405	.00122	.3012	820.214	3.320	3.248	10.783	21
22	321.184	.00311	.00094	.3009	1 067.3	3.323	3.265	10.848	22
23	417.539	.00239	.00072	.3007	1 388.5	3.325	3.278	10.901	23
24	542.800	.00184	.00055	.3006	1 806.0	3.327	3.289	10.943	24
25	705.640	.00142	.00043	.3004	2 348.8	3.329	3.298	10.977	25
26	917.332	.00109	.00033	.3003	3 054.4	3.330	3.305	11.005	26
27	1 192.5	.00084	.00025	.3003	3 971.8	3.331	3.311	11.026	27
28	1 550.3	.00065	.00019	.3002	5 164.3	3.331	3.315	11.044	28
29	2 015.4	.00050	.00015	.3001	6 714.6	3.332	3.319	11.058	29
30	2 620.0	.00038	.00011	.3001	8 730.0	3.332	3.322	11.069	30
31	3 406.0	.00029	.00009	.3001	11 350.0	3.332	3.324	11.078	31
32	4 427.8	.00023	.00007	.3001	14 756.0	3.333	3.326	11.085	32
33	5 756.1	.00017	.00005	.3001	19 183.7	3.333	3.328	11.090	33
34	7 483.0	.00013	.00004	.3000	24 939.9	3.333	3.329	11.094	34
35	9 727.8	.00010	.00003	.3000	32 422.8	3.333	3.330	11.098	35
40	36 118.8	.00003	.00001	.3000	120 392.6	3.333	3.332	11.107	40
45	134 106.5	.00001		.3000	447 018.3	3.333	3.333	11.110	45

35%					Compound Interest Factors					35%
	Single Payment		Uniform Payment Series				Arithmetic Gradient			
	Compound Amount Factor Find F Given P F/P	Present Worth Factor Find P Given F P/F	Sinking Fund Factor Find A Given F A/F	Capital Recovery Factor Find A Given P A/P	Compound Amount Factor Find F Given A F/A	Present Worth Factor Find P Given A P/A	Gradient Uniform Series Find A Given G A/G	Gradient Present Worth Find P Given G P/G	
n									n
1	1.350	.7407	1.0000	1.3500	1.000	0.741	0	0	1
2	1.822	.5487	.4255	.7755	2.350	1.289	0.426	0.549	2
3	2.460	.4064	.2397	.5897	4.173	1.696	0.803	1.362	3
4	3.322	.3011	.1508	.5008	6.633	1.997	1.134	2.265	4
5	4.484	.2230	.1005	.4505	9.954	2.220	1.422	3.157	5
6	6.053	.1652	.0693	.4193	14.438	2.385	1.670	3.983	6
7	8.172	.1224	.0488	.3988	20.492	2.508	1.881	4.717	7
8	11.032	.0906	.0349	.3849	28.664	2.598	2.060	5.352	8
9	14.894	.0671	.0252	.3752	39.696	2.665	2.209	5.889	9
10	20.107	.0497	.0183	.3683	54.590	2.715	2.334	6.336	10
11	27.144	.0368	.0134	.3634	74.697	2.752	2.436	6.705	11
12	36.644	.0273	.00982	.3598	101.841	2.779	2.520	7.005	12
13	49.470	.0202	.00722	.3572	138.485	2.799	2.589	7.247	13
14	66.784	.0150	.00532	.3553	187.954	2.814	2.644	7.442	14
15	90.158	.0111	.00393	.3539	254.739	2.825	2.689	7.597	15
16	121.714	.00822	.00290	.3529	344.897	2.834	2.725	7.721	16
17	164.314	.00609	.00214	.3521	466.611	2.840	2.753	7.818	17
18	221.824	.00451	.00158	.3516	630.925	2.844	2.776	7.895	18
19	299.462	.00334	.00117	.3512	852.748	2.848	2.793	7.955	19
20	404.274	.00247	.00087	.3509	1 152.2	2.850	2.808	8.002	20
21	545.769	.00183	.00064	.3506	1 556.5	2.852	2.819	8.038	21
22	736.789	.00136	.00048	.3505	2 102.3	2.853	2.827	8.067	22
23	994.665	.00101	.00035	.3504	2 839.0	2.854	2.834	8.089	23
24	1 342.8	.00074	.00026	.3503	3 833.7	2.855	2.839	8.106	24
25	1 812.8	.00055	.00019	.3502	5 176.5	2.856	2.843	8.119	25
26	2 447.2	.00041	.00014	.3501	6 989.3	2.856	2.847	8.130	26
27	3 303.8	.00030	.00011	.3501	9 436.5	2.856	2.849	8.137	27
28	4 460.1	.00022	.00008	.3501	12 740.3	2.857	2.851	8.143	28
29	6 021.1	.00017	.00006	.3501	17 200.4	2.857	2.852	8.148	29
30	8 128.5	.00012	.00004	.3500	23 221.6	2.857	2.853	8.152	30
31	10 973.5	.00009	.00003	.3500	31 350.1	2.857	2.854	8.154	31
32	14 814.3	.00007	.00002	.3500	42 323.7	2.857	2.855	8.157	32
33	19 999.3	.00005	.00002	.3500	57 137.9	2.857	2.855	8.158	33
34	26 999.0	.00004	.00001	.3500	77 137.2	2.857	2.856	8.159	34
35	36 448.7	.00003	.00001	.3500	104 136.3	2.857	2.856	8.160	35

40%				Compound Interest Factors					40%
	Single Payment		**Uniform Payment Series**				**Arithmetic Gradient**		
	Compound Amount Factor Find F Given P	Present Worth Factor Find P Given F	Sinking Fund Factor Find A Given F	Capital Recovery Factor Find A Given P	Compound Amount Factor Find F Given A	Present Worth Factor Find P Given A	Gradient Uniform Series Find A Given G	Gradient Present Worth Find P Given G	
n	F/P	P/F	A/F	A/P	F/A	P/A	A/G	P/G	n
1	1.400	.7143	1.0000	1.4000	1.000	0.714	0	0	1
2	1.960	.5102	.4167	.8167	2.400	1.224	0.417	0.510	2
3	2.744	.3644	.2294	.6294	4.360	1.589	0.780	1.239	3
4	3.842	.2603	.1408	.5408	7.104	1.849	1.092	2.020	4
5	5.378	.1859	.0914	.4914	10.946	2.035	1.358	2.764	5
6	7.530	.1328	.0613	.4613	16.324	2.168	1.581	3.428	6
7	10.541	.0949	.0419	.4419	23.853	2.263	1.766	3.997	7
8	14.758	.0678	.0291	.4291	34.395	2.331	1.919	4.471	8
9	20.661	.0484	.0203	.4203	49.153	2.379	2.042	4.858	9
10	28.925	.0346	.0143	.4143	69.814	2.414	2.142	5.170	10
11	40.496	.0247	.0101	.4101	98.739	2.438	2.221	5.417	11
12	56.694	.0176	.00718	.4072	139.235	2.456	2.285	5.611	12
13	79.371	.0126	.00510	.4051	195.929	2.469	2.334	5.762	13
14	111.120	.00900	.00363	.4036	275.300	2.478	2.373	5.879	14
15	155.568	.00643	.00259	.4026	386.420	2.484	2.403	5.969	15
16	217.795	.00459	.00185	.4018	541.988	2.489	2.426	6.038	16
17	304.913	.00328	.00132	.4013	759.783	2.492	2.444	6.090	17
18	426.879	.00234	.00094	.4009	1 064.7	2.494	2.458	6.130	18
19	597.630	.00167	.00067	.4007	1 419.6	2.496	2.468	6.160	19
20	836.682	.00120	.00048	.4005	2 089.2	2.497	2.476	6.183	20
21	1 171.4	.00085	.00034	.4003	2 925.9	2.498	2.482	6.200	21
22	1 639.9	.00061	.00024	.4002	4 097.2	2.498	2.487	6.213	22
23	2 295.9	.00044	.00017	.4002	5 737.1	2.499	2.490	6.222	23
24	3 214.2	.00031	.00012	.4001	8 033.0	2.499	2.493	6.229	24
25	4 499.9	.00022	.00009	.4001	11 247.2	2.499	2.494	6.235	25
26	6 299.8	.00016	.00006	.4001	15 747.1	2.500	2.496	6.239	26
27	8 819.8	.00011	.00005	.4000	22 046.9	2.500	2.497	6.242	27
28	12 347.7	.00008	.00003	.4000	30 866.7	2.500	2.498	6.244	28
29	17 286.7	.00006	.00002	.4000	43 214.3	2.500	2.498	6.245	29
30	24 201.4	.00004	.00002	.4000	60 501.0	2.500	2.499	6.247	30
31	33 882.0	.00003	.00001	.4000	84 702.5	2.500	2.499	6.248	31
32	47 434.8	.00002	.00001	.4000	118 584.4	2.500	2.499	6.248	32
33	66 408.7	.00002	.00001	.4000	166 019.2	2.500	2.500	6.249	33
34	92 972.1	.00001		.4000	232 427.9	2.500	2.500	6.249	34
35	130 161.0	.00001		.4000	325 400.0	2.500	2.500	6.249	35

45%   Compound Interest Factors   45%

| | Single Payment | | Uniform Payment Series | | | | Arithmetic Gradient | | |
| | Compound Amount Factor Find F Given P F/P | Present Worth Factor Find P Given F P/F | Sinking Fund Factor Find A Given F A/F | Capital Recovery Factor Find A Given P A/P | Compound Amount Factor Find F Given A F/A | Present Worth Factor Find P Given A P/A | Gradient Uniform Series Find A Given G A/G | Gradient Present Worth Find P Given G P/G | |
n									n
1	1.450	.6897	1.0000	1.4500	1.000	0.690	0	0	1
2	2.103	.4756	.4082	.8582	2.450	1.165	0.408	0.476	2
3	3.049	.3280	.2197	.6697	4.553	1.493	0.758	1.132	3
4	4.421	.2262	.1316	.5816	7.601	1.720	1.053	1.810	4
5	6.410	.1560	.0832	.5332	12.022	1.876	1.298	2.434	5
6	9.294	.1076	.0543	.5043	18.431	1.983	1.499	2.972	6
7	13.476	.0742	.0361	.4861	27.725	2.057	1.661	3.418	7
8	19.541	.0512	.0243	.4743	41.202	2.109	1.791	3.776	8
9	28.334	.0353	.0165	.4665	60.743	2.144	1.893	4.058	9
10	41.085	.0243	.0112	.4612	89.077	2.168	1.973	4.277	10
11	59.573	.0168	.00768	.4577	130.162	2.185	2.034	4.445	11
12	86.381	.0116	.00527	.4553	189.735	2.196	2.082	4.572	12
13	125.252	.00798	.00362	.4536	276.115	2.204	2.118	4.668	13
14	181.615	.00551	.00249	.4525	401.367	2.210	2.145	4.740	14
15	263.342	.00380	.00172	.4517	582.982	2.214	2.165	4.793	15
16	381.846	.00262	.00118	.4512	846.325	2.216	2.180	4.832	16
17	553.677	.00181	.00081	.4508	1 228.2	2.218	2.191	4.861	17
18	802.831	.00125	.00056	.4506	1 781.8	2.219	2.200	4.882	18
19	1 164.1	.00086	.00039	.4504	2 584.7	2.220	2.206	4.898	19
20	1 688.0	.00059	.00027	.4503	3 748.8	2.221	2.210	4.909	20
21	2 447.5	.00041	.00018	.4502	5 436.7	2.221	2.214	4.917	21
22	3 548.9	.00028	.00013	.4501	7 884.3	2.222	2.216	4.923	22
23	5 145.9	.00019	.00009	.4501	11 433.2	2.222	2.218	4.927	23
24	7 461.6	.00013	.00006	.4501	16 579.1	2.222	2.219	4.930	24
25	10 819.3	.00009	.00004	.4500	24 040.7	2.222	2.220	4.933	25
26	15 688.0	.00006	.00003	.4500	34 860.1	2.222	2.221	4.934	26
27	22 747.7	.00004	.00002	.4500	50 548.1	2.222	2.221	4.935	27
28	32 984.1	.00003	.00001	.4500	73 295.8	2.222	2.221	4.936	28
29	47 826.9	.00002	.00001	.4500	106 279.9	2.222	2.222	4.937	29
30	69 349.1	.00001	.00001	.4500	154 106.8	2.222	2.222	4.937	30
31	100 556.1	.00001		.4500	223 455.9	2.222	2.222	4.938	31
32	145 806.4	.00001		.4500	324 012.0	2.222	2.222	4.938	32
33	211 419.3			.4500	469 818.5	2.222	2.222	4.938	33
34	306 558.0			.4500	681 237.8	2.222	2.222	4.938	34
35	444 509.2			.4500	987 795.9	2.222	2.222	4.938	35

50%				Compound Interest Factors					50%
	Single Payment		Uniform Payment Series				Arithmetic Gradient		
	Compound Amount Factor Find F Given P F/P	Present Worth Factor Find P Given F P/F	Sinking Fund Factor Find A Given F A/F	Capital Recovery Factor Find A Given P A/P	Compound Amount Factor Find F Given A F/A	Present Worth Factor Find P Given A P/A	Gradient Uniform Series Find A Given G A/G	Gradient Present Worth Find P Given G P/G	
n									n
1	1.500	.6667	1.0000	1.5000	1.000	0.667	0	0	1
2	2.250	.4444	.4000	.9000	2.500	1.111	0.400	0.444	2
3	3.375	.2963	.2105	.7105	4.750	1.407	0.737	1.037	3
4	5.063	.1975	.1231	.6231	8.125	1.605	1.015	1.630	4
5	7.594	.1317	.0758	.5758	13.188	1.737	1.242	2.156	5
6	11.391	.0878	.0481	.5481	20.781	1.824	1.423	2.595	6
7	17.086	.0585	.0311	.5311	32.172	1.883	1.565	2.947	7
8	25.629	.0390	.0203	.5203	49.258	1.922	1.675	3.220	8
9	38.443	.0260	.0134	.5134	74.887	1.948	1.760	3.428	9
10	57.665	.0173	.00882	.5088	113.330	1.965	1.824	3.584	10
11	86.498	.0116	.00585	.5058	170.995	1.977	1.871	3.699	11
12	129.746	.00771	.00388	.5039	257.493	1.985	1.907	3.784	12
13	194.620	.00514	.00258	.5026	387.239	1.990	1.933	3.846	13
14	291.929	.00343	.00172	.5017	581.859	1.993	1.952	3.890	14
15	437.894	.00228	.00114	.5011	873.788	1.995	1.966	3.922	15
16	656.814	.00152	.00076	.5008	1311.7	1.997	1.976	3.945	16
17	985.261	.00101	.00051	.5005	1968.5	1.998	1.983	3.961	17
18	1477.9	.00068	.00034	.5003	2953.8	1.999	1.988	3.973	18
19	2216.8	.00045	.00023	.5002	4431.7	1.999	1.991	3.981	19
20	3325.3	.00030	.00015	.5002	6648.5	1.999	1.994	3.987	20
21	4987.9	.00020	.00010	.5001	9973.8	2.000	1.996	3.991	21
22	7481.8	.00013	.00007	.5001	14961.7	2.000	1.997	3.994	22
23	11222.7	.00009	.00004	.5000	22443.5	2.000	1.998	3.996	23
24	16834.1	.00006	.00003	.5000	33666.2	2.000	1.999	3.997	24
25	25251.2	.00004	.00002	.5000	50500.3	2.000	1.999	3.998	25
26	37876.8	.00003	.00001	.5000	75751.5	2.000	1.999	3.999	26
27	56815.1	.00002	.00001	.5000	113628.3	2.000	2.000	3.999	27
28	85222.7	.00001	.00001	.5000	170443.4	2.000	2.000	3.999	28
29	127834.0	.00001		.5000	255666.1	2.000	2.000	4.000	29
30	191751.1	.00001		.5000	383500.1	2.000	2.000	4.000	30
31	287626.6			.5000	575251.2	2.000	2.000	4.000	31
32	431439.9			.5000	862877.8	2.000	2.000	4.000	32

60%   Compound Interest Factors   **60%**

	Single Payment		Uniform Payment Series				Arithmetic Gradient		
	Compound Amount Factor Find F Given P	Present Worth Factor Find P Given F	Sinking Fund Factor Find A Given F	Capital Recovery Factor Find A Given P	Compound Amount Factor Find F Given A	Present Worth Factor Find P Given A	Gradient Uniform Series Find A Given G	Gradient Present Worth Find P Given G	
n	F/P	P/F	A/F	A/P	F/A	P/A	A/G	P/G	n
1	1.600	.6250	1.0000	1.6000	1.000	0.625	0	0	1
2	2.560	.3906	.3846	.9846	2.600	1.016	0.385	0.391	2
3	4.096	.2441	.1938	.7938	5.160	1.260	0.698	0.879	3
4	6.554	.1526	.1080	.7080	9.256	1.412	0.946	1.337	4
5	10.486	.0954	.0633	.6633	15.810	1.508	1.140	1.718	5
6	16.777	.0596	.0380	.6380	26.295	1.567	1.286	2.016	6
7	26.844	.0373	.0232	.6232	43.073	1.605	1.396	2.240	7
8	42.950	.0233	.0143	.6143	69.916	1.628	1.476	2.403	8
9	68.719	.0146	.00886	.6089	112.866	1.642	1.534	2.519	9
10	109.951	.00909	.00551	.6055	181.585	1.652	1.575	2.601	10
11	175.922	.00568	.00343	.6034	291.536	1.657	1.604	2.658	11
12	281.475	.00355	.00214	.6021	467.458	1.661	1.624	2.697	12
13	450.360	.00222	.00134	.6013	748.933	1.663	1.638	2.724	13
14	720.576	.00139	.00083	.6008	1 199.3	1.664	1.647	2.742	14
15	1 152.9	.00087	.00052	.6005	1 919.9	1.665	1.654	2.754	15
16	1 844.7	.00054	.00033	.6003	3 072.8	1.666	1.658	2.762	16
17	2 951.5	.00034	.00020	.6002	4 917.5	1.666	1.661	2.767	17
18	4 722.4	.00021	.00013	.6001	7 868.9	1.666	1.663	2.771	18
19	7 555.8	.00013	.00008	.6011	12 591.3	1.666	1.664	2.773	19
20	12 089.3	.00008	.00005	.6000	20 147.1	1.667	1.665	2.775	20
21	19 342.8	.00005	.00003	.6000	32 236.3	1.667	1.666	2.776	21
22	30 948.5	.00003	.00002	.6000	51 579.2	1.667	1.666	2.777	22
23	49 517.6	.00002	.00001	.6000	82 527.6	1.667	1.666	2.777	23
24	79 228.1	.00001	.00001	.6000	132 045.2	1.667	1.666	2.777	24
25	126 765.0	.00001		.6000	211 273.4	1.667	1.666	2.777	25
26	202 824.0			.6000	338 038.4	1.667	1.667	2.778	26
27	324 518.4			.6000	540 862.4	1.667	1.667	2.778	27
28	519 229.5			.6000	865 380.9	1.667	1.667	2.778	28

Continuous Compounding—Single Payment Factors

rn	Compound Amount Factor e^{rn} Find F Given P F/P	Present Worth Factor e^{-rn} Find P Find F P/F	rn	Compound Amount Factor e^{rn} Find F Given P F/P	Present Worth Factor e^{-rn} Find P Given F P/F
.01	1.0101	.9900	.51	1.6653	.6005
.02	1.0202	.9802	.52	1.6820	.5945
.03	1.0305	.9704	.53	1.6989	.5886
.04	1.0408	.9608	.54	1.7160	.5827
.05	1.0513	.9512	.55	1.7333	.5769
.06	1.0618	.9418	.56	1.7507	.5712
.07	1.0725	.9324	.57	1.7683	.5655
.08	1.0833	.9231	.58	1.7860	.5599
.09	1.0942	.9139	.59	1.8040	.5543
.10	1.1052	.9048	.60	1.8221	.5488
.11	1.1163	.8958	.61	1.8404	.5434
.12	1.1275	.8869	.62	1.8589	.5379
.13	1.1388	.8781	.63	1.8776	.5326
.14	1.1503	.8694	.64	1.8965	.5273
.15	1.1618	.8607	.65	1.9155	.5220
.16	1.1735	.8521	.66	1.9348	.5169
.17	1.1853	.8437	.67	1.9542	.5117
.18	1.1972	.8353	.68	1.9739	.5066
.19	1.2092	.8270	.69	1.9937	.5016
.20	1.2214	.8187	.70	2.0138	.4966
.21	1.2337	.8106	.71	2.0340	.4916
.22	1.2461	.8025	.72	2.0544	.4868
.23	1.2586	.7945	.73	2.0751	.4819
.24	1.2712	.7866	.74	2.0959	.4771
.25	1.2840	.7788	.75	2.1170	.4724
.26	1.2969	.7711	.76	2.1383	.4677
.27	1.3100	.7634	.77	2.1598	.4630
.28	1.3231	.7558	.78	2.1815	.4584
.29	1.3364	.7483	.79	2.2034	.4538
.30	1.3499	.7408	.80	2.2255	.4493
.31	1.3634	.7334	.81	2.2479	.4449
.32	1.3771	.7261	.82	2.2705	.4404
.33	1.3910	.7189	.83	2.2933	.4360
.34	1.4049	.7118	.84	2.3164	.4317
.35	1.4191	.7047	.85	2.3396	.4274
.36	1.4333	.6977	.86	2.3632	.4232
.37	1.4477	.6907	.87	2.3869	.4190
.38	1.4623	.6839	.88	2.4109	.4148
.39	1.4770	.6771	.89	2.4351	.4107
.40	1.4918	.6703	.90	2.4596	.4066
.41	1.5068	.6637	.91	2.4843	.4025
.42	1.5220	.6570	.92	2.5093	.3985
.43	1.5373	.6505	.93	2.5345	.3946
.44	1.5527	.6440	.94	2.5600	.3906
.45	1.5683	.6376	.95	2.5857	.3867
.46	1.5841	.6313	.96	2.6117	.3829
.47	1.6000	.6250	.97	2.6379	.3791
.48	1.6161	.6188	.98	2.6645	.3753
.49	1.6323	.6126	.99	2.6912	.3716
.50	1.6487	.6065	1.00	2.7183	.3679